REVIEWS IN ENGINEERING GEOLOGY
VOLUME XIV

THE ENVIRONMENTAL LEGACY OF MILITARY OPERATIONS

Edited by

JUDY EHLEN
U.S. Army Engineer Research and Development Center
7701 Telegraph Road
Alexandria, Virginia 22315-3864
USA

and

RUSSELL S. HARMON
U.S. Army Research Office
P.O. Box 12211
Research Triangle Park, North Carolina 27709-2211
USA

THE
GEOLOGICAL
SOCIETY
OF AMERICA

3300 Penrose Place, P.O. Box 9140 • Boulder, CO 80301-9140 USA

2001

The Reviews in Engineering Geology series was expanded in 1997 to include Engineering Geology Case Histories, 11 volumes of which were published by the Geological Society of America from 1957 to 1978 with ISBNs from 0-8137-4001-0 to 0-8137-4011-8. Beginning with Volume XI, Reviews in Engineering Geology may include both reviews and case histories, under the ISBN 0-8137-4111-4 and subsequent numbers.

Published by The Geological Society of America, Inc.
3300 Penrose Place, P.O. Box 9140, Boulder, Colorado 80301-9140, USA
www.geosociety.org

Printed in U.S.A.

GSA Books Science Editor Abhijit Basu
GSA Books Editor Rebecca Herr

Library of Congress Cataloging-in-Publication Data

The environmental legacy of military operations / edited by Judy Ehlen and Russell S. Harmon.
    p. cm. — (Reviews in engineering geology ; v. 14)
  Includes bibliographical references and index.
  ISBN 0-8137-4114-9
   1. Military geology. 2. Armed Forces—Environmental aspects. 3. War—Environmental aspects.
  4. Environmental degradation. I. Ehlen, Judy, 1944– II. Harmon, R. S. (Russell S.) III. Series.

TA705 .R4 vol. 14
[[UG465+]]
624.1'51 s—dc21
[355.4'7]

                                                                00-054426

Cover: The Rock of Gibraltar, viewed from the south. The two Quaternary wave-cut platforms that form the southern plateaus lie in the foreground and are occupied largely by military buildings and fortified with a defensive wall above the coastal cliffs. Behind, the 400-m-high main ridge of Jurassic dolomitic limestone slopes steeply toward the city and harbor on the west coast of the peninsula. Buildings set in the eastern scarp face of the Rock provide clues to the many caves and tunnels that penetrate it. Photo by E.P.F. Rose. Cover design by Heather L. Sutphin

10 9 8 7 6 5 4 3 2 1

Contents

Dedication

This volume is jointly dedicated to the memories of Paul Albertson and Christopher P. Cameron, both authors of papers in this volume who died during the course of its preparation. Paul died in an automobile accident near Jackson, Mississippi, in July 1999; Chris, of heart failure in February 2000 during field work in Nevada. To the editors and many of the authors contributing to this volume, both Paul and Chris were valued colleagues and friends. The untimely deaths of these two exemplary individuals are a great loss to their families, many friends, and the scientific profession they served.

Paul Albertson
(1955–1999)

Paul was a research geologist in the Engineering Geology Group of the Geotechnical Laboratory at the U.S. Army Corps of Engineers Waterways Experiment Station (WES) in Vicksburg, Mississippi; an adjunct professor at the University of Missouri, Rolla; and a contributor to two of the papers in this volume (Chapters 10 and 12). After obtaining a B.S. degree in geology from East Carolina University, Paul joined the Corps of Engineers, Nashville District, where he worked as a field geologist. In the mid-1980s, Paul transferred to the Vicksburg District and there began building a reputation in fluvial geomorphology through important studies undertaken on the Mississippi and Red Rivers.

Paul joined the Engineering Geology Branch of the Geotechnical Laboratory at WES in 1990 and, shortly thereafter, began collaborating with archaeologists and other scientists investigating and preserving fluvial archaeological sites. While at WES, Paul earned his M.S. in geology at Texas A&M University and then a Ph.D. in geological engineering at the University of Missouri, Rolla. Concurrent with his educational studies, Paul was a practicing engineering geologist for more than 20 years and was licensed in the states of

Indiana, Tennessee, Arkansas, and Missouri. Paul was an active member of the Lower Mississippi Valley Section of the Association of Engineering Geologists, the Mississippi Academy of Sciences, Society of American Archeology, American Society of Photogrammetry and Remote Sensing, Society of American Military Engineers, and Sigma Xi.

Chris Cameron
(1941–2000)

Chris was a faculty member of the Department of Geology at the University of Southern Mississippi (USM) at Hattiesburg, Mississippi. After receiving a B.S. degree in geology from the University of New Orleans in 1966 and a Ph.D. in geology from the University of Alaska in 1970, Chris worked for 14 years with the Exxon Corporation as a mining exploration geologist. It was during this time that Chris developed an expertise in subsurface geology.

After becoming a faculty member at USM in 1983, Chris was contracted by the Corps of Engineers Waterways Experiment Station to provide on-site support to the U.S. Army in the geophysical detection of clandestine tunnels under the Korean Demilitarized Zone. Chris was a member of the Panel of Experts in Tunnel Detection Technology, which served for six years from 1987 to 1993. Chris's paper in this volume (Chapter 6) discusses aspects of Korean geology that derive from this experience. In 1993, the Army awarded him the Outstanding Civilian Service award, and a year later, he received the Faculty Award for Applied Research from the University of Southern Mississippi.

Chris was a dedicated researcher and teacher, whose enthusiasm and love of geology inspired both students and colleagues at USM. Chris's interests in the fields of economic geology, geophysics, and remote sensing took him to more than a half-dozen countries over his academic and professional career. While at USM, Chris developed programs in geophysics and remote sensing that enhanced both educational and employment opportunities for students in the Department of Geology. He was an outstanding field geologist who taught the field methods course and who took every possible opportunity to work with students in the field. During his career, Chris authored or coauthored more than 40 published monographs, technical reports, journal articles, and abstracts, covering a wide range of geological and geophysical topics. A member of Sigma Xi since 1984, his professional affiliations also included the American Geophysical Union and the American Association of Petroleum Geologists.

Acknowledgments

The editors would like to thank the following people for reviewing the papers that appear in this volume. Their suggestions and advise have proved highly useful to the authors.

John E. Anderson, *Virginia Commonwealth University, Richmond, Virginia*

Douglas R. Caldwell, *U.S. Army Engineer Research and Development Center, Alexandria, Virginia*

Jeffrey D. Cawlfield, *University of Missouri, Rolla, Missouri*

Martin G. Culshaw, *British Geological Survey, Nottingham, England*

William S. Dershowitz, *Golder Associates, Inc., Redmond, Washington*

William W. Doe III, *Colorado State University, Fort Collins, Colorado*

Peter Doyle, *University of Greenwich, Chatham, England*

Herbert H. Einstein, *Massachusetts Institute of Technology, Cambridge, Massachusetts*

Paul R. Fisher, *U.S. Army Corps of Engineers (retired)*

Dennis Flannagan, *U.S. Department of Agriculture, West Lafayette, Indiana*

John Gerrard, *University of Birmingham, Birmingham, England*

Ron Gilmore, *U.S. Army Engineer Research and Development Center, Vicksburg, Mississippi*

John C. Jens, *U.S. Army Engineer Research and Development Center, Alexandria, Virginia*

Marie Johnson, *U.S. Army Military Academy, West Point, New York*

Robert A. Larson, *Los Angeles County Department of Public Works, Los Angeles, California*

William S. Leith, *U.S. Geological Survey, Reston, Virginia*

Major Kenneth MacDonald, *Fort Leonard Wood, Missouri*

Norbert H. Maerz, *University of Missouri, Rolla, Missouri*

David Montgomery, *University of Washington, Seattle, Washington*

Valerie A. Morrill, *Yuma Proving Ground, Yuma, Arizona*

Margaret A. Oliver, *University of Reading, Reading, England*

David Patrick, *University of Southern Mississippi, Hattiesburg, Mississippi*

Michael Rosenbaum, *Nottingham-Trent University, Nottingham, England*

Paul Santi, *University of Missouri, Rolla, Missouri*

Sally Shoop, *U.S. Army Engineer Research and Development Center, Hanover, New Hampshire*

Edward Tremba, *Defense Threat Reduction Agency, Albuquerque, New Mexico*

William K. Wedge, *Missouri Department of Natural Resources, Division of Geology and Land Survey, Rolla, Missouri*

Clinton S. Wilson, *Louisiana State University, Baton Rouge, Louisiana*

Foreword

The indefatigable lessons of history are replete with examples reflecting the criticality of the physical environment in the practice of the military arts. Consider Niccolo Machiavelli (1469–1527; cited in Collins, 1998, p. 27), who postulated, "In peace, soldiers must learn the nature of the land, how steep the mountains are, how the valleys debouch, where the plains lie, and understand the nature of rivers and swamps—then by means of the knowledge and experience gained in one locality, one can easily understand any other." In this volume, the impact of terrain and geology on military operations, particularly from an environmental viewpoint, is considered from several different perspectives.

Machiavelli's message has proved truly prophetic with the subsequent history of war: "In peace, soldiers must learn the nature of the land." Military forces can use geologic knowledge of the land surface to military advantage and must be able train on diverse and realistic terrain to adequately prepare for their military mission. Today, and even more so in the future, training and testing lands will be critical and finite resources. At a time when military doctrine is changing to increase the range and mobility of military operations and, thus, the need for larger land areas on which to train, base closures and the continuing growth of civilian suburban development in the vicinity of previously remote military installations (e.g., Camp Pendleton in southern California or the Fort Bragg area in central North Carolina) are reducing available training and testing space. Carrying-capacity estimates (Shaw and Kowalski, 1996) indicate that the U.S. Army is short of enough usable land to meet its training mission in an ecologically sustainable manner. The army both must understand the effects of its land use practices in the past and must use this knowledge to leverage all available tools to sustain and enhance the training effectiveness of existing lands. It is critical that sustainable development and effective training area management be practiced if the army is going to have the lands needed to train forces in the future. Unfortunate examples have clearly demonstrated that failure to sustain these lands can cost the military their use.

In a bigger picture, military training lands are a part of the public land trust, valuable natural resources that must be protected. At the same time, that land space is shrinking, and impacts grow as the intense pressure applied by modern military equipment increasingly wears on training lands. A 60-ton, fire-breathing armored vehicle moving cross-country at 30 miles per hour while concurrently firing multiple weapon systems is as environmentally challenging as it can get. In military terms, environmental geologists have a target-rich environment in which to practice their trade.

As concern for the environment has grown within the American public over the past three decades, so has the level of environmental legislation and regulation. Under the terms of the Federal Facilities Compliance Act of 1993, every federal department and agency is governed by current federal environmental regulations to the same extent as private sector entities, organizations, and businesses. As a result, every federal organization must comply with all environmental legislation, and each agency and its employees are legally responsible for their actions vis-à-vis the environment to the same extent as organizations and individuals in the private sector. For example, the U.S. Army is required to meet the conditions of the Clean Air Act, the Clean Water Act, the Toxic Substances Control Act, the Noise Control Act, the Resource Conservation and Recovery Act, the Endangered Species Act, and the Historic and Archaeological Preservation Act—just to name a few major pieces of legislation that currently affect the army.

   In addition to land use sustainability, base closures and heightened levels of environmental awareness by the general public have introduced new challenges for cleaning and restoring lands that have served as military installations for decades. Our legacy of environmental protection at military installations is not the most exemplary part of our military history. Until recently, it was generally considered by both the public and private sectors that nature would take care of itself. Also, there was the general assumption that natural resources were free and, therefore, it did not matter how military operations and facilities affected the environment. Certainly, these viewpoints prevailed within the Department of Defense and Department of Energy during the preparations for two world wars and throughout most of the subsequent half-century of the Cold War. The legacy of the hazardous substances developed, tested, and manufactured during this time—together with the toxic waste by-products arising from such activities, the impact of training activities on the natural landscape and its biodiversity, and the improper disposal of liquid and solid waste materials from normal day-to-day operations and activities—has had a significant adverse impact on the environment. Industrial operations, such as explosives manufacturing and vehicle maintenance as just two examples, have generated massive quantities of toxic wastes that, in some cases, have been disposed of through dangerous practices, mostly with ineffective land disposal practices. In addition, air, water, and soil pollution, training area abuses of the landscape, and mismanagement of toxic wastes at U.S. Army installations represent very real costs to the service. Currently, there are more than 10 000 sites on some 1200 present and past army installations in the territorial United States that are contaminated and in need of cleanup, the cost of which is estimated to be in excess of $25–30 billion. These costs include fines paid to state regulatory agencies, time and resources used to clean up spills of hazardous substances, lost training areas, delays in manufacturing operations, and negative impacts on overall military readiness. Therefore, the U.S. Army must care about the environment, and its senior leadership has taken a very proactive position in this context. Much money has already been spent, but there is not enough money to complete the cleanups without innovation. Today, the expense and technical complexity of cleaning up these contaminated sites challenge scientists to find cost-effective solutions that achieve protection of the public health and can be used to rehabilitate closed facilities for postmilitary, private sector use. As pointed out in the paper in this volume concerning Aberdeen Proving Ground (Dunbar et al.), arguably one of the U.S. Army's most significant cleanup challenges, accurate characterization of the subsurface is just one example of an absolutely critical tool to implementing effective solutions in contaminated site cleanups. In this context, the army has made its intent clear: "The army will be a national leader in environmental and natural resource stewardship for present and future generations as an integral part of our mission." (U.S. Army, 1992).

   The needs in the U.S. Army are great: proactive, sustainable training and testing lands management, innovation in land restoration, cost-effective environmental cleanup technology—the list goes on. The papers presented in this volume offer an informative view of the ongoing accomplishments of military geologists and allow a little peek at a bright future. I hope you find them valuable; I did.

Wendell "Chris" King, Ph.D.
Colonel, United States Army
Professor and Head
Department of Geography and
    Environmental Engineering
United States Military Academy
West Point, New York

REFERENCES CITED

Collins, J., 1998, Military geography: For professionals and the
    public: Washington, D.C., Brassey's, 437 p.
Shaw, R.B., and Kowalski, D.G., 1996, U.S. Army lands: A national
    survey: Fort Collins, Colorado, Center for Ecological Man-
    agement of Military Lands, Publication TPS 96-1, 44 p.
U.S. Army, 1992, Environmental strategy into the 21st century:
    Washington, D.C., U.S. Army, 20 p.

Geological Society of America
Reviews in Engineering Geology, Volume XIV
2001

Introduction

Allen W. Hatheway

*FGSA, Col. (EN, AUS, Retired), International Consultant on Mitigation, Remediation, and Forensics,
Rolla, Missouri, and Big Arm, Montana, USA*

ABSTRACT

It is with sadness, yet without reservation on the part of this retired soldier, that the findings of the twelve associated chapters in this volume portray a distressing military fact. Again, the traditional peacekeeping nations are flagging in their resolve to support democracy and peace among nations. The new millennium opens to a generational gap in which the young cannot sense that real dictators are far worse than cinema villains. Today's youth breathes the fresh air purchased by the toil of their oppressed predecessors. Citizens suffer a declining interest in maintenance of armed forces worldwide, yet we must be conscious of the force-multiplication factors that weigh heavily on providing the means for fewer soldiers, sailors, and airmen to keep the peace most effectively through constant and fervent attention to military geology. Professional soldiers and civilian members of the military forces must train more diligently to keep the peace, and must do so with constant regard for preservation of the training environment. First-world military forces now bear serious financial constraints and stringent requirements from their civilian leaders to care for the natural environment during training. I thank the authors for presenting their evidence of the new and expanded roles in conservation, maintenance of training, and preservation of peace at favorable cost-benefit ratios for and by those nations that are dedicated to peace through judicious military strength.

"What little you good people know of what we soldiers undergo,
when taking up arms to rid our country of alarms!"
—*U.S. Confederate States battle lament*

It's a fact that nobody loves a soldier when there is not a war going on. In fact, whatever attractions there are to soldiering are rapidly being lost on a world of young people no longer facing the spectre of traditional nuclear warfare. The concept of patriotic military service by the world's citizenry has drifted to a "Let George do it" situation. At the same time, those who do serve in defense of their nations must do so on reduced financial resources at the beginning of the new millennium—one fraught with superior weapons of mass destruction and weapons systems capable of supporting irrational, fanatic, or terrorist regimes. Entire regions are placed off balance and are suffering various degrees of intimidation by local dictators armed with "suitcase" destruc-

tion. At the root of the physical threat of the new-world terrorist regimes is guerrilla warfare, the age-old concept of the small-assets attacker choosing the time and place to confront the thinly spread world power or the less capable neighbor.

Since the days of Sun Tzu, the founding military strategist of ancient China, ca. 300 B.C., informed military commanders have known that military action is only the expression of national policy and that as such it is applied most often in the defense of democracy when diplomacy fails. Today's military forces—air, sea, and ground—are financially strapped by leaders and politicians who seek and address social issues as the highest priority in a world economy that is rapidly changing in

E-mail: allen@hatheway.net

Hatheway, A.W., 2001, Introduction, *in* Ehlen, J., and Harmon, R.S., eds., The Environmental Legacy of Military Operations: Boulder, Colorado, Geological Society of America Reviews in Engineering Geology, v. XIV, p. 1–6.

terms of national wealth and financial resources. Additional financial stress affects the U.S. military in the concept of total budgeting for all troop activities with respect to environmental protection and restoration imperatives. The cost of unfortunate events that may negatively affect the environment of training grounds must be taken from the total budget, and the quick result is diminishment of soldier training.

In the new "world economy," no superpower can be expected to carry the brunt of being world policeman and to be willing to constantly sacrifice the lives of its citizens for the sake of maintaining peace. But, aside from this situation, those responsible nations field military forces to maintain peace must have all of the advantages that science and technology can provide.

Even with smart bombs; depleted-uranium, tank-killing gun rounds; laser targeting; satellite communications and positioning; and radiological, biological, and chemical protective equipment, world peace will still ride on the shoulders of the individual ground soldier. Just as in Caesar's legions, the troops must occupy the right ground at the right time in order to protect and defend tomorrow's ever-challenged need to support rational and law-abiding forces of world peace.

Since the days of the world's first military logistician, General U.S. Grant, winning forces have come to realize that the key to ultimate victory is not only genius, courage, hard steel, and God's will and/or luck (depending on one's point of view), but placing the right number of well-equipped troops in the right place on the ground in the shortest period of time. Stretched worldwide, this is a nearly impossible task for the United Nations and the responsible nations that support its constant and ultimate goal of seeking and sustaining world peace.

The ground, yes, the ground. The ultimate proof of military capability lies in control and advantageous use of the ground. The ground is geology, and that geology is military geology. Modern military strategists and commanders know that the simple World War II concept of the "combat multiplier" must be achieved and that that number must be boosted to the ultimate achievable value, especially to counter the new threat in which the aggressor chooses the time and the place and can produce weapons of mass destruction from the suitcase of the world armaments industry.

This is the third volume of a worldwide contribution of geologists of many lands and many disciplinary backgrounds, brought together partially by citizen-soldier geologists and their civilian counterparts. (The first volume, *Military geology in war and peace*, edited by James R. Underwood, Jr., and Peter L. Guth, was published in 1998 by the Geological Society of America as Reviews in Engineering Geology, v. 13; the second volume, *Geology and warfare: Examples of the influence of terrain and geologists on military operations*, edited by E.P.F. Rose and C.P. Nathanail, was published by the Geological Society of London in 2000.) The authors of this volume have worked, or are working, in some aspect of the application of military geology, and it is their good works that support the day-to-day readiness and tomorrow's rapid response, all in the maintenance of peace.

Military geology remains a constant positive factor in preserving the force and in giving it sound advantages capable of increasing the combat multipliers of nations devoted to achievement and maintenance of world peace. Military geology now also includes measures to protect the environment and to conserve the allocated military training funds.

The chapters herein represent the efforts of Judy Ehlen and Russell Harmon, two professional geologists who live and work in and around the U.S. Army and whose daily lives are never without constant attention to improving the combat multiplier of the forces of democracy. The editors track active contributors to military geology and have invited a broad spread of specialists to speak and write about their contributions.

The reader likely will be surprised to learn of the many ways in which military geology appears in the "how, when, and where" equation of peacekeeping by the United Nations, as well as by NATO and the several other world-region defense treaty organizations. Nathanail (Chapter 2) provides a valuable peek at the conduct of military geologic operations that otherwise would not be available at the time of their conduct in "Terrain evaluation for peacekeeping with examples from Bosnia Herzegovina." We are faced with the author's realistic computation that limited wars are now occurring at the rate of 58 major military engagements ("wars") per year. Into this scenario, inject the prevalent use of armored fighting vehicles and the land-destruction capacity of such equipment, along with the employment of "smarter" weapons of greater physical-damage potential, and it is easy to see that more military geologic knowledge is of supreme use in carrying out a mission, especially far from the home base of most forces called to fight at least one side of the war.

In introducing Bosnia to the reader, Nathanail sketches in the geologic conditions of heavy influence in several historic campaigns and then sets out to deal with the current situation in the former Yugoslavia, which has escalated from his own first-hand experiences of just a few years ago.

Nathanail's message is twofold: (1) campaigns conducted without geologically based terrain intelligence likely will experience a turning point based on just that information, and (2) we are instructively reminded that military geologists can offer up-to-the-moment advice to the commander, advice that is more valuable for its rapid delivery than for the amount of detail.

Guth's chapter, "Quantifying terrain fabric in digital elevation models" (Chapter 3), is a mathematical representation of what is now possible in fast-acquisition military geologic studies, employing the astounding capabilities of digital elevation models (DEMs) and geographic information systems (GIS). With this data-acquisition and data-recovery capability, Guth pours relevant data into a DEM and emerges with a totally quantitative representation of the ground surface, in terms of whatever its repeatable geomorphic signature is, that is overwhelming.

This chapter is a fine example of the analysis of terrain information that previously was unaffordable to collect, both in time and effort, and that can be applied to denied areas. This is just the tip of an iceberg of terrain information, which, when converted to military geologic intelligence, can assist in focusing the combat commander's tactical options.

Jacobi, Eastler, and Xu (Chapter 4) and Ehlen (Chapter 5) are contemporary workers in the stark realization that masses of hard rock represent the most difficult of all terrain in which to detect and neutralize enemy installations. Free World interests have, for some years, been carried into the employment of defensive and offensive weapons to counter threats from enemy forces that would make extensive use of the underground.

"Hard-rock" engineering geologists have long known that the behavior of rock masses depends almost solely on the nature, frequency, orientation, and persistence of rock joints (discontinuities), as separated by an occasional shear zone or fault. The quantification of geologic information for resolution of many tactical combat threats, the embedded theme of this third military geology volume, is emerging from the enhanced capability (byte resolution) of remotely sensed imagery to provide what the foot soldier or officer specialist cannot obtain from denied areas occupied by the enemy.

The message Jacobi, Eastler, and Xu present in "Methodology for remote characterization of fracture systems in bedrock of enemy underground facilities" is simply that underground facilities sited in fractured bedrock will be extensively controlled, as to orientation and dimension, by the geometry of the rock-mass fracture system. This is one of the rules that engineering geologists follow when performing in rock-engineering roles, but here the rule can be extended to include remotely sensed, ground-surface evidence of such fracturing. The authors build on the message of Ehlen's earlier work (Ehlen, 1998) and make the point that lineament detection and fractal identification and interpretation may be the only geologic information available in areas denied to entry. Furthermore, the transformation of military geologic input into bedrock fracture system interpretation is nearly always available, because of scale deficiencies of existing geologic maps, in the uninterpreted form of today's standard military-intelligence imagery. The present paper serves as a strong reminder to be "modern" in seeking and using state-of-the-art military remotely sensed imagery.

Ehlen is a "hard-rocker" and hers is a true specialty of military geology. She has pioneered the application of remotely sensed and interpreted rock joints, as applied to established geologic work in rock engineering, but for the purpose of detection and to take combat advantage of the only forms of weakness in rock masses. In her 1998 paper, she investigated and proved certain first-hand statistical relationships among the various measurement parameters of rock discontinuities.

In "Predicting fracture properties in weathered granite in denied areas" (Chapter 5), Ehlen brings together the proven relationships and their relative levels of predictability by using a commercially available, three-dimensional (3-D) computer program to generate and graphically visualize rock fractures. Here, as is the general goal of 3-D plotting models, the idea is to graphically represent trends and associations that should serve for direct military interpretation for exploitation of rock-mass weaknesses. Ehlen

concludes that the 3-D mapping simulation produces useful, graphically plotted fractures representing as close and reliable a statistical summary as combat-support military geologists will be able to apply in advising combat commanders.

Ample evidence of the continuing need to develop means of employment of neutralization tactics is readily seen in the presence of North Korean invasion tunnels facing the United Nations Command in the Korean Demilitarized Zone, exemplified by the late Chris Cameron's "Battlefield terrain and engineering geology in the eastern Chorwon Valley, central Korean Peninsula" (Chapter 6). Cameron, another experienced hard-rock geologist and former U.S. Navy seaman, brought the lessons of Korean War military geology into his work and his work product. The nature of Cameron's work was identical to that of this reviewer: detection and neutralization of North Korean invasion tunnels, constructed in violation of the 1953 Armistice. Successful tunnel-hunting military geologists must also appreciate the inherent and historic North Korean affection for use of underground space.

Cameron's categorical findings are so fundamental, proven, and reliable as to constitute "rules" for conduct of military geology on the Korean Peninsula. These same findings constitute good, sound principles for employment in other mid-latitude granitic and metamorphic terranes, worldwide.

Fortress Gibraltar, a structural block of dolomitic limestone about 6 km^2 in area and in military use for more than 800 years, felt the impact of military defensive construction in perhaps the extreme sense, relative to other militarized areas in the world. With the end of the Cold War, a relaxed degree of control allowed for concepts of degrees of conversion to nonmilitary land use. Withdrawal of the last unit of the Royal Engineers to be stationed on Gibraltar gave Rose (Chapter 7, "Military engineering on the Rock of Gibraltar and its geoenvironmental legacy") a timely opportunity to reveal the military geologic "secrets" of his own long geologic and military involvement with this bastion.

Rose makes definitive connections between the options and constraints that have dominated what is possible in terms of siting, layout, and construction on the fortress rock. Geologic connections are stark; you deal with either Jurassic rock or less consolidated Quaternary materials. There is much from this chapter that can be adopted, worldwide, to maneuver and combat locations in which geologic conditions are as stark and controlling, but where it is necessary to accommodate populations or activities in areas of limited space.

Military forces nearly worldwide have been tightly confined to reservations set aside for training. No longer are the soils of these training areas subject to the passage of groups of soldiers marching or running with only their boots and bellies touching the ground. Thin-skinned and armored vehicles have been designed to traverse nearly all manner of terrain, geologic and vegetative. Consequently, the potential for forceful abuse of the terrain has increased immensely and has done so in the face of increased scientific and public concern for preservation of the landscape, if only to decrease the sedimentation induced by careless use of maneuver lands. Attendant also is concern for preservation of threatened and endangered species. There is one budget to cover all expenses, including ammunition and the costs of environmental damage. On the one hand, the commander is charged with being ready to fight, in terms of combat readiness, and at the same time, is also liable for "charges" of environmental damage. Any assistance that can be rendered to the commander, who must prepare soldiers to fight on a worldwide basis in the chaos of battle, is welcome, whereas all the while a "third eye" must guard against environmental damage. The chapters by Nichols and Bierman; Patrick and Boyd; Albertson; Gatto, Halvorson, and McCool; and Isaacson, Hurst, Miller, and Albertson address these issues.

Camp Iron Mountain was a key facility in the vast California-Arizona Maneuver Area (CAMA) created by General George Patton on his personal initiative just weeks after the Pearl Harbor attack on 7 December 1941. Patton was on site in January 1942 and had troops in training by March of that year. In fact, I was raised, in youth, not far from the western boundary of CAMA, and I geologically mapped and drilled in the early 1970s for a never-built nuclear power station at the former Rice Army Airfield within CAMA. The historic sense of military geology was with me throughout my mapping of hard-rock and unconsolidated units. Patton and his troops departed CAMA by July 1942 for the invasion of North Africa, but the ground at CAMA was indeed subjected to heavy maneuver use by other Army ground forces well into 1944.

In "Fifty-four years of ephemeral channel response to two years of intense World War II military activity, Camp Iron Mountain, Mojave Desert, California" (Chapter 8), Nichols and Bierman have discovered a fragile environmental record of military maneuver. We are indebted to them for sensing this and for recording and interpreting the long-term effects of such disturbances. Their work comes at a critical period in which the causative activities are interpretable in terms of long-term effects.

Nichols and Bierman's field methodology is solid and instructive for applied geomorphic studies of arid environments affected by quickly induced anthropogenic features. The authors' micro-topographic technique emphasizes capabilities of the Global Positioning System (GPS) in which planar locations have a greater study impact in the arid environment, whereas vertical positions can be averaged for the surface-water flow paths that are the main independent variable.

Patrick and Boyd's contribution (Chapter 9) "Wetlands and erosion studies in support of military training, Camp Shelby Training Site, Mississippi, USA," and other chapters in the book, clearly point out that the prime means of preservation of natural ground is by way of applied geomorphic classification of the land surface. The techniques of quantitative geomorphology and of incorporation of certain principles of soil science were ready and waiting in 1969 when the National Environmental Policy Act was passed in the United States and attention was directed toward incorporation of environmental stewardship at military reservations.

There is a distinct and rational gap between the interests of environmental preservation fostered by nonmilitary interests and the momentary tactical requirements placed on military commanders, who are charged with training and leading soldiers. The conceptual answer is simple: geoscientists will delimit geologically based areas in which the physical damage of combat training is to be minimized or denied, and then wildlife and watershed scientists will develop rules for conduct on areas allowed for active training use. Geoscience information is also imparted to the civil construction engineers who design training ranges scheduled for high-impact munitions and explosives. Patrick and Boyd leave us with a protocol for developing such geoscience templates.

The late Paul Albertson, an engineering geomorphologist, completed many military geologic assignments during his 22-year civilian career with the Corps of Engineers. As in the case of his other, co-authored chapter in this volume (described subsequently), Albertson has concentrated on the environmental protection aspect of military geology in "Sustainability of military lands: Historic erosion trends at Fort Leonard Wood, Missouri" (Chapter 10). Emphasis is on conserving the soldier-training dollar while husbanding the landscape.

In this study Albertson visited with the commander and his representatives and then devised an outgrowth application of soil science, as linked through soil-loss relationships, to the geologic setting of the military installation. A technique was developed whereby existing aerial photographs formed the basis of good engineering geologic mapping as the means of areal coverage of the active military installation, for the purpose of arresting and preventing future maneuver-generated damage to the land, practicing what the U.S. Army terms "landscape stewardship."

Albertson's useful contribution is fundamental. Take a close look at 60 years of information linking evidence of historic military land use impacts, then project backward into the Pleistocene epoch to judge relative forms of geologic susceptibility to geomorphic agents, and then project ahead to reduce sensitive impacts. Simple and understandable conceptual models were developed to extrapolate and extend proven relationships and sensitivities.

Gatto, Halvorson, and McCool (Chapter 11) have seized on a realistic basis for mitigating environmental-training damage in two naturally fragile terrains in the northern latitudes (Washington state and Vermont) in "Freeze-thaw–induced geomorphic and soil changes in vehicle ruts and natural rills." The solution is a blend of geomorphic and geotechnical engineering techniques where the depth of major concern is but 10–15 cm. Fragile crusts develop on soils in both areas, and thereafter control erosion rills developed along combat-vehicle ruts.

Simple, repeatable soil properties were measured, and statistically arrayed parameters led to indications related to freeze-thaw structures developed in the fragile soils during winters. From these indicators came simple suggestions for directional control of traffic that may limit erosion related to soil-crust damage.

The outstanding message of "Unsurfaced road investigation and management plan, Fort Leonard Wood, Missouri," by Isaacson, Hurst, Miller, and Albertson (Chapter 12) is that the utility of military geologic studies knows no end in terms of how such information can be developed, interpreted, and managed, for a wide variety of contemporary uses. Unlike the 1942–1944 situation of the California-Arizona Maneuver Area studied by Nichols and Bierman (previously described), that same type of vehicle-intensive maneuver training is going on today by the armies of the developed nations.

Fully arrived environmental sensitivity in the U.S. Army puts the commander in a nearly impossible situation: train the troops for maximum combat efficiency, but do so without environmental impairment. The same dollar that funds combat training also has to pay for environmental management and the maintenance of training-area roads; these are but a few of the competing uses of the training dollar.

Albertson and Miller, both experienced engineering geomorphologists, took on the Fort Leonard Wood "opportunity" as one of the training-management problems facing the commander at the Army's only combat engineer training post. Fort Leonard Wood, located in a fragile environment of lower Paleozoic karsts and residual soil of carbonate rocks, also trains engineer troops of all U.S. military forces, as well as engineer officers of many other nations. Working with Isaacson and Hurst, two geological engineering seniors, Albertson and Miller, took existing civil-engineering technology brought forward from the rural roads of the 1930s, arranged a series of seven road-damage and repair parameters and devised a means for "quick-and-dirty" assessments to direct priority, low-cost, road-maintenance measurements and repair measures to keep the commander's training mission on target with safety, access, and minimal dollars. The student authors played the role of experienced combat-engineer, noncommissioned officers and tested the ratings and interpretations.

Not surprisingly, modern (post-1900) military forces have produced their own "brownfields," also known as "derelict lands." Most of this ground now, in the new millennium, is pressed by some form of urban encroachment and ensuing desires to allow for multiple societal uses in a time mandating reduction of environmental threats stemming from the prior land use. Aberdeen Proving Ground (APG), such a societally stressed area, is described by Dunbar, Wakeley, Miller, and Swartzel in their paper "Geology without borders: A conceptual model for Aberdeen Proving Ground" (Chapter 13). APG was established in 1917 for the specialized role of developing both weapons and munitions.

As with most military reservations that are being reevaluated with respect to environmental concerns, there is much to be learned from the geologic case history of APG, and certainly as an eastern U.S. geologic analog as regards appropriate remediation. A disconformable downward sequence of Pleistocene to Cretaceous rocks, mostly unconsolidated sediments, presents the predictable high degree of impact on ground water quality. Additionally, the U.S. Superfund innovation of "operable units" and "solid-waste-management units" is well defined here and serves as an excellent introduction to a cross-linked military and civilian geoenvironmental technology.

Blake, in "Geoenvironmental factors in the regeneration of military airfields in Great Britain" (Chapter 14) produced a topical study regarding reutilization of military airfields as facilities no longer required for defense purposes. His message has far-ranging implications for postmilitary planning and implementation for all nations and also impinges on "brownfields" redevelopment of derelict industrial lands everywhere.

Particularly useful are Blake's summaries of the interrelationships of airfield and airport impacts on land use management and of geoscience considerations involved in airport siting. All the better that Blake is reflective of lessons learned, both positive and negative, and that geologic constraints and uncontrolled sources of hazardous waste are fully recognized.

Since the advent of quantitative geomorphology in the early 1960s, military geology has embraced most of this technology and has continued to observe the two primary divisions of practice, strategic and tactical. Actual applications of military geology continue to follow this now-traditional dichotomous nature, strategic military geologic studies being more speculative in terms of their potential use and derived mainly from remotely sensed imagery, as opposed to the tactical products, which are typically rapidly produced, more on demand, for actual planned or ongoing military operations.

In the same way, strategic military geologic work projects tend to employ mathematically based techniques that are more amenable to automatic imagery-scanning or the result of electromagnetic signatures returned and analyzed for statistically significant characteristics related mainly to trafficability, as well as effects of the deployment of special-effects weapons.

In both senses, the successful military geologist functions as a consultant of sorts, having a client in need of useful intelligence that can be derived in a short period of time, with sufficient accuracy to affect the outcome of battle. In almost all cases, strategic or tactical, the military geologic product emphasizes two essential philosophies, those of "go or no-go" and those involving relative degrees of qualitative importance, such as "high," "medium," and "low," in terms of factors affecting the military mission and the commander's choices of actions.

As practitioners of engineering geology, those who specialize in military geology are faced with a constant array of challenges to collect relevant data and to convert such data, as indicators of military geologic impact, to meaningful input to the commander, whose mind already is inundated with an endless chain of decisions affecting lives and the mission.

Those who practice in military geology should always strive to be part soldier and to envision the basic military tactics of "shoot, move, and communicate," as well as the concept of combat multipliers in which geologic conditions contribute strongly, either positively or negatively, toward the effectiveness of soldiers who can perform today's mission and yet survive to fight again, perhaps tomorrow.

There are many hidden messages in this broad compilation of technical geologic information. The editors have carefully included chapters that bring out one or more techniques that will be equally important to the broad practice of engineering geology, especially in such roles as resource management (particularly in forestry), land use planning, and international aid. This book should be read and referred to in terms of how its technology can be applied to generating useful interpretations dealing with the land.

REFERENCE CITED

Ehlen, J., 1998, A proposed method for characterizing fracture patterns in denied areas, *in* Underwood, J.R., Jr., and Guth, P.L., eds., Military geology in war and peace: Boulder, Colorado, Geological Society of America, Reviews in Engineering Geology, v. 13, p. 151–163.

MANUSCRIPT ACCEPTED BY THE SOCIETY OCTOBER 27, 2000

Geological Society of America
Reviews in Engineering Geology, Volume XIV
2001

Terrain evaluation for peacekeeping with examples from Bosnia Herzegovina

C. Paul Nathanail

Land Quality Management, School of Chemical, Environmental and Mining Engineering, University of Nottingham,
University Park, Nottingham NG7 2RD, UK

ABSTRACT

Geology has influenced military commanders and the outcome of military operations since ancient times. Terrain evaluation was developed in the 1960s and has benefited greatly from recent developments in GIS (geographic information systems). Peacekeeping operations are increasingly becoming a component of armed forces workload. Geologic support based on terrain evaluation principles was provided to the UN and NATO during peacekeeping and humanitarian relief operations in Bosnia Herzegovina. This included assessments of slope stability, seismic hazard, flood risk, groundwater potential, and construction materials.

The role of the geologist advising military commanders during peace support operations essentially becomes a hybrid of those roles of military geologists and conventional civilian engineering geologists. As ever, training in the engineering operations of the "client" is essential to delivering a successful product—usually defined as an approximate answer within a very limited time frame rather than a "good" answer late.

INTRODUCTION

The end of the Cold War at the beginning of the 1990s should, in theory, have led to a reduction in armed forces across the world. However, armed conflicts abound and peacekeeping operations have expanded. Since 1989 there have been, on average, 58 wars a year (Smith, 1997). It should be noted that Smith has defined a war as a conflict with at least 25 battle-related deaths. Increasingly, multinational forces are being deployed either to maintain or to enforce peace in various parts of the world. The recently ratified Ottawa Convention made the use of antipersonnel mines illegal. The United Kingdom has passed directives to its own armed forces that prohibit the use of antipersonnel mines in warfare. One of the major deployments of British troops in recent years was to the Balkans—the former Yugoslav republics of Macedonia, Croatia, Slovenia, and Bosnia Herzegovina. Geological advice has contributed to the success of the operations under the United Nations Protection Force (UNPROFOR), the North Atlantic Treaty Organization (NATO) Implementation Force (IFOR), and later the Stabilization Force (SFOR). Geological advice has drawn on the principles of terrain evaluation developed in the 1960s and has made use of digital data availability and the technologies of geographic information systems (GIS) and remote sensors. As summarized herein, the terrain has had an impact on military activities since ancient times. Work to formalize understanding of this impact was carried out in the 1960s in the UK and is reviewed later. However, it was not until the advent of GIS and digital data that the techniques could be put to realistic use, as shown here with the UNPROFOR effort in Bosnia Herzegovina.

TERRAIN AND MILITARY ACTIVITIES

It has been said that terrain always influences and sometimes controls the outcome of military operations. To this should be added that the information available about the terrain can greatly influence a commander's tactics. Historical examples of how terrain can affect military decisions are given by many authors (e.g., Eggenberger, 1967; Spink, 1996; Rose and Pareyn, 1998).

E-mail: paul.nathanail@nottingham.ac.uk

Nathanail, C.P., 2001, Terrain evaluation for peacekeeping with examples from Bosnia Herzegovina, *in* Ehlen, J., and Harmon, R.S., eds., The Environmental Legacy of Military Operations: Boulder, Colorado, Geological Society of America Reviews in Engineering Geology, v. XIV, p. 7–12.

Rose and Pareyn described how British military geologists, armed with aerial photographs and maps, demonstrated both the limitations of the Contentin Peninsula (amply demonstrated by the struggle the U.S. armed forces had in clearing the peninsula of Axis forces) and the advantages of the Normandy beach area. Of course, nothing is better than seeing the ground, and a military geologist was flown over the Normandy area, at low height and upside down, to afford a better view (Ladd, 1983).

Mitchell (1991) reviewed two twentieth-century examples: the Somme-Flanders battlefield in World War I and the Falkland Islands battlefields in 1982.

The Somme-Flanders lowland is strategically vital, not only because it is the narrowest point on the northern European plain, but specifically because it covers the gap between the Artois and Ardennes barriers. It forms the only route into France from Germany without significant terrain obstacles. Battles during both world wars centered on the lowland via command of the surrounding heights. The Artois barrier is a chalk upland, terminated on the north by the Vimy ridge (Rosenbaum, 1989), and the Ardennes barrier is a Paleozoic upland reaching a height of about 600 m. Some of the fiercest battles of World War I were fought on the Flanders clay plain and on the rolling chalk plain of the Somme. The geology had significant and inadequately appreciated impacts on the armed forces of both sides. The Flanders clay is especially fine grained and usually wet: it has a very low permeability. In this condition, vehicle, animal, and human mobility were significantly decreased. Troops were exposed for a longer time to enemy observation because they moved slowly, if at all; weapons effectiveness decreased; equipment became mired and could not be moved easily, and the wounded suffocated. Digging was difficult, trench stability was reduced, and excavations soon filled with water. Water, which is in itself essential for survival, was abundant, but frequently contaminated. Natural construction materials were usually absent.

British success in the Falklands conflict in 1982 hinged on the rapid availability of terrain intelligence following the unexpected invasion of a little-known area (Rosenbaum, 1998). Despite a poorly populated database and limited time, information was provided regarding potential landing sites for aircraft and paratroops, predicting site conditions at beaches, trafficability over boggy and open terrain, and outcrops offering command points of tactical importance. In contrast to World War I, commanders had good, timely terrain information that could be used in planning.

TERRAIN EVALUATION

Terrain evaluation developed in response to the need for an understanding of terrain by a number of disciplines, including geology, hydrology, geography, botany, zoology, ecology, pedology, and meteorology, as well as applied sciences such as agriculture, forestry, civil and military engineering, and landscape planning (Anon., 1982; Mitchell, 1991).

Mitchell (1991) pointed out that "terrain" comprises a tract of country considered with regard to its natural features and con-

figuration, whereas "evaluation" is defined as the act or result of expressing the numerical value of or judging the worth of an object. Therefore, "terrain evaluation" is the process of expressing properties about the terrain in terms of numerical values and/or making some sort of judgment about the properties of that terrain for a particular use. The term "terrain evaluation" grew from research carried out in the 1960s in the UK under the auspices of the Military Engineering Experimental Establishment (MEXE; later the Military Vehicles and Engineering Establishment, MVEE, and now part of the Defence Evaluation and Research Agency, DERA). Terrain evaluation involves the collection of information about the terrain; the abstraction, classification, storage, and reproduction of such information to make it available quickly and cheaply to others; and finally, the means by which this result can be achieved. The sorts of information required for the earth sciences include the nature and distribution of near-surface materials, information on past processes and likely future processes, and the impact of these processes on those materials.

The MEXE system used a tiered classification of land with information stored at each tier in such a way that it could be made rapidly available and could also be extrapolated to unknown areas on the basis of physiographic similarities recognized on either remotely sensed imagery or aerial photography (the "analog" concept). Although developed in the 1960s, terrain evaluation was essentially a solution waiting for a technology to allow it to gain widespread use. GIS, which arrived in the late 1970s and 1980s, was that technology. At a MEXE conference in the 1960s, Brigadier J.R. Blomfield (1967, p. 29) asked: "Is the thing going to die in six months time when we say we have no money or effort left or is there some other means of carrying on?" He went on to speculate that, by the multiple nature of use, "I mean that whereas it started off here at MEXE, obviously as a principally military use, it is now clear that it involves or can have many engineering usages: agricultural, econometric, transport, operational planning, resource, raw materials uses, and so on." A.O. Barrie, Group Leader at MEXE, recognized that "if you really want to know what a piece of ground is like or what it is good for you have got to go there" (Barrie, 1967, p. 34). He went on to suggest that "if you use the proposed terrain evaluation technique it would tell you where to sample instead of doing what they had all been taught as young engineers, that is to sample every 500 feet or so." He suggested that the technique would tell you that "perhaps over 100 miles of road alignment, you would only have to check this technique to tell you that over 100 miles of a proposed road location you may only have to check perhaps three points."

In fact, one of the advantages of terrain evaluation is that it can help one say a lot about a piece of ground *without* ever having been there. This was the basis on which J.D. Bernel suggested the use of a beach near Brancaster, Norfolk, on the east coast of England, for training special forces prior to deploying for a reconnaissance of the geologically similar beaches at Arromanches where one of the two floating Mulberry Harbours was to be constructed for the invasion of Normandy in 1944 (Ladd, 1983). It also provides the basis for the work described in this chapter.

So terrain evaluation was born in response to a need for timely and acceptably imperfect answers to assist commanders in making decisions about military operations. For military activities (which may be thought of as essentially civil engineering operations, but with emphasis on less permanent works and those requiring very rapid response times) interest focuses on lines of sight; suitability of the ground for excavating trenches and fortifications; holding of posts, pegs, and mines; accepting parachute drops; and sustaining the passage of troops and vehicles. Terrain evaluation also includes finding sufficient quantities of water and construction materials. Terrain evaluation, under various names, is routinely used by geologists in both civil and military engineering applications.

THE ROLE OF MILITARY GEOLOGY IN PEACEKEEPING

Military geology has benefited greatly from the development of the theory of terrain evaluation and of such tools as GIS and remote sensing. The role of a geological advisor to a military commander is to understand the commander's intent; to grasp any geologic or terrain constraints on the commander's actions; to deduce the influence of geologic and other terrain factors on those actions; to interpret the ground conditions; and, finally, to communicate findings to the commander in a simple, easily understood manner.

As such, the geologist needs to understand both how military operations evolve and how the geology might influence that evolution. This knowledge requires professional competence in geology, preferably in an applied subdiscipline such as engineering geology, and military competence both to understand operations and to convince commanders of their opinions. The principal tasks of military geologists are to assist in the protection of troops and equipment, to select suitable sites, to predict mobility of men and vehicles, and to locate resources such as water and construction materials.

Time is often tight and information usually inadequate. Nevertheless, a timely, imperfect answer is of some use, whereas a perfect but tardy answer would be of no use. For this reason, the British Army in the 1960s expended considerable resources, through MEXE, in developing templates for terrain evaluation in a variety of geologic conditions.

Peacekeeping may involve any or all of the following:
• Observation of treaty boundaries, especially soon after treaties have been signed
• Maintaining peace between former belligerents
• Imposing peace between warring factions

The delivery of humanitarian aid or the assistance of nongovernmental organizations in such delivery may take place during any of these tasks or indeed without any of them.

Nathanail (1995) described work to improve trafficability and visibility along the "green line" between the southern part of the Republic of Cyprus and the Turkish-occupied northern part of the island. Nathanail (1998) highlighted the role of geology in

the first deployment of the British Army's well-drillers to Bosnia to secure water supplies for the British and Dutch contingents of UNPROFOR troops. Holland (1999) described the construction of a septic tank to service 4800 British soldiers deployed to Macedonia during *Operation Upminster*. The design was based on ground conditions and proximity to a water-supply borehole as well as a desire to operate to European Union standards.

UNPROFOR

UNPROFOR is reputed to be the biggest, most expensive, and most complex peace operation in the history of the UN. Its goals were to keep the peace and build confidence between the warring sides to help achieve a final political solution and restore normal life to Croatia, where it was initially deployed. UNPROFOR was initially established as an interim arrangement to create the conditions for peace and security required for the negotiation of an overall settlement of the Yugoslav crisis (http://www.un.org/Depts/DPKO/Missions/unprofor.htm). In June 1992, as the conflict extended to Bosnia and Herzegovina (Fig. 1), UNPROFOR's mandate and strength were enlarged to ensure the security and functioning of the airport at Sarajevo as well as the delivery of humanitarian assistance to that city and its environs. In September 1992, UNPROFOR's mandate was further enlarged to enable it to support efforts by the UN High Commissioner for Refugees to deliver humanitarian relief throughout Bosnia Herzegovina and to protect convoys of released civilian detainees, if the International Committee of the Red Cross so requested. UNPROFOR also monitored the implementation of a cease-fire agreement signed by the Bosnian government and Bosnian Croat forces in February 1994, and the cease-fire arrangements negotiated between the Bosnian government and Bosnian Serb forces that went into effect on 1 January 1995.

Geology of Bosnia Herzegovina

Bosnia Herzegovina is located in the Dinarids, part of the Alpine mountain chain that marks the collision between Africa and the European continental plate (Embleton, 1984). Two collision events seem to have taken place, one lasting from the Late Jurassic through the middle Cretaceous and the second possibly beginning as early as the Paleocene and going on through the Pleistocene (Ager, 1980). The Dinaric Alps comprise mainly carbonate rocks that have been folded parallel to the coastline of former Yugoslavia. The Middle Triassic-to-Cretaceous limestones were strongly folded and thrust upward during the Eocene. Additional uplift and erosion by major rivers followed in the Miocene. The whole length of the former Yugoslavia contains many classic karst features, and many type localities for karst terrain are located in this area of the world (Bridges, 1991).

The Dinarids take their name from Mount Dinara and comprise eight tectonic and paleogeographic zones (Fig. 2): Serbo Macedonian massif, Vardar zone, Golija zone, Serbian zone, Bosnian zone, High Karst zone, Budva zone, and Dalmatian zone.

Figure 1. Location of Bosnia Herzegovina (shaded area; after http://www.graphicmaps.com/graphic_maps.htm).

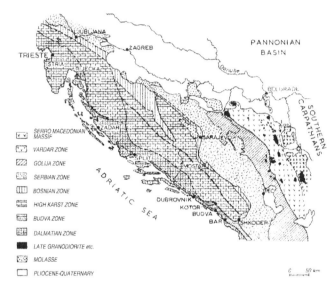

Figure 2. Main tectonic zones in the Dinarides (after Ager, 1980).

Bosnia contains terrain from the Dalmatian zone, the High Karst zone, the Bosnian zone, and the Serbian zone (Ager, 1980). The Dalmatian zone extends from a peninsula of Istria, on the Italian border, all the way down to Albania. The general northwesterly strike of the rocks is evidenced by the extremely elongated islands off the Croatian coast at Zadar and north of Dubrovnik (Fig. 2). The zone is lithologically dominated by Triassic limestone, other carbonates, and some evaporites.

The High Karst zone comprises white limestone mountains that have been eroded into deep valleys and caves. Much of the surface water has disappeared underground and given rise to karst terrain. The limestones range from Middle Triassic to Late Cretaceous in age and are in places intercalated with bauxites. They rest on basal Triassic rocks, which in turn lie on a Paleozoic floor.

Flysch constitutes the main part of the narrow Bosnian zone between two major thrusts and represents a trough that persisted at least from the beginning of the Jurassic until the Late Cretaceous (Ager, 1980). Sarajevo is built on the Bosnian zone flysch. The Jurassic succession generally comprises pelagic limestone with chert passing up to radiolarites, then into the thick Bosnian flysch.

Much of this zone and the Serbian zone discussed subsequently are concealed beneath postorogenic Oligocene-Miocene molasse.

The Serbian zone largely comprises ophiolites whose dark color gives Montenegro its name. In places the preophiolite continental crust comprising Paleozoic basement is exposed, overlain by Lower Triassic red sandstone. Within Bosnia, the ophiolite sequence is overlain conformably by flysch that spans the Jurassic-Cretaceous boundary and corresponds with the flysch of the Bosnian zone to the southwest. Ager (1980) reported that this is one of the rare places in Europe where the direct relationship of ophiolites and flysch can be seen.

Dearman et al. (1989) recognized that Bosnia lies within one of the tectonically active regions of the world where tectonism would affect the distribution of the principal types of weathering. The country is characterized by complex mountain relief and extensive geodynamic processes. The lower and middle levels undergo chemical weathering of the rocks, resulting in the deposition of a thick, clayey cover over bedrock. Abundant rainfall and groundwater enhance the development of landslides.

The mean annual precipitation in the Dinaric Alps is about 1000 mm (extreme values are 258 mm and 4926 mm), and runoff averages $15.31 \cdot m^2 \cdot sec$. The role of surface runoff in the evolution and dissection of the relief is evident; the flysch and molasse hills in eastern Serbia, with annual precipitation of under 600 mm, are less dissected than are the western parts of Slovenia, which receive more rain.

Many geomorphologic terms have been derived from the Slovenian and Serbo-Croatian languages, such as *doline*, a circular depression; *polje*, a linear depression; *ponor*, a sink hole; and *uvala*, a large depression due to the coalescence of dolines.

In the Dinarids, the carbonate series of the Dinarid zone and the inner Dinarian syncline region are subject to extensive karstification. Seismic activity of the region is high and has a high rate of recurrence. The southeastern end of the region is the most active. The mountainous part of the Dinarids represents a system of extensive faulted and folded block structures. Large parts are formed from Mesozoic limestone. As the intramontane basin and some poljes lagged behind during the general tectonic uplift of the Dinarids in the Neogene, sediment that once formed part of a larger mantle is preserved in them (e.g., in the Sarajevo basin).

TABLE 1. LANDSLIDE POTENTIAL FOR BOSNIA HERZEGOVINA

Unit	Age of rocks	Gradient	Landslide potential	Lithology
Q	Quaternary	Low	Low	Glacial and river sediments
J,K	Jurassic, Cretaceous	Medium–high	High	Clastic rocks, limestone, mudstone, limestone interfaces
P_3	Permian	Medium	High	Permian clastic rocks and schists
D	Devonian	Medium	High	Devonian sedimentary rocks
S,D	Silurian–Devonian	Medium	High	Silurian–Devonian carbonates and shales
M	Unknown	Medium	High	Marbles

Terrain-evaluation tasks

Several terrain-evaluation tasks arose during the time that UNPROFOR, IFOR, and SFOR were deployed in Bosnia Herzegovina. These included assessments of slope stability, seismic hazard, flood risk, groundwater potential, and construction materials.

Slope stability. The efforts to secure peace and provide humanitarian aid relied upon the main supply routes (MSRs) being trafficable. Concern was therefore expressed about the potential for ground movement that would lead to MSR closure.

The first task was to evaluate slope failure and the angle at which slope failure was likely to occur for a range of different soils throughout Bosnia. Geologic maps at a scale of 1:500 000 were interpreted in terms of landslide potential purely on the basis of the geologic materials within each map unit (Table 1). A digital terrain model was used to derive slope angles. Slopes were then grouped into the following classes:

$<12°$
$12° – <25°$
$25° – <45°$
$45° – <70°$
$70° – <90°$

An overall slope stability rating was then assigned by combining slope angle and geologic landslide potential.

Once IFOR had deployed, teams of military engineers were assigned to maintain and upgrade the MSRs. One such task involved reconstructing a high gabion wall to support a hairpin bend on a road. Geological advice centered on assessing slope stability and the feasibility of the conceptual design.

Seismic hazard assessment. Bosnia is a tectonically active country, and an assessment was required of likely seismic hazard. A literature review was conducted in an attempt to identify a preexisting seismic hazard assessment map or study. Many papers on individual seismic events and on seismological studies on individual fault zones or across regions were retrieved. However, none dealt with the distribution of seismic hazards across the country. It became apparent, however, that the entire country may be thought of as tectonically active, judging from the brief review of the history of seismic activity and predictions of future activity. It was obvious that earthquakes would occur, but the questions of where and when they would occur could not be addressed in any useful manner. The approach adopted, therefore, was to assume an earthquake could take place anywhere and to try to predict the influence of such movement on soil properties and therefore on any affected structures. In essence the country was classified into two areas: (1) areas comprising silt or fine-sand deposits that may be expected to attenuate seismic movement, and (2) areas comprising solid rock, clay, and gravel that would not be expected to incur undue ground motions. The locations of sensitive structures and of high population density above susceptible soils represented the areas of principal concern.

Flood risk assessment. During IFOR's time in Bosnia, concern was raised about the possibility of flooding from the collapse of dams weakened either through lack of maintenance or through damage during the fighting. The solution involved assessing the physiography downstream of the dam in order to evaluate how high floodwaters would be likely to rise and whether settlements or other important structures would be affected. The geology was a secondary factor in the evaluation. This task proved impossible to complete from the UK with the limited availability of large-scale mapping that is essential to assess the likely downstream response to a dam collapse. Therefore the task was handled by terrain analysts in the field.

Groundwater potential. Secure sources of drinking water became a critical concern to British Forces during *Operation Grapple*, the British contribution to the UN humanitarian relief operation in Bosnia. A geologist was deployed to Bosnia to assess groundwater conditions at four British bases and one Dutch base (Nathanail, 1998). A well-drilling team deployed several times and successfully constructed wells at many UN bases throughout the former Republic of Yugoslavia (Wye, 1994).

Construction materials assessment. Quarrying operations were conducted by UN and NATO troops from the early days of British involvement in *Operation Grapple* onward (Jackson, 1997). The initial need was for material to use in widening and maintaining MSRs. Material was extracted from local borrow pits to minimize the need for haulage and the risk of convoys being compromised by warring parties.

It was not feasible to have a geologist on the ground at all times. Instead, ground reconnaissance was conducted with the military plant foreman (MPF) in order to assess the likely types of ground that would yield significant quantities of usable material (Nathanail, 1998). Areas highly unlikely to yield good material were also identified. This enabled the MPF and his staff to carry out detailed reconnaissance of future borrow-pit sites with a preliminary geologic conceptual model and/or mental map.

IFOR requirements were for camp construction, major route construction, and maintenance works for which higher-quality crushed rock aggregate was needed. For these, the MPF used geologic maps dating from World War II, ground and heliborne reconnaissance, and limited testing of samples to evaluate ground conditions and material suitability (Jackson, 1997).

CONCLUSIONS

Peacekeeping operations are increasingly becoming a component of armed forces workload. The role of the geologist advising military commanders essentially becomes a hybrid of those of military geologists and conventional civilian-engineering geologists. As ever, training in the engineering operations of the "client" is essential to delivering a successful product—usually defined as an approximate answer within a very limited time frame rather than a "good" answer late. By applying basic principles of terrain evaluation and modern technology, relevant and useful geological advice was provided to UN and NATO forces in Bosnia Herzegovina within the operational time frame.

REFERENCES CITED

Ager, D.V., 1980, The geology of Europe: London, McGraw-Hill Book Company, 634 p.

Anonymous, 1982, Land surface evaluation for engineering practice: Report by a working party under the auspices of the Geological Society [London]: Quarterly Journal of Engineering Geology, v. 15, p. 265–316.

Barrie, A.O., 1967, General Discussion. Terrain Evaluation Symposium held at MEXE Christchurch: Hampshire, UK: London, Ministry of Defence, MEXE Report No. 1053, p. 34.

Blomfield, J.R., 1967, General discussion. Terrain Evaluation Symposium held at MEXE Christchurch: Hampshire, UK: London, Ministry of Defence, MEXE Report No. 1053, p. 29.

Bridges, E.M., 1991, World geomorphology: Cambridge, Cambridge University Press, 260 p.

Dearman, W.R., Sergev, E.M., and Shibakova, V.S., 1989, Engineering geology of the earth: Moscow, Nauka Publishers, 247 p.

Eggenberger, D., 1967, A dictionary of battles: From 1479 to the present: London, George Allen and Unwin, Ltd., 526 p.

Embleton, C., 1984, Geomorphology of Europe: London, Macmillan Press, 465 p.

Holland, G.R.N., 1999, And they thought it was another swimming pool: The Royal Engineers Journal, v. 113, p. 194–199.

Jackson, P., 1997, Quarrying operations in Bosnia Hercegovina: The Royal Engineers Journal, v. 111, p. 72–75.

Ladd, J.D., 1983, SBS, the invisible raiders: The history of the Special Boat Squadron from World War Two to the present: Glasgow, Fontana, 381 p.

Mitchell, C.W., 1991, Terrain evaluation (second edition): Oxford, Longman Scientific and Technical, 441 p.

Nathanail, C.P., 1995, Assessments of ease of blasting in Troodos Sheeted Dyke Complex and Lower Pillow Lava Series, *in* Eddleston, M., et al., eds., Engineering geology in construction: Engineering Geology Special Publication 10, p. 355–359.

Nathanail, C.P., 1998, Hydrogeological assessments of United Nations bases in Bosnia Hercegovina, *in* Underwood, J.R., Jr., and Guth, P.L., eds., Military geology in war and peace: Geological Society of America, Reviews in Engineering Geology, v. 13, p. 211–216.

Rose, E.P.F., and Pareyn, C., 1998, British applications of military geology for Operation Overlord and the battle in Normandy, France, 1944, *in* Underwood, J.R., Jr., and Guth, P.L., eds., Military geology in war and peace: Geological Society of America, Reviews in Engineering Geology, v. 13, p. 55–66.

Rosenbaum, M.S., 1989, Geological influence of tunnelling under the western front at Vimy Ridge: Proceedings of the Geologists' Association, v. 100, p. 135–140.

Rosenbaum, M.S., 1998, Background and recent applications of military geology in the British armed forces, *in* Underwood, J.R., Jr., and Guth, P.L., eds., Military geology in war and peace: Geological Society of America, Reviews in Engineering Geology, v. 13, p. 125–134.

Smith, D., 1997, The state of war and peace atlas: London, Penguin, 128 p.

Spink, K., 1996, Geological constraints at the battle of Waterloo: Bath, Geological Society [London], Applied Geoscience, Warwick, Abstracts, p. 27.

Wye, T., 1994, Well drilling in Bosnia: The Royal Engineers Journal, v. 108, p. 149–153.

MANUSCRIPT ACCEPTED BY THE SOCIETY OCTOBER 27, 2001

Geological Society of America
Reviews in Engineering Geology, Volume XIV
2001

Quantifying terrain fabric in digital elevation models

Peter L. Guth
Department of Oceanography, 572 Holloway Road, U.S. Naval Academy, Annapolis MD 21402-5026, USA

ABSTRACT

Eigenvector analysis of a topographic landform reveals a directional fabric consisting of surface roughness or slope, organization or fabric strength, and preferred orientation. This analysis uses a digital elevation model (DEM) to compute slope and aspect at all points in a region and uses those values to define the normal surface. Standard techniques contour the distributions, extract eigenvectors and eigenvalues from the matrix of the sum of cross products of the directional cosines, and compute eigenvalue ratios. The terrain fabric at a point depends on the size of the region used for the computation and reveals different scales over which directional fabrics operate. WIth large-scale DEMs, the directional fabric varies in a systematic manner and proves relatively insensitive to the horizontal resolution of the DEM or its quality and creation method. Quantitative measurement of terrain fabric belongs in all studies of terrain analysis and geomorphometry.

INTRODUCTION

Digital elevation models (DEMs) provide the fundamental data set for digital terrain analysis and geomorphometry. DEMs create base maps for display of other map data, allow rapid and easy visualization of surface landforms, and automate calculations previously done laboriously by hand by using measurements from paper maps. Other data sets—satellite imagery, aerial photography, digitized maps, or vector overlays—can supplement and enhance a DEM, but rarely with as much geomorphological information in as compact a data file.

Pike (1988) listed a dozen groups of parameters used as terrain descriptors, about half dealing with spatial (*x, y*) characters and half with vertical (*z*) parameters. Pike (1988) focused his discussion on five descriptive categories: altitude, slope between topographic reversals, slope at constant slope length, slope curvature, and the power spectrum. He used manually digitized data at 30 m resolution and a resulting "geometric signature" to categorize terrain characteristics and suggest the degree of danger from landslides. Since his work, an increasing number of high-quality DEMs have appeared to make geomorphometry increasingly accurate and automated.

Pike et al. (1989) documented the unfortunate definition of the term "grain" in the literature. An intuitive definition of topographic grain, for the strength and orientation of ridges and valleys, corresponds with the grain of wood and other natural materials. Pike et al. (1989) focused on the characteristic horizontal spacing of major ridges and valleys as topographic grain, which would only be part of a broader definition of grain. Here, the term "fabric" refers to the orientation in space of the elements making up the landscape, an approach consistent with the usage of the term in structural geology and petrology. This concept of terrain fabric includes both strength, ranging from highly organized to random, and direction, corresponding to the orientation of the ridges and valleys.

Investigations of the spatial patterns of terrain have used the variogram (e.g., Vergne and Souriau, 1993) or the power spectrum (e.g., Pike and Rozema, 1975). These analyses have generally determined the strength and spacing of periodic landforms. Pattern recognition with DEMs uses many of the same techniques associated with image analysis and has focused primarily on lineament extraction (e.g., Raghavan et al., 1993; Koike et al., 1998). Numerous researchers (e.g., Gardner et al., 1990) have investigated the extraction of geomorphometric parameters relat-

E-mail: pguth@usna.edu

Guth, P.L., 2001, Quantifying terrain fabric in digital elevation models, *in* Ehlen, J., and Harmon, R.S., eds., The Environmental Legacy of Military Operations: Boulder, Colorado, Geological Society of America Reviews in Engineering Geology, v. XIV, p. 13–25.

ing to drainage patterns and basins from DEMs. This chapter presents an eigenvector routine to determine the strength orientation of topographic fabric. Although topographic fabric could be used for terrain classification on scales from global to local, this study focuses on fabric as a point descriptor of terrain that provides a suitable input for terrain analysis and ultimately for cross-country mobility studies.

METHODS

Chapman (1952) proposed a quantitative technique of topographic analysis, i.e., the contouring of normal vectors to the earth's surface by using standard structural geology procedures. He manually computed slope and aspect (downhill direction) from topographic maps and plotted and contoured the diagrams by hand. Guth (1995) computerized the process using a DEM. In this method, the slope and aspect define a vector normal to the earth's surface, plotted onto the lower hemisphere of an equal-area projection (also called a Lambert projection or Schmidt net). Contouring the resulting density distribution creates a visual representation of the fabric. Densities are expressed in terms of the percentage of points within a 1% area on the plot. Because of the difficulty involved in manual computations, plotting, and contouring, Chapman's method, termed a statistical slope orientation (SSO) diagram, never became popular.

Woodcock (1977) discussed an eigenvalue method for the representation of fabric shapes in structural geology, paleomagnetism, sedimentology, and glaciology. This method is applied here to DEMs to quantify Chapman's (1952) technique. As modified for topographic fabric, Woodcock's algorithm uses the following steps: (1) At each point within the region of interest, calculate the slope and aspect. (The slope and aspect define a vector normal to the earth's surface. This work used a hybrid algorithm involving the steepest adjacent neighbor for slopes and unweighted eight nearest neighbors for aspect.) (2) Plot each point on a lower-hemisphere, equal-area projection. (3) Compute the direction cosines of the normal vector. (4) Create a 3×3 matrix of the sums of the cross products of the direction cosines for all points in the analysis region. (5) Contour the graphical projections by using the traditional method of counting points in a 1% circle (Guth, 1987) to create an SSO diagram. (6) Extract the eigenvalues and eigenvectors from the 3×3 matrix, by using an algorithm from Press et al. (1986). (7) Normalize the three eigenvalues; S_1 is the largest. (8) Compute and graph the ratios $\ln(S_1/S_2)$ and $\ln(S_2/S_3)$. (9) The ratio $K = \ln(S_1/S_2)/\ln(S_2/S_3)$ and the term $c = \ln(S_1/S_3)$ define a shape and strength factor, respectively.

Guth (1999a) reported on results from eigenvector analysis of terrain organization. He concentrated on using subsets of at least 10 000 points from DEMs ranging from 30 m to 30 arc second (roughly 1 km) spacing. The reported analysis for large geographic areas involved four generalizations: (1) Normalized eigenvalues $S_1 \gg S_2 \approx S_3$. (2) Eigenvector S_1 is essentially vertical because the average orientation is nearly horizontal. (3) Eigenvector S_3 defines the dominant direction of topographic fabric.

(4) The term $\ln(S_1/S_2)$ correlates strongly with strength factor (c) and defines a flatness parameter of terrain, and $\ln(S_2/S_3)$ correlates strongly with shape factor (K) and defines the organization of the terrain.

Guth (1999a) sought regional-terrain classification, clearly possible with eigenvector analysis from DEMs. The present study seeks to extend the analysis to point calculations of much smaller regions, for which some of the four listed generalizations need modification.

This work uses square regions about a point. Region sizes range from 9 pixels to about 300 pixels on a side, the size of a 1:24 000 DEM, which creates sample sizes of 81 to 90 000 orientations. Square regions were chosen for computational simplicity and speed; the modest change in area coverage with circular regions does not appear to justify the extra processing.

DEMS USED

A DEM consists of elevations stored on a regular rectangular grid. DEMs use either a geographic grid with spacing along parallels and meridians, in which case the data spacing changes because of curvature of the earth, or they use a projected grid like the Universal Transverse Mercator (UTM), in which case merging data sets eventually becomes a problem because of curvature of the earth. Smaller-scale DEMs generally use geographic grids, whereas large-scale DEMs can use either grid type.

The two primary U.S. producers of DEMs, the National Imagery and Mapping Agency (NIMA) and the U.S. Geological Survey (USGS), have an unfortunate difference in their use of the term "level." For the USGS, "level" refers to the quality of the data: Level 1 has the lowest quality, and Level 2 has a higher quality. Level 1 data come from the National High-Altitude Photography Program or equivalent imagery compiled by using stereo profiling or image correlation. Level 2 data are derived from hypsographic and hydrographic information collected photogrammetrically or digitized from maps. Increasing amounts of Level 2 data are being produced. Except for an unfortunate artifact of contour line "ghosts" in the Level 2 data (Guth, 1999b), Level 2 data present a much better visual representation of the earth's surface. The subjective visual quality of Level 1 data varies greatly; some subsets appear almost identical to Level 2 data, and some have numerous immediately obvious flaws. Level 2 DEMs have too many elevations corresponding to the source-map contour lines; their average "ghost ratio" of 1.30 means that contour line elevations occur about 30% more often than they should. Level 1 DEMs have ghost ratios of 1.00, with contour line elevations no more likely to occur than any other elevations (Guth, 1999b).

Figure 1 shows elevation contours derived from each of four USGS DEMs covering the same 1 km² in Wyoming. Table 1 shows key characteristics of the four DEMs. Note the clear limitations of the 1:250 000 DEM (Fig. 1D) in two key areas: only the gross trends of the topography appear in the map, and because of the large "ghost ratio," the contour lines come in clusters of

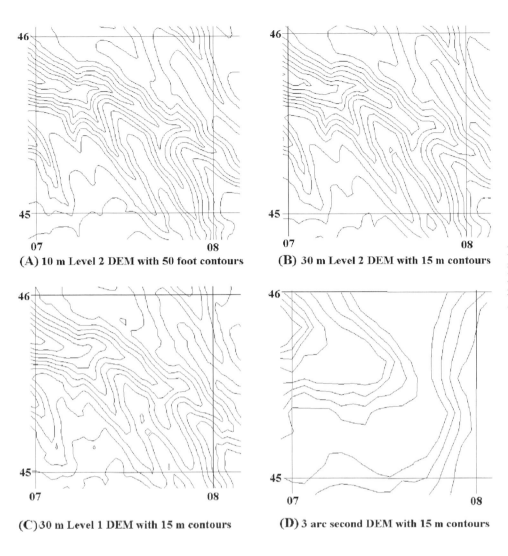

(A) 10 m Level 2 DEM with 50 foot contours

(B) 30 m Level 2 DEM with 15 m contours

(C) 30 m Level 1 DEM with 15 m contours

(D) 3 arc second DEM with 15 m contours

Figure 1. DEM-derived contours for a 1 km square from four independent DEMs of the Mount Jackson, Wyoming, 1:24 000 quadrangle. Note the increasing level of generalization from upper left to lower right.

four. With the 15 m contour interval, this corresponds to the 200 foot (60 m) contour interval of the source maps used to create this DEM. The two Level 2 1:24 000 DEMs (Figs. 1A and 1B) have much smaller ghost ratios, not apparent in the contour maps, but that exert some influence on the DEM and especially derived calculations like slope. The contour lines from the 10 m DEM (Fig. 1A) show some displacement from the 30 m DEMs because of the different elevation units; 50 foot contours do not exactly replicate 15 m contours. The 10 m DEM contours also show fewer anomalous closed contours along the ridges and in general exhibit a more rounded, realistic pattern. For this DEM pair, the two 30 m DEMs (Fig. 1B and 1C) produce very similar results, although the Level 2 (Fig. 1B) produces slightly better contour lines. Except in the case of particularly poor Level 1 DEMs, only three-dimensional shaded relief depictions show the tremendous improvements with Level 2 DEMs and with 10 m data.

This study used USGS DEMs, primarily the 1:24 000 series. All have elevations recorded in meters, or feet for the flatter quadrangles. Preliminary analysis of about 3000 DEMs showed the range of variation for the fabric measures and suggested DEMs

for the detailed study presented here. Some comparisons of the 1:24 000 and 1:250 000 DEMs allow extrapolation of the results to smaller-scale DEMs, even though the USGS 1:250 000 DEM has many quirks (particularly severe ghost ratios), reflecting its status as one of the first wide-coverage DEM series ever produced.

This choice of data allowed three comparisons to see how fabric measures can be recovered from DEMs: (1) DEM quality reflected in the Level 1 and Level 2 data; (2) horizontal spacing, ranging from 10 m to 30 m and from 60 to 90 m for the 1:250 000 data; and (3) terrain variability, because the available DEMs span the range of topographic landforms found in the continental United States.

RESULTS

Results of the fabric analysis can be displayed in a number of formats: (1) SSO diagrams, which are contoured plots of the distribution of surface normals in the region around a point (the SSO diagrams shown here include the values of the flatness, organization, strength, shape, and preferred orientation calculated

P.L. Guth

**TABLE 1. CHARACTERISTICS OF THE DEMS SHOWN IN FIGURE 1,
PART OF THE MOUNT JACKSON, WYOMING, QUADRANGLE**

DEM	Elevation units	Points in 1 km^2	Ghost ratio	Source contours
10 m Level 2	feet	100 x 100	1.18	20 ft
30 m Level 2	meters	33 x 33	1.11	40 ft
30 m Level 2	meters	33 x 33	1.01	—
3″ 1:250 000	meters	15 x 11	10.09	200 ft

for the contoured region); (2) graphs showing the variation of fabric measures at a single point as the size of the region varies; (3) overlay of fabric strength and orientation for a given region size superimposed on a base map; and (4) color maps that show the variation of fabric measures in space, for a given region size.

This chapter presents results from four quadrangles, selected to show a variety of terrain fabrics. Mount Jackson, Wyoming (Fig. 1), forms part of the Yellowstone Plateau. Bright Angel Point, Arizona (Figs. 2 and 3), shows extreme vertical relief and steep slopes. Aughwick, Pennsylvania (Figs. 4 and 5), demonstrates the epitome of linear fabric in the folded ridges of the Appalachians. Montara Mountain, California (Figs. 6 and 7), shows dissected, rugged terrain, with weak preferred orientation. Except as explicitly noted, all analyses refer to 30 m 1:24 000 DEMs.

Sensitivity to slope algorithm

Most terrain analysis studies show that different algorithms produce almost identical results for slope and, except for the nearest-neighbor algorithms, very similar results for aspect (Skidmore, 1989; Guth, 1995; Hodgson, 1998). Guth (1995) reported correlation coefficients exceeding 0.89 for any pair from six distinct slope algorithms and exceeding 0.95 for the most common algorithms. He also showed that some terrain categories account for many of the differences between algorithms because of the ambiguity in what slope value should be accepted. Ridge tops and valley bottoms present a dilemma for a slope algorithm: should the value reflect the low slope along the stream channel, or the much higher slope climbing out of the valley? Smoothing algorithms such as the four- or eight-closest-neighbor algorithms choose the first value, whereas the steepest-adjacent-neighbor algorithms determine that the second will be used. The choice of algorithm for aspect leads to significant differences, because the adjacent-neighbor methods can return aspect directions only in the eight principal compass directions. The use of only eight bins would be unacceptable for computations such as fabric orientation. Guth (1995) advocated the use of an unweighted eight-nearest-neighbor algorithm because it showed the fewest artifacts in the aspect distribution, although all of the common four- and eight-nearest-neighbor algorithms produced very similar results.

Tests with the Montara Mountain 30 m Level 2 DEM showed that the choice of slope algorithm did not significantly affect the fabric results. The comparison employed two algorithms: (1) the hybrid algorithm advocated by Guth (1995), which selects the steepest adjacent neighbor for the slope and uses an unweighted

eight-adjacent-neighbor method for the aspect and (2) a four-nearest-neighbor method for both slope and aspect, probably the most widespread method used (e.g., Skidmore, 1989). Slopes computed with the steepest-adjacent-neighbor and the four-closest-neighbor algorithms showed a correlation coefficient of 0.926. The algorithms calculated a different average slope: the steepest-adjacent-neighbor method yielded an average slope of 37.64%, and the four-closest-neighbor method gave an average slope of 30.66%. Even though the averages differed, the two algorithms correlated strongly and generally produced very similar results. Maps of the slope differences closely reproduced the drainage pattern; the large differences were almost exclusively in valley bottoms.

Use of the different slope algorithms changed the values of the organization parameter slightly. Organization parameters with a region size of 900 m had a correlation coefficient of 0.963; the steepest-adjacent-neighbor algorithm calculated an average of 0.670, and the four-nearest-neighbor algorithm estimated the average as 0.644, somewhat less organized. The fabric direction changes only slightly with the two algorithms. With a 900 m region, the average difference in orientation was 4.6° but the median difference was under 2°. More than 80% of the points differed by less than 5°, more than 90% of the points differed by less than 10°, and more than 96% differed by less than 20°. As with the differences for slope, differences in aspect and hence overall fabric reflected differences in handling points like ridge crests and valley bottoms. Differences between the slope algorithms proved to be much less than differences between independent DEMs (discussed subsequently), and within reason, the choice of algorithm did not significantly change the results.

Fabrics from SSO diagrams

Figure 2 shows overlays of the topographic fabric over a part of the Bright Angel Point 1:24 000 DEM in the Grand Canyon. The figure compares the Level 1 (Figs. 2A and 2B) and Level 2 (Figs. 2C and 2D) DEMs as well as the use of the strength and organization parameters to show the fabric. The underlying topography may not be clear with the fabric overlays, but the Level 2 DEM has much greater roughness and captures the small-scale structure of the canyon wall. This difference is manifest most strongly in the intermediate slopes, where the Level 2 DEM (Figs. 2C and 2D) shows a northeast-southwest fabric at right angles to the larger-scale northeast-southwest fabric, and the Level 1 DEM (Figs. 2A and 2B) does not capture this finer struc-

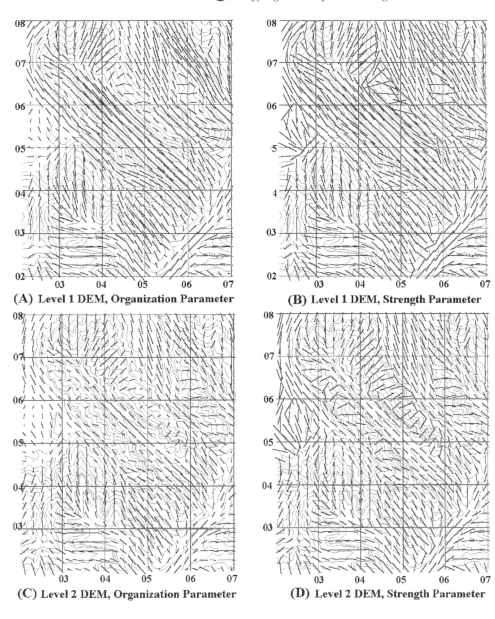

(A) Level 1 DEM, Organization Parameter

(B) Level 1 DEM, Strength Parameter

(C) Level 2 DEM, Organization Parameter

(D) Level 2 DEM, Strength Parameter

Figure 2. Terrain fabric of part of the Bright Angel Point, Arizona, quadrangle, with 100 m contours and 1 km UTM grid. A and B: Level 1 DEM C, and D, Level 2 DEM. Left-hand plots (A and C) illustrate the organization parameter, and right-hand plots (B and D) portray the strength parameter. Points plotted every 200 m with an 800 m region size. Note the difference in fabric on the intermediate slopes, for example, near grid coordinates 0506, and the greater depiction in the Level 2 DEM of the northeast-southwest fabric at the same location.

ture. The strength and organization parameters require different scaling factors for the map overlay because they have a different range of values, but they generally record similar patterns. The organization parameter shows the difference in fabric intensity more clearly because it records a wider range of values.

Figure 3 shows SSO diagrams for two points (A and B) in the Grand Canyon for three region sizes from 300 m to 1500 m. The map has 100 m contours, and the clustered contours represent the cliff-forming formations and benches, not artifacts of the DEM creation process. Point A, located on a ridge, shows the same fabric orientation (within 6°) at all three scales. By contrast, point B, which is located along the canyon sides, shows a change in orientation and strength. At a 300 m scale, the fabric is oriented perpendicular to the canyon and reflects the small ridges and valleys cut into the sidewalls of the canyon. With a 900 m region the fabric has negligible strength, representing the transition to the

fabric (seen at 1500 m region size) that records the major ridges parallel to the canyon sides. The organization parameter goes from 1.81 at 300 m, to 0.14 at 900 m, and then to 0.81 at 1200 m. This point records a 90° change in fabric orientation, from 35.8° to 318°, over the range of spatial scales considered. With their extreme slopes along the edge of the SSO diagram, this map area represents an extreme of rugged topography. Because of the relief and consequent orientations of the three eigenvectors, which are not vertical and horizontal, the two potential estimators for fabric strength, organization parameter $\ln(S_2/S_3)$, and strength parameter K, produce different results that are qualitatively similar but quantitatively different in details.

Figures 4 and 5 show a series of analyses for the Aughwick, Pennsylvania, quadrangle. This quadrangle has the highest organization at the quadrangle scale of the 3000 DEMs examined in the course of this study. This region in the folded Appalachians is

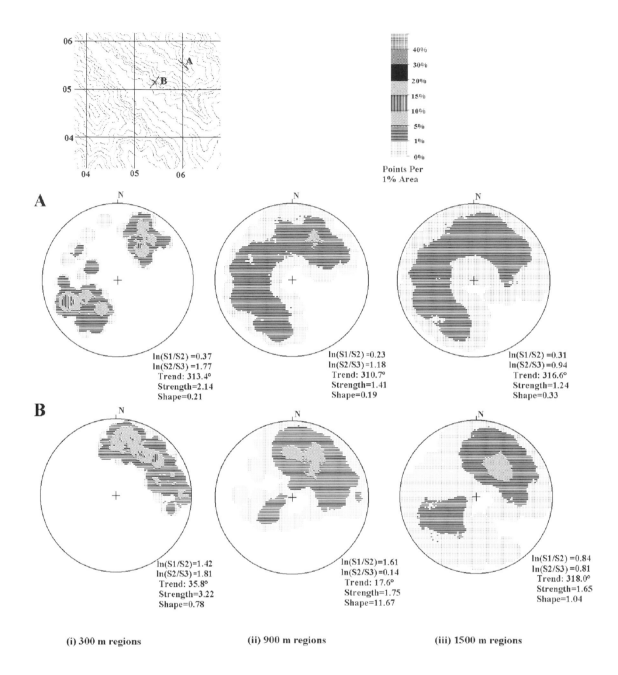

Figure 3. Location map of part of the Bright Angel Point, Arizona, Level 2 DEM, with the location of points A and B indicated along with the direction and strength of the terrain fabric. Statistical slope-orientation diagrams for the two points with region sizes of 300, 900, and 1500 m. This map is a subset of the area shown in Figure 2.

much less rugged than the Grand Canyon; the average slope over the entire map is 25.6% (14.3°) compared to 81.7% (39.2°). Figure 4 shows the calculated direction and strength of the fabric, which clearly picks up the trends of the ridges. This type of presentation can be prepared with any region size and any desired spacing of the calculation points. Figure 5 shows a series of calculations at four points. The SSO diagrams show all points clustered near the center of the diagram, in contrast to the Grand Canyon, and as a result the first eigenvector is nearly vertical. The steep upper ridges and ridge crests (locations D and E) show a strong girdle fabric, and the ridge asymmetry appears in both diagrams with a different pattern for the northwest- and southeast-facing slopes. The bottom slopes and valley bottoms (locations B and C) show a cluster orientation with the contours nearly in a circular pattern. Ridge points D and E have organization values of 3.86 and 3.59, compared to the value of 1.18 for ridge location A in the Grand Canyon (Fig. 2) at comparable region size. This map shows a consistent pattern of decreasing organization from the ridge crests down to the valley bottom.

Fabric, region size, and source DEM

Figure 6 shows graphs of fabric direction (A), organization (B), and flatness (C) for a single location in the Montara Mountain quadrangle. The graphs show the results of changing the region size and the differences among four independent DEMs of the region. Measures of terrain organization clearly vary with the size of the region considered. On all three graphs, a change in fabric occurs with a region size of about 700 m. A smaller region captures the small northeast-trending ridge, whereas the larger regions capture the dominant northwest-trending fabric of the major ridges. Flatness, the ratio $\ln(S_1/S_2)$, increases for small regions and then decreases, as more and more rugged terrain is included in the analysis region (Fig. 6C). Alternatively, the steepness generally increases as the size of the region increases to include more diverse terrain. Organization, the ratio $\ln(S_2/S_3)$, shows the greatest variability (Fig. 6B). It shows the greatest values at the smallest region sizes, reflecting a single ridge with a 25° trend (compare with the orientation graph). Organization reaches a minimum at 700 m region size and then increases as the 135° major ridge dominates the analysis (Fig. 6B). Larger regions show a decline in organization as more diverse terrain enters the sampling box. The orientation parameter (Fig. 6A) mirrors the results of organization; small regions show the small ridges orthogonal to the main ridges.

The four DEMs in Figure 6 produce similar results. The 1:250 000 DEM (3″ spacing), with its larger data spacing and consequent generalization, does not capture the smaller-scale features—in particular, it misses the change in fabric seen at the region size of 700 m. In part this is simply because the coarse 3″ data spacing does not allow computation for regions much smaller than 700 m. All four DEMs provide very similar results for the fabric direction. Trends in the organization parameter correlate very well, but they show a consistent pattern: the greater the generalization in the DEM, the greater the calculated organization. Thus the 1:250 000 DEM shows the greatest organization, the 30 m DEMs intermediate values, and the 10 m DEM the lowest organization because it captures so much of the microfabric. Of the two 30 m DEMs, the greater generalization of the Level 1 product gives it more apparent organization. The values of flatness for the 10 and 30 m DEMs essentially do not differ, and they mirror the trends seen in the 3″ DEM.

Graphs such as Figure 6 can show only the effects of DEM parameters such as spacing or quality at a single point, but they can point out major differences in terrain organization. Figure 7 shows a similar graph from a ridge crest (point E in Fig. 5) from the Aughwick quadrangle. Note that the lowest organization values from this point exceed the highest values from the 1:24 000

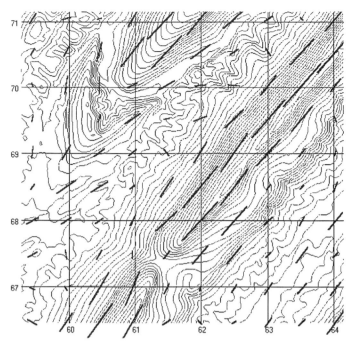

Figure 4. Computed topographic fabric overlaid on contour map of part of the Aughwick, Pennsylvania, quadrangle. Fabric computed every 500 m from region 800 m on a side. Length of the line is proportional to the strength of the fabric, with the line oriented in the direction of the fabric. The fabric is strongest along the strike ridges of the Appalachians and weakest in the valley bottoms.

Montara Mountain DEMs. In addition, note that in this case the Level 2 DEM records higher organization. Two procedures assess the relationship across an entire DEM. In the first, the correlations between the organization parameters calculated from independent DEMs are shown in correlation matrices. In the second, graphs show the covariance of fabric direction and organization.

Tables 2 through 5 show correlation matrices for two quadrangles, Mount Jackson, Wyoming, and Montara Mountain, California. These sampled the fabric on a 200 m grid and computed the organization parameter from four independent DEMs. The procedure was repeated for 900 m and 1800 m region sizes. In all cases the 3″ 1:250 000 DEM correlates poorly with the others; for Montara Mountain with a 900 m region size, the 3″ DEM shows random correlation with the three 1:24 000 DEMs. Organizations calculated from the Level 1 and Level 2 DEM correlate very well; r ranges from 0.777 to 0.909. Similarly the Level 2 data with 10 m and 30 m resolution also correlates very well, with r between 0.778 and 0.989. Although DEM quality and resolution obviously affect fabric analysis, within the 1:24 000 USGS quadrangles, DEM results correlate highly between Level 1 and Level 2 data and between 10 m and 30 m DEMs.

Figure 8 shows how fabric organization and orientation vary depending both on the DEM and the region size, using the Montara Mountain DEM. The left side of the figure (Figure 8, A–C) compares 30 m Level 1 and Level 2 DEMs, and the right side (Figure 8, D–F) compares 10 m and 30 m Level 2 DEMs. Each

P.L. Guth

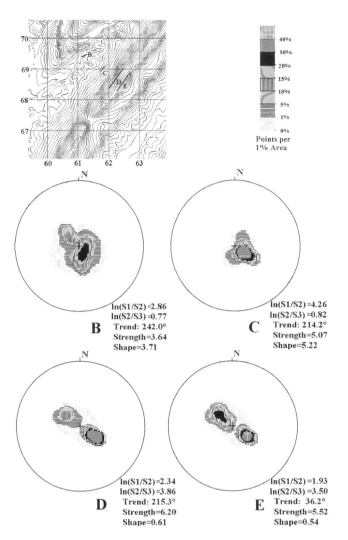

Figure 5. Location map showing part of the Aughwick, Pennsylvania, Level 2 USGS 1:24 000 DEM. The map has 50-foot contour lines and a 1 km UTM grid superimposed. The locations of sample points B–E are indicated. The SSO diagrams show the results at each location for 900 m regions.

row compares a different region size, from 300 m at the top to 1800 m on the bottom. This analysis used all points in the central part of the DEM, which had sufficient neighbors to calculate the required region and which had relief exceeding 20 m. Examination of color maps of the difference in fabric between the two DEMs shows that almost all large differences occur in very flat terrain, where DEMs perform poorly. The contours show the percentage of points with a difference in orientation and organization smaller than the contour value. The lower left corner of the graph shows identical results from the two DEMs; in all cases this is just less than 10% or 20% of the points. The upper right corner shows significant disagreement. For example, in Figure 8C comparing the two 30 m DEMs for 1800 m region size, more than 90% of the points show a difference in fabric orienta-

tion less than 15° and a difference in organization less than 0.20. The organization values vary with the region size, becoming less organized as the region increases, as seen in Figure 6 and Figure 7. For the 30 m Level 2 DEM, maximum organization decreases from 9.62 for the 300 m region, to 2.21 for the 900 m region, and to 1.20 for the 1800 m region. Thus the differences between the two independent DEMs represent a fairly small part of the data range. The very small percentage of points with large differences in the fabric orientation occurs almost exclusively in relatively flat, poorly organized areas.

DISCUSSION

Terrain fabric can be treated as a point property composed of three parts: roughness (defined by Woodcock's [1977] choice of ratios as a flatness parameter), organization, and orientation. Table 6 summarizes these and other parameters discussed in this chapter. Eigenvector analysis recovers these parameters, roughness as the inverse of the ratio $\ln(S_1/S_2)$, organization as ratio $\ln(S_2/S_3)$, and the orientation as the direction of eigenvector S_3. The three eigenvectors define an ellipsoid that best describes the pattern of the "cloud" formed by the normals to the earth's surface in three-dimensional space. Except in small regions in extremely rugged terrain (such as the Grand Canyon seen in Fig. 3), the first eigenvector will be nearly vertical. Its orientation marks the average slope and aspect of the region, and its magnitude compared to the other two eigenvectors' measures the ruggedness of the terrain. The second and third eigenvectors define a horizontal ellipse; the more elliptical, or the greater the difference between these eigenvalues, the greater the tendency for the terrain to have a girdle distribution on the SSO and for the terrain to show linear organization.

The choice of using the roughness (or flatness) and organization parameters versus the strength and shape parameters does not lend itself to an easy answer. There are three eigenvectors, but through the normalization process, only two remain independent. Woodcock (1977, Fig. 1) graphically shows the relationships among the four parameters. Any consideration of fabric needs to address two parameters together. For example, two terrain regions, both with high strength but differing shapes, will have dramatically different properties: the uniaxial cluster (high strength and high shape, or low roughness and low organization) will be a flat plane, and the uniaxial girdle (high strength and low shape, or high roughness and high organization) will have an extremely strong fabric. Because slope (roughness) has always been a key characterization of terrain, the use of roughness and organization are preferred as the key characterization. As seen in the comparative diagrams from the Grand Canyon (Fig. 2), the organization parameter also appears to produce a better pattern than the strength parameter.

The 1:24 000 DEMs from the USGS produce consistent, meaningful results. Except for a small number of the worst examples of Level 1 DEMs, Level 1 and Level 2 DEMs produce very similar results. Most differences appear only with very small

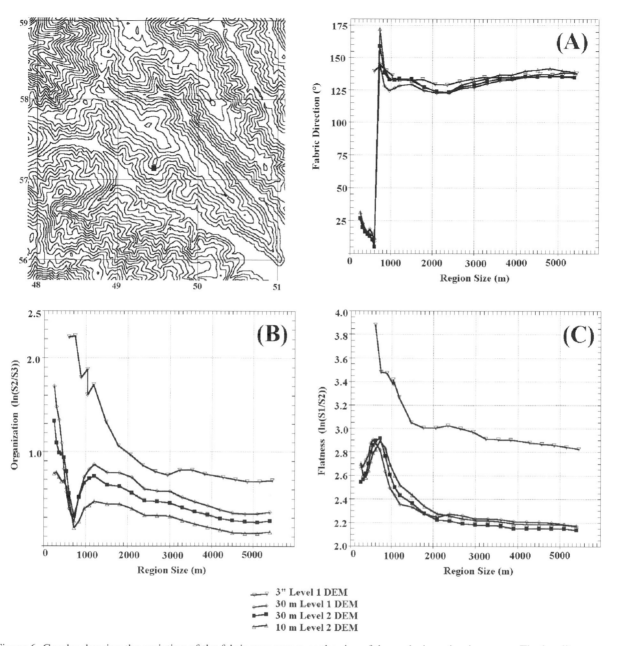

Figure 6. Graphs showing the variation of the fabric parameters as the size of the analysis region increases. The locality map, with 50-foot contours and a 1 km UTM grid, shows the location of the point. Each graph shows results calculated with four independent DEMs.

region sizes, where the small sample sizes enhance statistical variability in the results, and for the smallest scale variations in the topographic fabric. Differences also appear in flat regions, where the "stairstepping" in the elevations in the DEM produces artifacts in the slope distribution, which will carry into fabric analysis. Many Level 1 DEMs actually have a true point spacing several times greater than 30 m, but that does not appear to greatly affect these fabric calculations. Somewhat surprisingly, the 10 m Level 2 DEMs do not provide a very noticeable improvement over the 30 m DEMs for the calculation of terrain

fabric. This may be due to horizontal resolution of the DEMs, especially for those with elevations in meters. With horizontal resolution of 10 m and vertical resolution of 1 m, only certain slopes can be calculated. Expressing vertical elevations in feet helps somewhat with this quantification problem, but large-scale DEMs probably need elevations expressed in decimeters. Decimeter elevations would also help alleviate the problems encountered with the eigenvector analysis in very flat terrain, although DEMs will probably always have difficulty capturing true terrain variation in very gentle topography.

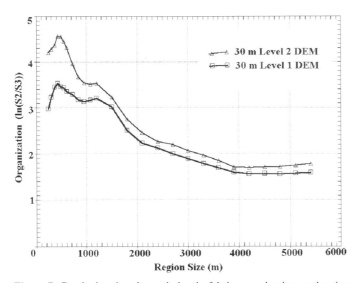

Figure 7. Graph showing the variation in fabric organization as the size of the analysis region increases at point E of Figure 5. The Level 1 DEM is depicted with squares (□), and the Level 2 DEM with triangles. Note the much greater organization in the folded Appalachians compared to the nearly isotropic topography in Figure 6.

The 1:250 000 DEMs from the USGS should be used primarily for small-scale, large regional fabric studies and only with extreme caution for large-scale studies. Its generalized depiction of the terrain retains the gross fabric but not the fine details. It can recover the fabric orientation but only a very generalized value for organization.

Although a point parameter, terrain fabric depends on the scale of the region used for computation. In one sense this resembles the well-known dependence of DEM parameters like slope or aspect on the cell size used for computation (Guth, 1995; Hodgson, 1995), but those parameters have some "true" value masked by the complexity of the DEM sampling and calculation process. Fabric may truly vary with the scale of the region shown; several of the examples shown in this chapter show small-scale fabric superimposed on larger-scale features, often at 90° angles. Qualitative experience suggests that region sizes of about 900 m provide good estimates of overall terrain fabric with USGS 1:24 000 DEMs. More work needs to be done to support this assessment, and it will require sophisticated visualization techniques such as color animations (showing the effect of changing the region size) or color overlays (showing the fabric computed with different DEMs or slope algorithms) (Guth, 1999c).

In addition to the effect that quantification of topographic fabric will have on quantitative terrain analysis and geomorphometry, the work promises to have applications for military models of cross-country mobility and trafficability. The current military model for trafficability, the NATO Reference Mobility Model (NRMM), was used in the Comprehensive Army Mobility Model System—Developmental (CAMMS-D), which provided a geographic information system (GIS) interface for users (Lessem et al., 1992, 1996; Williamson and Deliman, 1996), and will also

TABLE 2. CORRELATION MATRIX FOR ORGANIZATION PARAMETER FROM INDEPENDENT DEMS, MOUNT JACKSON, WYOMING, 900 m REGIONS, N = 2604

	3″ Level 1	30 m Level 1	30 m Level 2	10 m Level 2
3″ Level 1	1.000	0.323	0.364	0.306
30 m Level 1	0.323	1.000	0.777	0.767
30 m Level 2	0.364	0.777	1.000	0.982
10 m Level 2	0.306	0.767	0.982	1.000

TABLE 3. CORRELATION MATRIX FOR ORGANIZATION PARAMETER FROM INDEPENDENT DEMS, MOUNT JACKSON, WYOMING, 1800 m REGIONS, N = 2204

	3″ Level 1	30 m Level 1	30 m Level 2	10 m Level 2
3″ Level 1	1.000	0.405	0.348	0.281
30 m Level 1	0.405	1.000	0.785	0.773
30 m Level 2	0.348	0.785	1.000	0.989
10 m Level 2	0.281	0.773	0.989	1.000

TABLE 4. CORRELATION MATRIX FOR ORGANIZATION PARAMETER FROM INDEPENDENT DEMS, MONTARA MOUNTAIN, CALIFORNIA, 900 m REGIONS, N = 3037

	3″ Level 1	30 m Level 1	30 m Level 2	10 m Level 2
3″ Level 1	1.000	0.151	0.001	-0.114
30 m Level 1	0.151	1.000	0.853	0.605
30 m Level 2	0.001	0.853	1.000	0.778
10 m Level 2	-0.114	0.605	0.778	1.000

TABLE 5. CORRELATION MATRIX FOR ORGANIZATION PARAMETER FROM INDEPENDENT DEMS, MONTARA MOUNTAIN, CALIFORNIA, 1800 m REGIONS, N = 2610

	3″ Level 1	30 m Level 1	30 m Level 2	10 m Level 2
3″ Level 1	1.000	0.486	0.325	0.060
30 m Level 1	0.486	1.000	0.909	0.749
30 m Level 2	0.325	0.909	1.000	0.887
10 m Level 2	0.060	0.749	0.887	1.000

be part of the Maneuver Control System—Engineer (MCS-E) planned for field deployment starting in the year 2000 (Army Engineer School, 1998). The NRMM considers a number of terrain factors that contribute to trafficability, including soil strength, terrain slope, and obstacles—especially vegetation (Lessem et al., 1992). NRMM lacks any consideration of terrain fabric or directionality (N.C. Deliman, 1998, USA Waterways Experiment Station, personal commun.). This eigenvector analysis has the potential to improve those models, because it provides a quantitative measure terrain organization and the direction of the fabric. To be useful for the models, work will have to determine the

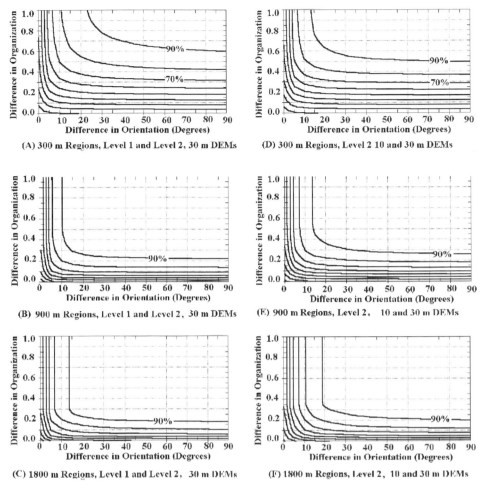

Figure 8. Graphs showing the agreement between two pairs of DEMs for the Montara Mountain, California, DEM. The three graphs on the left compare Level 1 and Level 2 30 m DEMs, and the three graphs on the right compare 10 m and 30 m Level 2 DEMs. From top to bottom the graphs show the effect of increasing the region size from 300 to 1800 m. The contour lines, at 10% intervals, show the differences between results computed with the two DEMs. See the text for a full discussion.

region size most suitable for trafficability measurements and exactly how the organization and roughness parameters relate to mobility. The models already use point slope, which correlates strongly with macroroughness, but organization has not previously been used in terrain models.

Calculation of the orientation parameters will not pose a severe burden on military systems. Tests with a 333 MHz Pentium II computer with 64 Mb of RAM (a fairly modest machine in early 1999) showed that it could compute the fabric parameters for about 1.4 million points per second. This is the product of the number of points in the DEM times the number of points in the analysis region. For military standard DTED Level 1 and a 900 m region size, this would require about 2.5 min to process a 1 degree by 1 degree cell and calculate the values for every point. For an area of operations of 4 to 20 square degrees, the processing could be completed in 10 to 60 min on a single laptop computer. Fairly simple optimizations could cut this time dramatically. Because organization changes slowly and repre-

sents a regional value, values would not have to be calculated at every point in the DEM. An improved algorithm could exploit the fact that adjacent regions overlap and intermediate values could be stored temporarily instead of being recalculated. The organization parameters could also be calculated in advance and stored for use as needed. Two files the size of the DEM would store the organization value and its orientation for every point in the DEM. DEMs now typically require significantly less storage space than associated imagery, so tripling the storage requirements for the DEMs would not strain field systems. Higher-resolution DEMs will increase the requirements, but computing power and storage capacity will likely increase faster than DEM resolution.

CONCLUSION

Eigenvector analysis of digital topography produces a meaningful, quantitative measure of terrain fabric, defined by roughness and organization parameters, and fabric orientation direction.

TABLE 6. GEOMORPHOMETRIC PARAMETERS DISCUSSED IN THIS PAPER

Parameter	Formula	Interpretation of values
Flatness	ln (S_1/S_2)	Large values indicate flat terrain, low values indicate rugged terrain. Correlates strongly and negatively with slope or relief.
Organization	ln (S_2/S_3)	Large values indicate a dominant linear fabric to the terrain; small values indicate isotropic topography.
Orientation	Trend of S_3)	Dominant trend to the terrain fabric; direction between 0 and 180°.
Strength, c	ln (S_1/S_3)	Large values indicate flat terrain; small values indicate rugged terrain. Very similar to the flatness parameter. Correlates strongly and negatively with slope or relief.
Shape, k	ln (S_1/S_2)/ ln (S_2/S_3)	Large values indicate a dominant linear fabric to the terrain; small values indicate isotropic topography. Correlates moderately with organization.
Ghost ratio	(Percentage points on contour lines) / (Percentage elevations that are contour lines)	Indicates the overrepresentation of contour line elevations in the DEM, an artifact of the digitizing process if the ghost ratio exceeds 1. The ghost ratio is never significantly less than 1.

S_1, S_2, and S_3 are the eigenvalues from the 3 x 3 matrix of the sums of the cross products of the direction cosines for all points in the analysis region; $S_1 > S_2 > S_3$.

USGS 1:24000 DEMs with 30 m data spacing provide consistent results for regions as small as a few hundred meters in size and potentially even for regions 100 m in size with 10 m data. These results prove surprisingly insensitive to DEM quality or resolution, as both 30 m Level 1 and Level 2 DEMs, and 10 m and 30 m Level 2 DEMs, produce very similar results. Fabric exists on a variety of scales, and as the analysis region size increases, larger features of the terrain emerge.

Within the next few years a variety of improved DEMs will become available. Global elevation data from the Shuttle Radar Topography Mission (SRTM) was collected in 1999 and will provide data at 30–100 m elevation spacing (Baltuck, 1997). Complete coverage of the United States with USGS 30 m DEMs will soon be available, and increasing numbers of 10 m DEMs are being produced. Selected areas will have GeoSAR DEMs with 1–5 m resolution (Freedman et al., 1998). These will offer significant opportunities for terrain analysis and classification and for automated extraction of terrain fabric.

ACKNOWLEDGMENTS

This work was done with the MICRODEM program for 32-bit Windows, available at http://www.usna.edu/Users/oceano/pguth/website/microdem.htm (this address is case sensitive). The U.S. Army Engineer School and the Naval Academy have funded work the last two summers (1998 and 1999) on terrain analysis training and DEM manipulation that indirectly contributed to the work reported here. I thank reviewers D.R. Caldwell and R.H. Gilmore for thorough and thoughtful critiques that significantly improved the final paper.

REFERENCES CITED

Army Engineer School, 1998, Engineer Systems handbook, http://www.wood.army.mil/DCD/no_limitations/systems_pw/book.htm.

Baltuck, M., 1997, Solid earth programs meet Coolfont goals: Eos (Transactions, American Geophysical Union), v. 78, p. 537, 540.

Chapman, C.A., 1952, A new quantitative method of topographic analysis: American Journal of Science, v. 250, p. 428–452.

Freedman, A.P., Hensley, S., and Chapin, E., 1998, GeoSAR: A system for obtaining high-resolution, true ground surface, digital elevation models at regional scales: Eos (Transactions, American Geophysical Union), v. 79, p. S5.

Gardner, T.W., Sasowsky, K.C., and Day, R.L., 1990, Automated extraction of geomorphometric properties from digital elevation models: Zeitschrift für Geomorphologie Neue Folge Supplementband 80, p. 57–68.

Guth, P.L., 1987, MicroNET: Interactive equal-area and equal-angle nets: Computers and Geosciences, v. 13, p. 541–543.

Guth, P.L., 1995, Slope and aspect calculations on gridded digital elevation models: Examples from a geomorphometric toolbox for personal computers: Zeitschrift für Geomorphologie Neue Folge Supplementband 101, p. 31–52.

Guth, P.L., 1999a, Quantifying topographic fabric: Eigenvector analysis using digital elevation models, in Merisko, R.J., ed., Applied imagery pattern recognition (AIPR) workshop: Advances in computer-assisted recognition, 27th: Proceedings of the International Society for Optical Engineering, v. 3584, p. 233–243.

Guth, P.L., 1999b, Contour line "ghosts" in USGS Level 2 DEMs: Photogrammetric Engineering and Remote Sensing, v. 65, p. 289–296.

Guth, P.L., 1999c, Quantifying and visualizing terrain fabric from digital elevation models, in Diaz, J. Tynes, R., Caldwell, D., and Ehlen, J., eds., Geocomputation 99: Proceedings of the 4th International Conference on GeoComputation, Fredericksburg, Virginia, USA: Greenwich, UK, GeoComputation, CD-ROM.

Hodgson, M.E., 1995, What cell size does the computed slope/aspect angle represent?: Photogrammetric Engineering and Remote Sensing, v. 61, p. 513–517.

Hodgson, M.E., 1998, Comparison of angles from surface slope/aspect algorithms: Cartography and Geographic Information Systems, v. 25, p. 173–185.

Koike, K., Nagano, S., and Kawaba, K., 1998, Construction and analysis of interpreted fracture planes through combination of satellite-image derived lineaments and digital terrain elevation data: Computers and Geosciences, v. 24, p. 573–584.

Lessem, A., Ahlvin, R., and Mason, G., 1992, Stochastic vehicle mobility forecasts using the NATO reference mobility model: Report 1. Basic concepts and procedures: Vicksburg, Mississippi, USA Waterways Experiment Station Technical Report GL-92-11, AD-A255 682, 51 p.

Lessem, A., Mason, G., and Ahlvin, R., 1996, Stochastic vehicle mobility forecasts using the NATO reference mobility model: Journal of Terramechanics, v. 33, p. 273–280.

Pike, R.J., 1988, The geometric signature: Quantifying landslide-terrain types from digital elevation models: Mathematical Geology, v. 20, p. 491–512.

Pike, R.J., Acevedo, W., and Card, D.H., 1989, Topographic grain automated from digital elevation models, *in* Proceedings, International Symposium on Computer Assisted Cartography, 9th: Baltimore, Maryland: American Society for Photogrammetry and Remote Sensing–American Congress on Surveying and Mapping, p.128–137.

Pike, R.J., and Rozema, W.J., 1975, Spectral analysis of landforms: Annals of the Association of American Geographers, v. 65, p. 449–516.

Press, W.H., Flannery, B.P., Teukolsky, S.A., and Vetterling, W.T., 1986, Numerical recipes: The art of scientific computing: Cambridge, Cambridge University Press, 818 p.

Raghavan, V., Wadatsumi, K., and Masumoto, S., 1993, Automatic extraction of lineament information of satellite images using digital elevation data: Nonrenewable Resources, v. 2, p. 148–155.

Skidmore, A.K., 1989, A comparison of techniques for calculating gradient and aspect from a gridded digital elevation model: International Journal of Geographical Information Systems, v. 3, p. 323–334.

Vergne, M., and Souriau, M., 1993, Quantifying the transition between tectonic trend and mes-scale texture in topographic data: Geophysical Research Letters, v. 20, p. 2139–2141.

Williamson, J.L., and Deliman, N.C., 1996, A user's guide for creating risk-based mobility products in CAMMS-D: Vicksburg, Mississippi, USA Waterways Experiment Station Technical Report GL-96-9, AD-A310420, 155 p.

Woodcock, N.H., 1977, Specification of fabric shapes using an eigenvalue method: Geological Society of America Bulletin, v. 88, p. 1231–1236.

MANUSCRIPT ACCEPTED BY THE SOCIETY OCTOBER 27, 2000

Geological Society of America
Reviews in Engineering Geology, Volume XIV
2001

Methodology for remote characterization of fracture systems in bedrock of enemy underground facilities

Robert D. Jacobi
Department of Geology, 876 NSC, SUNY at Buffalo, Buffalo, NY 14260, USA
Thomas E. Eastler
Natural Science Department, University of Maine at Farmington, Farmington, ME 04938, USA
Jiandong Xu
Department of Geology, 876 NSC, SUNY at Buffalo, Buffalo, NY 14260, USA

ABSTRACT

Weaponry can be conveniently and safely concealed in enemy underground bedrock facilities (UGF). The bedrock environment surrounding UGF offers a high degree of protection for the assets contained within. Physical characteristics of the surrounding bedrock constrain the effects of conventional and even nuclear weapons. Brittle structures in the bedrock such as fracture systems have anisotropic characteristics and present a formidable obstacle to the survival of penetrating weapons. Knowledge of the three-dimensional (3-D) characteristics of bedrock fracture systems in enemy UGF, which may be covered by soil or vegetation, is of paramount importance to the weapons development community in its quest to penetrate anisotropic environments.

We utilize rigorous methodologies to predict fracture characteristics in overburden-covered regions from outcrop, core, borehole, and remote sensing data. We have established digital scanline and scangrid methodologies to characterize fracture geometries. The digital data allow us to easily analyze the fractures in terms of fractal and more advanced geostatistical techniques. We have developed theoretical and practical guidelines for determining the two-dimensional (2-D) density of fractures from one-dimentional (1-D) (scanline) data. Additionally, we have developed theoretical relationships between 2-D and 3-D fracture densities. Integration of digital field data with density and spatial structure of the fracture networks allows us to predict the distribution of fractures in areas removed from the outcrop. These methodologies, once refined, fully tested, and verified, will allow us to characterize three-dimensional fracture systems in potential target areas worldwide by remote sensing means alone.

INTRODUCTION

The nature of the bedrock environment in and around military underground facilities (UGF) controls the effectiveness of an incoming weapon when it strikes that bedrock environment. Although the characterization of bedrock in enemy territory can be quite problematic due to the inability to sample the bedrock directly, remote detection of certain characteristics, such as the fracture pattern, may allow the weaponeer to select more appropriate weapons and tactics to increase the probability of neutralizing the underground facility. This chapter represents the combined efforts of a military and penetration trajectory geologist (Eastler) and fracture characterization researchers (Jacobi and Xu). We examine the nature of bedrock UGF with respect to the existence of detectable surface bedrock fracture systems (Eastler), discuss the relationship between penetration trajectory and brittle fabrics (Eastler), and discuss methodologies for remote characterization of fracture systems surrounding UGF (Jacobi and Xu).

Jacobi, R.D., Eastler, T.E., and Xu, J. 2001, Methodology for remote characterization of fracture systems in bedrock of enemy underground facilities, *in* Ehlen, J., and Harmon, R.S., eds., The Environmental Legacy of Military Operations: Boulder, Colorado, Geological Society of America Reviews in Engineering Geology, v. XIV, p. 27–59.

BEDROCK UGF

Bedrock UGF is defined as underground facilities in bedrock. These facilities may be civilian or military in nature, but all can be used for a military function if necessary (Fig. 1). Typical bedrock UGFs have an entrance/exit portal, tunnel access, and interior functional spaces (Fig. 2). From the exterior only the entrance/exit portal is visible (Fig. 3).

The number of bedrock UGFs worldwide is unknown but assumed to be substantial. Underground mines are potential military UGFs, and as such, number in the thousands or tens of thousands. Add to this the unknown number of bedrock facilities constructed primarily for military purposes, and the number of UGFs climbs. To categorize all such facilities, known and unknown, would be a formidable task replete with errors. It is safe to assume, however, that virtually all of these civilian and military bedrock UGFs are developed in bedrock that has a fabric such as bedding, flow structure, or brittle cleavage/fracture.

UGF AND BEDROCK SURFACE FRACTURE SYSTEMS

Langberg and Davis (1993), in their literature analysis of attack on deep underground target entrances with penetrating warheads, discussed literature dealing primarily with collapse and slide mechanisms and only peripherally discussed orientation of penetrative foliation as it relates to damage mechanisms (Fig. 4). It is clear, from the lack of literature on the effect of jointing (fracture systems) and penetrative foliation on projectile trajectory, that much work remains to be done on the subject. What little is known, however, suggests that fracture system orientation specifically, and planar anisotropy in general, strongly affect the trajectory of penetrating weapons at all scales.

Austin et al. (1982) showed in their weapon-target interaction that 40-mm rounds fired at 2900 feet per second into in situ Dugway schist from a full-tracked M42 self-propelled gun with twin 40-mm cannon (T141) (Fig. 5) were controlled by the schistose foliation. Rounds fired normal to foliation were able to penetrate some distance, and rounds fired obliquely to foliation would ricochet. Those fired parallel to foliation would follow the foliation and were often expelled from the outcrop before the rounds had expended all of their energy by turning a full 180 degrees and exiting the same way they entered.

Eastler (1985) and Eastler and Andersen (1988) showed that much more robust warheads were also trajectory constrained by the penetrative fabric of the host rock. Indeed, in all studies to date, from calibers ranging from 40 mm to much more massive warheads, the data suggest that brittle fabric controls final trajectory (Figs. 6, 7A and 7B).

Once we understand how fracture systems govern projectile trajectory beneath the ground surface, we must further understand how to obtain the needed spatial fracture geometry data. Because the penetration depth of warheads is small (on the order of a few meters), only near-surface bedrock fabrics need to be determined for trajectory prediction. These fabrics can be observed on bare bedrock surfaces, but overburden (e.g., soil, vegetation) is an important factor in determining whether we can detect these structures. For example, the structural fabric of bedrock under a thick soil overlay is usually very difficult to determine (Fig. 8). With lessening amounts of soil cover, the nature of the bedrock structure becomes more discernible (Figs. 9 and 10) because frac-

Figure 1. Fuselage assembly line in the Junkers underground factory located 490 m below the surface in a salt mine at Tarthun, Soviet Zone, Germany. This military weapons production plant occupied approximately 32,500 square meters of floor space in the formerly civilian mine (from Department of the Air Force, 1954).

tures are often reflected upward through thin overburden because of their anisotropic nature and the spectral characteristics that accompany such heterogeneity. With no soil or vegetative cover, the structure is easily detected (Figs. 11 and 12).

Methods need to be developed to accurately assess fracture systems remotely and to predict the 2-D and 3-D nature of the fracture environment beneath areas masked by overburden, vegetation, or camouflage. Only then can we hope to increase the probability of neutralizing enemy bedrock UGF under all target conditions.

The following discussion will address the development of rigorous methodologies to predict fracture systems in overburden-covered regions from a combination of outcrop, core, borehole, and remote sensing data.

STATISTICAL CHARACTERIZATION AND EXTRAPOLATION OF FRACTURE PATTERNS

Introduction

In an ongoing program over the past 10 years, the UB Rock Fracture Group at the State University of New York at Buffalo has utilized both traditional and innovative techniques to characterize fracture patterns. These techniques can be used to detect subtle or hidden faults and to aid in predicting fracture patterns in covered or denied access areas. These research efforts were directed toward fracture systems in the heavily vegetated Appalachian Plateau of western New York, where information concerning fractures was needed for considerations related to potential radioactive waste disposal, salt mine collapse, oil and gas exploration, and remediation of toxic-waste sites. We have now compiled fracture data, including orientation, abutting relationships and intersection geometries, length, height, spacing, planarity, and fracture surface structures, for well over 70 000 fractures from over 1300 outcrops in western New York State (Fig. 13). These fracture data, from scanlines and scangrids in

primarily interbedded sandstones and shales, make up the basic library we have utilized for constructing and testing techniques that characterize fractures and that promote extrapolation of the fracture patterns into covered areas. This section reviews these techniques that can be applied directly to the problem of predicting fracture patterns in denied areas. This review is intended to serve as a basic introduction for those interested in, but not necessarily yet conversant with, (1) some of the modern fracture analysis techniques, (2) practical problems of these techniques, and (3) resolution of these problems. The fractal analysis section includes a case study.

Fractal analyses

Introduction and operations. One of the techniques used for analyzing fracture patterns is fractal analysis. About 15 years ago researchers began suggesting that fractal analysis, originally developed by Mandelbrot (1967, 1975, 1983), could be used to compare patterns of geological phenomena (e.g., fractures) at different scales (Barton and Larsen, 1985; Brown and Scholz, 1985; Barton et al., 1986; Turcotte, 1986a, 1986b, 1986c; Smalley et al., 1987; Brown, 1987; Chiles, 1988; La Pointe, 1989; Barton and Hsieh, 1989; Turcotte, 1989a, 1989b). These seminal reports were followed by numerous fractal studies, summarized in four publications (Turcotte, 1992; Barton and La Pointe, 1995a, 1995b; Cowie et al., 1996). Recently, fractal analysis was proposed as a methodology for fracture characterization in denied areas (Ehlen, 1998, Ehlen this volume).

A fractal set, or pattern, is defined by the following equation:

$$N_i = \frac{C}{(r_i)^D} \qquad (1)$$

where N_i is the number of objects with a characteristic linear dimension r_i, D is the fractal dimension, and C is a constant of proportionality. Other forms of the basic equation can be written as:

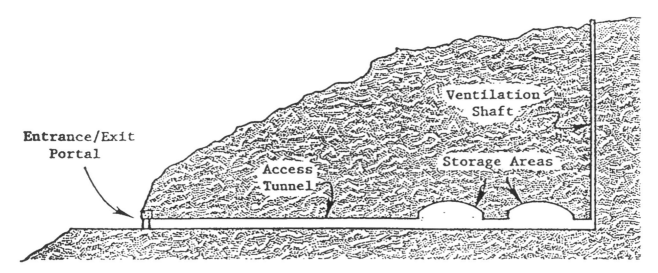

Figure 2. Cross section of a hypothetical UGF showing the key physical features of such facilities (from Langberg and Davis, 1993).

Figure 3. UGF entranceway. A: External view of an aircraft capable UGF entranceway constructed in heavily fractured bedrock. Note the existence of conjugate joints and prominent fault zones with heavy vegetation in otherwise barren rock. B: External close-up view of an aircraft capable UGF entranceway. Note poor placement of entranceway with respect to orientation of conjugate fracture system.

$$\frac{N_2}{N_1} = r^{-D} \qquad (2)$$

or

$$D = \frac{\ln N_i}{\ln \left(\dfrac{l}{r_i}\right)} \qquad (3)$$

where N_1 is the number of boxes needed to describe the pattern at a certain size of box, N_2 is the number of boxes needed to describe the pattern if the original box size is multiplied by the scaling fac-

tor r, and ln is the logarithm to the base e. From equation (3), it is clear that if a pattern is fractal, then the relation between the scale of observation and the number of observed fragments will describe a straight line on a ln-ln (or log-log) graph. The slope of this straight line will be the fractal dimension, D.

This constant relationship between scale of observation and number of observed objects is the power behind self-similar fractals, for such patterns are statistically scale invariant. Scale invariance implies that these fractal patterns can be compared at different scales, or extrapolated to different scales (e.g., Barton, 1995). Self-similar fractals are isotropic, that is, they follow the same scaling law in all Euclidian axes. In 2-D space all fracture properties that we address are regarded as self-similar, but in 3-D space only those fracture properties generated in isotropic media (e.g., unfoliated granite) and under very special stress conditions can be assumed to be self similar.

Other fractals, called self affine, obey different scaling laws along different Euclidian space axes (e.g., Dubuc et al., 1989; Turcotte, 1992; Wilson and Dominic, 1998; Wilson, 1999). For example, topography commonly exhibits both self-similar and self-affine fractals. A single topographic contour is commonly a self-similar fractal in the horizontal plane, but if fractal elevation is plotted against either horizontal axis, it is apparent that the scaling factor, r, is not the same for both elevation and either horizontal axis. Thus, elevation is commonly a self-affine fractal (Turcotte, 1992). Fracture properties that involve interbedded units with different rheologies may exhibit self-affine fractals in 3-D. For example, a self-similar fractal pattern may characterize the 2-D fracture pattern on a sandstone bedding surface, but if the interbedded sequence is examined in the third dimension,

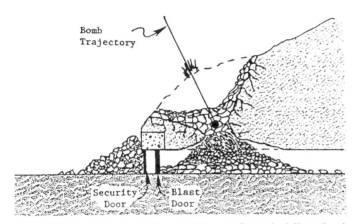

Figure 4. External and internal tunnel closure from air delivered ordnance showing implied collapse mechanisms without regard to orientation of penetrative foliation (from Langberg and Davis, 1993).

Figure 5. Full-tracked M42 self-propelled gun with twin 40-mm canon (T141) used to test penetration characteristics of schistose rocks with respect to the deviation of the foliation orientation away from the path of incoming projectiles (from Austin et al., 1982).

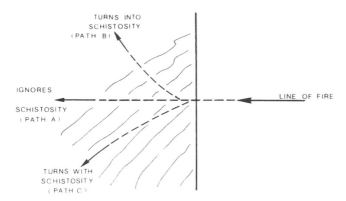

Figure 6. Possible pathways available to a penetrator in a rock with penetrative foliation. The penetrator not impacting parallel to foliation will most likely turn into the foliation, path C (from Austin et al., 1982).

extra fractures in the interbedded shales may result in a self-affine fractal pattern.

If the patterns are self similar, then fractal analysis provides a method of comparing patterns that were imaged at different scales. For example, if fractal Landsat lineaments have a fractal dimension similar to that of a fracture pattern observed on a flat bedding surface, then the lineaments may have an origin related to the fractures observed on the outcrop (subject to the problems discussed below). Thus, the lineaments could be used as a guide for extrapolating outcrop fracture patterns away from the outcrop.

An important aspect of fractal analysis is that a fractal dimension can be used to characterize the natural groupings of fractures (e.g., Velde et al., 1991, 1993; Gillespie et al., 1993; Ehlen, 1998; Xu and Jacobi, 1998). If the spacing of the fractures approaches a regular interval, then the fractal dimension will be relatively high, whereas if the spacing is clustered, then the fractal dimension will be relatively low. Thus, the degree of fracture clustering can be described by the fractal dimension. Although clustering can result from random processes (e.g., Turcotte, 1989a; Hestir et al., 1987), clustering of fractures can indicate the presence of a fault. Fracture intensification domains (FIDs) were defined as zones where closely spaced master fractures occur within a relatively narrow structural domain that is oriented parallel to the strike of the master fractures (Jacobi and Fountain, 1996; Jacobi and Zhao, 1996a; Jacobi and Xu, 1998). These researchers showed that FIDs are commonly associated with lineaments, faults, and zones of higher fluid flow (e.g., gas) in western New York, as evidenced by seismic reflection profiles, image analysis, field observations, soil gas anomalies, and well log analyses. Similar relationships between fracture spacing and various geological attributes such as lineaments, hydrocarbon production, and faults have been observed elsewhere (e.g., Lottman-Craig and Malone, 1991; Doe, 1993; Mabee et al., 1994; Hardcastle, 1995; Bashilov and Kuprin, 1995; Guo, 1997).

Another advantage of fractals is the theoretical ease of calculating the fractal dimension in 2-D space using data collected in 1-D space (e.g., a scanline), as long as the same fracture sets

are considered (e.g., Barton, 1995). Theoretically, one should add the integer 1 to the fractal dimension for each additional dimension considered. Barton (1995) demonstrated that such is the case in the spacing of veins in Alaska, where in 1-D space, the D_1 was found to be 0.41-0.62 with an average of 0.5, whereas 2-D sampling of the same veins showed that D_2 was 1.48. However, calculating the fractal dimension in 3-D space from 2-D data is not necessarily simple (discussed in problem section).

Fractal Analysis by the UB Rock Fracture Group. In order to "ground-truth" the lineaments and to extend the fracture patterns away from the outcrops, we typically compare lineament patterns to fracture patterns. Our operations include:

Step 1. Acquiring digital fracture data

Step 2a. Determining whether the lineaments and the observed fracture patterns are fractal

Step 2b. Determining the fractal dimension of the lineament and fracture patterns (if the patterns are fractal)

Step 3. Comparing outcrop fracture patterns to lineaments patterns recognized in various remotely sensed images (Landsat, SLAR, air photos) and topographic maps (a case study)

Step 4. Extrapolating the fracture patterns based on similarities to lineaments

Step 1. Acquiring digital fracture data. In order to acquire 2-D fracture trace data in the field, we first lay a 1 m square grid constructed of meter rulers over a portion of the bedding surface where the range in fracture lengths for each set of fractures is greater than one order of magnitude. Then a photograph is taken which is corrected for lens and view angle distortions by correcting the length and orthogonality of the rulers in Adobe Photoshop. The fractures are then digitized at a 0.1 cm resolution, resulting in a digital fracture trace. We have constructed larger scangrids by combining multiple meter-square scangrids or by laying out orthogonal 100 m tapes and taking a large view photograph from a nearby cliff.

In order to acquire 1-D digital data, we lay one or more scanlines across the outcrop, preferably so that the predominant fracture sets are adequately sampled. Sampling errors from scanlines are important issues, but most of the errors can be corrected (see following example).

Step 2a. Determining whether the lineaments and the observed fracture patterns are fractal. In order to determine the fractal dimension of lineament and fracture patterns, we must first determine if the patterns are fractal by assessing the curve used for calculating D_2. For calculating the D_2 curve, we have used Jacobi and Zhao's (1996a, 1996b) method, which rasterizes the trace map in ARC/INFO (e.g., Jacobi and Fountain, 1991; Wawrzynski and Jacobi, 1992; Zhao and Jacobi, 1993), a technique that is based on the box-counting method (e.g., Barton, 1995; Preuss, 1995). For calculating the $D1$ curve, we have used a computer program, GEO (Xu and Jacobi, 1998), which is based on Cantor's Dust method (e.g., Barton, 1995; Pruess, 1995). Several other options exist to calculate fractal dimension curves, including the computer program of Barton et al. (1989), commercial computer program packages; or for 1-D one can use the spacing population method (Gillespie et

Figure 7A. Vertical cross section through the path of a penetrator. Note the flattening of the lowermost part of the penetration path, illustrating the effect of joints in the rock (from Eastler, 1985).

Figure 7B. Penetrator lying parallel to prominent joint surface in fractured bedrock. Final orientation of penetrator does not equal initial orientation upon impact. The penetrator has been rotated during penetration to come to rest parallel to prominent joint surface.

al., 1993), in which the cumulative spacing between fracture pairs is plotted against spacing.

In the ARC/INFO rasterization method for 2-D patterns, an east-west/north-south grid is laid over the rotated fracture trace map. The fracture trace map has been rotated so that the grid will cover the maximum area of the fracture trace map without the grid extending beyond the boundaries of the fracture trace map. For fractal dimension calculations of single fracture sets, we rotate the fracture trace map so that the fractures in question are parallel to gridlines. The boxes defined by the grid that contain fractures are then counted. The grid scale (box size) is then changed by the scaling factor, r, and the grid boxes with fractures are counted again. We use a geometric, rather than an arithmetic, scaling factor so that the points on the ln N/ln($1/r$) graph have a constant spacing on the y-axis. This box-counting process is repeated for different box sizes. The minimum box size is determined by the approximate spacing of the fractures, and the maximum is determined by the fracture trace map size (with the narrow dimension of the fracture trace map divided into two east-west/north-south grid boxes.

To determine whether the pattern is fractal, all the box count/box size points are plotted on a ln N/ln($1/r$) graph. If a constant relation exists between the different scales of observation (i.e., if a straight regression line can be passed through the points), then the pattern is considered fractal. To determine more rigorously whether portions of the curve do have a constant slope, we plot the slope of the regression curve between each successive pair of points and also plot the residuals of the points (distance of the point away from the regression line). Problems with this simple method for determining which patterns are fractal are discussed in the "Fractal analysis problems and resolutions" section below.

In the GEO program for 1-D patterns, the input can be either fracture spacings or fracture lengths along a scanline, and the output includes both a curve of $1 - D_1$ for different scales of observation and a plot of the slopes between each two successive pairs of calculations. If the slopes remain constant across observation scales, then the D_1 pattern is considered fractal.

Step 2b. Determining the fractal dimension of the lineament and fracture patterns (if the patterns are fractal). If the entire regression curve has a fairly constant slope, as revealed by (1) the ln N/ln($1/r$) graph, or (2) the graph portraying the slope of the regression line, or (3) the residual curve, then D_2 is simply the slope of that regression line. Similarly, for D_1, the stable slope portion of the curve determined from GEO is subtracted from 1 to arrive at the D_1 value. If the regression curve has one or both tails with a non-constant slope, then the tail is removed from the data, and the regression curve is recalculated. The slope of the new regression curve is D_2. If the entire regression curve has multifractal characteristics (i.e., the curve has two or more sections with different, but constant, slopes), then the slope for each section of the curve can be calculated. However, if we are comparing fracture patterns to larger patterns of lineaments, then we generally discard the small-box tail. Other lineament and fracture patterns

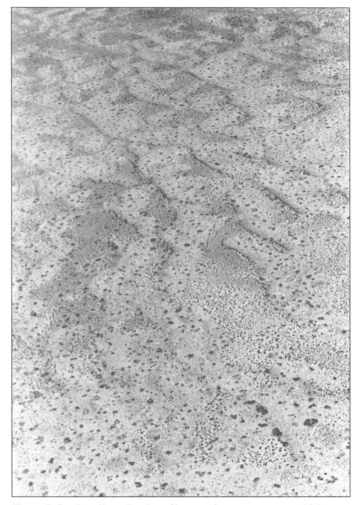

Figure 8. Sandy soil overburden of just centimeters to a meter thick completely obliterates the nature of the underlying bedrock in this air photo taken approximately 500 m above ground level. Presence or absence and orientation of fracture pattern cannot be ascertained from visual remote sensing of this locality.

have equivocal fractal dimensions, as illustrated and discussed in the "Fractal analysis problems and resolutions" section to follow.

Step 3. Comparing outcrop fracture patterns to lineament patterns recognized in various remotely sensed images (Landsat, SLAR, air photos) and topographic maps (a case study from the Appalachian Plateau of western New York). Figure 14 displays lineaments identified on the Fillmore 7.5′ topographic map (Wawrzynski and Jacobi, 1992), located in western New York State (Fig. 13). The regression curve on the *log N/log 1/r* of the lineament pattern (Fig. 15A) has a fairly constant slope with *log 1/r* values between 0.2 and 1.0 (Figs. 15B and 15C). The large instability in the slope of the large box tail (*log 1/r* < ~0.15) is a function of the box-counting method; this tail should be truncated and the regression curve recalculated (Fig. 15D; see the "Fractal analysis problems and resolutions" section for further discussion on truncations). The smaller excursions of the curve between *log 1/r* = 0.15 and 0.4 are also a function of large box sizes, but the

Figure 9. Shallow sandy soils in area near Figure 8 show presence of conjugate joints outlined by phreatophytic vegetation in some "windows" through the soil overburden in this air photo taken approximately 500 m above ground level.

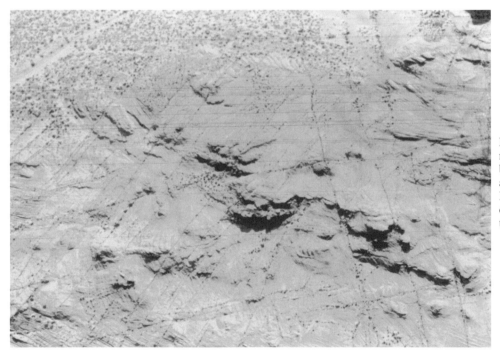

Figure 10. Fracture pattern becomes more readily apparent as the amount of exposed bedrock increases in this air photo taken approximately 500 m above ground level. Information here, as in Figure 9, is sufficient to characterize the nature of the fracture system.

instabilities are not judged sufficiently serious to truncate this section of the curve. The small box tail ($log\ 1/r > \sim 1$) with increasing residuals (Fig. 15C) should also be truncated. The new regression line, without either tail, yields a single slope with a slightly different D_2 value of 1.779 (vs. 1.756 for the original D_2). This truncated regression line has a slightly higher correlation coefficient than the original regression curve (0.999 vs. 0.998).

Lineaments identified in air photos that are located in the upper third of the Fillmore 7.5′ topographic quadrangle are shown in Figure 16 (Wawrzynski and Jacobi, 1992). The regression curve on the *log N/log 1/r* of the air photo lineament pattern (Fig. 17A) can be interpreted as fractal, and the large deviation from a best fit straight line in the small box sizes (Figs. 17B and 17C) could be interpreted as a function of short lineaments that are increasingly unidentified as their size decreases. However, a second interpretation is that the lineament pattern is actually multifractal (see the "Fractal analysis problems and resolutions" section for further discussion), and the sharp change in slope at about *log 1/r* = 0.8 marks the break in fractal domains. If the small box tail (that part of the curve with values of *log 1/r* >1) is removed and the regression line recalculated, a good best fit is found with a correlation coefficient of 0.999. This curve of the truncated population yields a D_2 value of 1.691 for the air photo lineaments (Fig. 17D). This value is lower than the 1.779 value found for the entire Fillmore quadrangle (Fig. 15). However, D_2 of the topographic map lineaments in only the area covered by the air photos (the northern third of the quadrangle, Fig. 14) does agree quite well with the air photo D_2 for the same area (1.685 for topographic map lineaments vs. 1.691 for air photo lineaments). The variance in D_2 between the entire topographic quadrangle and the northern third is discussed in the "Fractal analysis problems and resolutions" section. Because the lineament patterns observed in both the air photos and the northern third of the Fillmore topographic map have a statistically similar pattern, they can be integrated to construct a composite lineament map.

How do these lineament patterns from air photos and topographic maps compare with the fracture patterns on bedding surfaces at outcrops in the same area as the air photos and topographic maps? The qualitative answer is that lineaments patterns in the Appalachian Plateau of western New York do have the same patterns as the fractures. For example, lineaments observed on the Fillmore 7.5′ topographic map trend either northwest or northeast, with a smaller number striking north-south (Fig. 14). The air photo lineaments display similar relationships in the same area (Fig. 16). A local contrast to this general condition is seen in Figure 18, part of the Portageville 7.5′ topographic map, where a prominent north-striking lineament appears to truncate (i.e., it is the "master") northwest-, northeast-, and east-striking lineaments. The primary fracture sets in the area of these two topographic maps have the same pattern: a systematic northwest set (the "cross-fold set"; e.g., Engelder and Geiser, 1980; Engelder, 1985; Zhao and Jacobi, 1997) is generally abutted by a systematic northeast set (the "fold-parallel set") (Fig. 19). In much of the region, north-striking fractures are not present (Fig. 19b), but where they are present, they are usually nonsystematic and abut the northeast and northwest-striking sets (Fig. 19A). A causative relationship between the lineaments and the fracture orientations can be understood from Figure 20, where the trend of Wiscoy Creek (a prominent lineament in the topographic map of Figure 18) is clearly controlled by the systematic fracture set. This qualitative observation, that the lineaments from remotely sensed data and topographic maps have the same pattern as fractures in outcrop, can be tested by fractal analyses.

Many fracture patterns from hand-traced scangrids are not fractal in a rigorous sense. For example, the box count/box size curve (Fig. 21A) for the fracture pattern on a bedding surface of a thin sandstone (Fig. 19A) does not have a constant slope (Figs. 21A, 21B, and 21C). Although the slopes calculated between

Figure 11. Complete absence of overlying soil and vegetative cover in high relief terrain reveals the fracture system very well in two dimensions and quite well in three dimensions in the oblique view air photo from approximately 750 m above ground level.

adjacent points on the box count/box size curve appear fairly constant between a range of 0.5 < *log 1/r*<1.5 (Fig. 21B), the residuals (Fig. 21C) between the box count/box size curve (Fig. 21A) and a best fit straight line with a slope of D_2 = 1.19 are not stable; rather, the residuals indicate that the box count/box size curve has a constantly changing slope. The low D_2 value, 1.190, is consistent with the fracture pattern, but is clearly not consistent with the topographic and air photo D_2 values in the same area. Although unrecognized short fractures certainly contribute to the low-slope tail of small box sizes (see the "Fractal analysis problems and resolutions" section), in several outcrops of thin sandstones, careful inspection did not reveal a range of fracture lengths and spacings significantly larger than that indicated by the hand tracings. This observation suggests that some of the outcrop fracture patterns in these thin sandstones may not be inherently fractal at all dimensions of observation.

In another hand-traced fracture pattern on the surface of a thin sandstone (Fig. 19B), the fracture pattern has characteris-

Figure 12. Complete absence of overlying soil and vegetative cover in low to no relief terrain reveals the fracture system geometry very well in two dimensions, but not in three. For scale, the drill hole has a 4" (~10 cm) diameter (from Eastler and Andersen, 1988).

tics (Figs. 21E, 21F, and 21G) similar to those discussed before. Although the fracture pattern in Figure 19B has some fractal tendencies (the residuals are stable between $0.5 < log\ 1/r < 1.0$), the fractal dimension is much too low to be consistent with the lineament fractal dimensions ($D_2 = 1.248$ for the scangrid vs. ~1.6 to 1.79 for the lineament patterns). This disparity in fractal dimensions is certainly at least partly a function of the equivocal fractal nature of the fracture hand-traced scangrids, but the low D_2 values for the sandstones may also suggest that these sandstone fracture patterns do not control the lineament formation as much as the interbedded, thicker, and more highly fractured shales do.

In contrast to the hand-traced scangrids, photo scangrids of bedding surface fracture patterns in both sandstones and more shaley units (Fig. 22A and 22B, respectively) do exhibit fractal regression curves (Fig. 23). That photo scangrids, with higher resolution, do display fractal fracture patterns suggests that in many cases the nonfractal nature of the hand-traced fracture patterns was a result of untraced short fractures either because of nonrecognition or because the fracture length fell below an arbitrary length threshold. The fractal regression curves (Fig. 23) of the fracture patterns on the photo scangrids agree both in form and D_2 value with those of the lineament patterns; compare the D_2 values from the photo scangrids, 1.618 and 1.73, with those of the topographic map lineaments, 1.691 and 1.779, and the air photo lineaments, 1.685. That the lineament patterns from the 7.5′ topographic map and air photos, as well as the fracture patterns from photo scangrids, all have very similar fractal dimensions, and thus have statistically similar patterns, confirms the qualitative observation that there is a close relationship between

patterns of outcropping fractures and lineaments. A more rigorous exercise would be to compare the fractal dimension of each systematic set of fractures (e.g., northwest- or northeast-striking) and lineaments in a single structural domain.

Step 4. Extrapolating the fracture patterns based on similarities to lineaments. The relationship between fractures and lineaments is not a simple one in western New York. Jacobi and Fountain (1996) and Jacobi and Xu (1998) found that in the Appalachian Plateau of New York State, relatively long lineaments are related to FIDs, and thus to fault locations. The FIDs generally have different fracture patterns than the areas outside the FIDs. In order to predict fracture patterns and fault locations in covered (or denied) areas, one must therefore establish whether the lineaments that will be used as a guide for fracture/fault extrapolation are related to "general" fracture patterns or to FIDs. We extrapolated the fracture patterns characteristic of FIDs along associated lineaments (Fig. 24). The FIDs extended along lineaments define an interlocking grid of structural domains in which the gridlines (FIDs) have a fracture spacing and orientation that can be predicted from the fracture pattern in outcrops along the FIDs. These gridlines are characterized by: (1) a fracture spacing that is tighter than the "general" case, (2) master fractures parallel to the strike of the FID, and (3) a higher fractal dimension than the surrounding areas.

Fractured outcrops that do not display FIDs represent the "general" fracture pattern in the immediate region bounded by FIDs. If the fractal dimension of these fractures and the lineaments are similar, then it is possible to extrapolate the fracture pattern into denied (covered) areas bounded by the major lineaments. In practice, we assumed that the area bounded by FIDs is

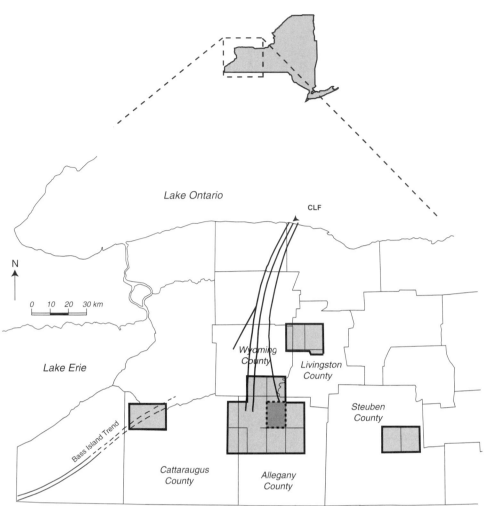

Figure 13. General location map displaying areas (shaded) in western New York State where the UB Rock Fracture Group has collected digital scangrid and scanline data that comprise over 70,000 fractures. Thin lines in shaded areas indicate 7.5′ topographic quadrangle boundaries. The shading in Allegany County indicates the outline of Figure 24. The darker shading in Allegany County indicates the Fillmore 7.5′ topographic quadrangle of Figure 14. CLF = Clarendon-Linden Fault System from Van Tyne (1975). Bass Island Trend from Van Tyne et al. (1980).

characterized by fracture patterns found in outcrops located within the area of question, whether or not there are sufficient lineaments to test the fractal dimensions. We were forced to make this assumption, based on multiple outcrops in the inter-FID areas, because there were insufficient lineaments to conduct a valid fractal dimension test in many inter-FID areas of New York State. To a limited extent, the validity of the fracture extrapolations can be tested by semivariograms (see subsequent section).

Fractal analysis problems and resolutions

1. Nondirectionality of fractals. An important consideration is that a fractal dimension is a non-directional quantity. For example, an east-striking fracture system with a certain spacing and length function will have the same fractal dimension as a north-striking fracture system that has the same spacing and length function. Thus, fractal analyses of the complete, or composite, fracture pattern in outcrop can be used only as a measure (and comparison) of the complexity of the fracture pattern, not as a measure of the similarity of orientations.

A simple solution for the nondirectional quality of fractals is to separate the observed fracture or lineament pattern into its component sets. The recognition and separation of fracture sets can be accomplished by analyzing the fracture orientation population for multiple Gaussian distributions (e.g., Gillespie et al., 1993), or by determining the range of orientations for each fracture set by grouping fractures that have common characteristics, such as orientation, abutting relationships, and style (e.g., Hestir et al., 1987; Zhao and Jacobi, 1994). Once the sets have been established, each set is analyzed separately for its fractal nature and fractal dimension. Then the fractal dimension of, for example, north-striking fractures in outcrop can be compared to the fractal dimension of north-striking lineaments observed in Landsat images.

2. Box-counting method drawback. The fractal dimension calculated from the box counting method is the result of a complex function of fracture spacing, fracture length, and box orientation/shape (e.g., Gillespie et al., 1993). Thus, not only do fractals lose the directionality of the fracture data, they also link the effects of spacing, length, and box characteristics. It is therefore possible that two fracture patterns with quite different spacing and length

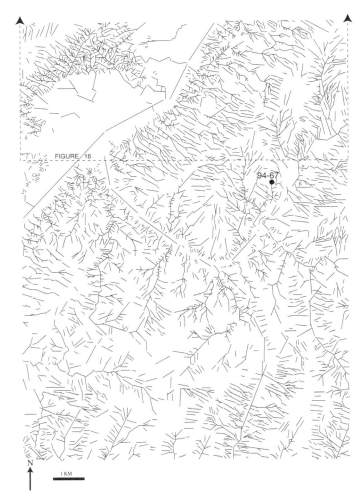

Figure 14. Lineaments identified on the Fillmore 7.5′ topographic quadrangle map, western New York State (location of quadrangle shown in Figure 13). Annotated dot indicates location of scangrid in Figure 22A (Site 94–67). Lineaments after Wawrzynski and Jacobi (1992).

characteristics could have the same fractal dimension. This basic inadequacy in fractal analysis is not easily surmountable. We reduce the box shape/orientation effect by rotating the single fracture set so that it is orthogonal and parallel to the sides of the counting box. Fracture spacing can be analyzed separately in 1-D scanline data sets by the spacing population method or the box-counting method (e.g., Gillespie, et al., 1993). For a 2-D fracture trace map, the box-counting method cannot distinguish between length vs. spacing, and thus fractals calculated in this manner are fairly insensitive to pattern changes. Fracture semivariograms (discussed subsequently) are attempts to refine the fractal approach, as are various fracture counting methods that count the number or orientation of fractures in the counting box (e.g., La Pointe, 1989; Gillespie, et al., 1993; Hardcastle, 1995). Gillespie et al. (1993) found that fracture-number interval counting (number of fractures in the counting box) is also of little value for discrimination among different fracture patterns, including discriminating between fractal and nonfractal fracture patterns.

3. Discrimination between fractal and nonfractal patterns. To determine if a pattern is fractal, the best-fit line that relates observation scale (box size) to number of boxes needed to fully cover the pattern (box count) must be straight on a log-log graph. Early analyses of fractures suggested that all fracture patterns were fractal (e.g., Barton, 1995). Careful inspection of Barton's (1995) data, however, shows that the data actually describe curvilinear regression lines at all sites. The question becomes: how much deviation in slope can be accommodated before a pattern is said to be nonfractal? There are no working guidelines at present. For example, Walsh and Watterson (1993) and Gillespie et al. (1993) suggested that Barton and Larsen's (1985) fracture systems with relatively small, gradual changes in slope are essentially nonfractal. Others, however, believe that slight curving of the regression line relating box size to box count is normal for fractal patterns (e.g., Feder, 1988). We have found that for 1-D space, the Cantor's Dust method demonstrates that on the box size/box count graph, some fracture patterns can be described with a tight clustering of points about a linear regression line (with a correlation coefficient of 0.999), whereas other patterns have a relatively high degree of spread away from a linear best-fit line (with a correlation coefficient of 0.90–0.990). We have regarded the latter as nonfractal patterns (e.g., Appendix, Fig. A1, and possibly Fig. 21C). Velde et al. (1991) used 0.97 as the minimum correlation coefficient value for assuming the pattern was fractal. However, nonfractal synthetic fractures can also result in linear regression lines with correlation coefficients as high as 0.999 (e.g., Gillespie et al., 1993; Zhao et al., 1994). Gillespie et al. (1993) therefore suggested that at least for spacing of 1-D data, fractal testing be conducted with the spacing-population method.

4. Tails of the regression curve in the ln N/ln(1/r) graph. A practical corollary to the curving regression line of the box size/box count relationship is the tails of the curve with different slopes that are related to methodology. For example, in 2-D space, the fractal dimension will be 2.0 for all box counting sizes greater than the size of the scangrid and greater than the widest fracture spacing (below S_{max} in Figure 25). The transition curve between the oversized box counting size and useful range of box counting sizes should also be disregarded (at S_{max} in Figure 25). At the other end of the scale, selected box counting sizes that are smaller than the resolution of the scangrid, and smaller than the spacing of the imaged fractures, yield unstable fractal dimensions that tend toward 0. The average slope is too low for box sizes smaller than the resolution of the scangrid ($log\ 1/r > S_{min}$ in Figure 25), compared to the true fractal dimension of the scangrid. Pruess (1995) pointed out that spurious D values can result from incorrect choices for the box size, and that a large range of box sizes is necessary to guard against such incorrect D values.

5. Multifractal patterns. In some data sets the regression line relating box size to box count does not have a single slope across all scales of observation; rather, the regression line has different slopes restricted to different scales of observation (e.g., Cowie, et al., 1995; Xu and Jacobi, 1998; Fig. 26). Each slope represents a different fractal dimension. In these cases,

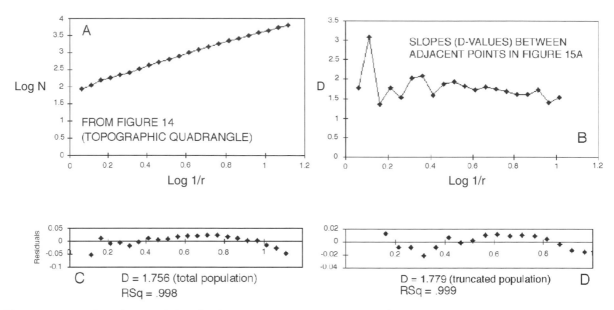

Figure 15. Fractal dimension calculations for lineament patterns in the Fillmore 7.5′ topographic quadrangle of Figure 14. A: A *log N/log 1/r* plot of the lineament pattern. B: Slopes (*D* values) between adjacent points in "A". C: Residual values after a least squares linear regression line has been fitted to curve in "A", with a *D* value (slope) and correlation coefficient annotated below the graph. D: Residual values after a least squares linear regression line has been fitted to a truncated curve of "A", with a *D* value (slope) and correlation coefficient annotated below the graph. In all fractal calculations the dimension of the counting box size varies from about half the narrow dimension of the map analyzed to a minimum size equal to the distance between the closest line element pairs. The fractal curve is similar to those for the lineament patterns from air photos (Figs. 16 and 17) and the third of the top Fillmore topographic map (Appendix, Fig. A1), but the *D* value is higher for the entire Fillmore quadrangle. The variation in *D* values is not entirely a result of different map resolutions since the difference also occurs between different parts of the same map.

the fractal dimension depends on the scale of the observation, with threshold observation sizes, T, separating different fractal dimensions. Patterns that display two or more distinct slopes are said to be multifractal. Multifractals have been observed in both natural fracture systems (e.g., Berkowitz and Hadad, 1997; Xu and Jacobi,1998; Wilson, 1999) and in computer generated fracture systems (Cowie, et al., 1995). Xu and Jacobi (1998) found that for scanline data in western New York, T ranges from 0.15 m to 1.15 m, and that the fractal dimension at observation scales larger than T is on the order of fractal dimensions expected from calculations from large 2-D scangrids (0.11 to 0.85, with an average of 0.52). Both laboratory experiments (Cowie et al., 1995; Wu and Pollard, 1995) and outcrop abutting relationships (Xu and Jacobi, 1998) suggested that fracture sets with a single fractal dimension have had sufficient time and space to develop fractures with relatively long lengths and equal spacing. In western New York, the older fracture sets, based on abutting relationships, are more mature (i.e., are not multifractal). In contrast, Barton (1995) suggested that the apparent multifractal nature of fractures may be a counting problem related to the aperture of the visible fractures counted.

One obvious problem for fracture patterns with multifractal properties is that it is not possible to definitively extrapolate from mesoscale fracture patterns to macroscale lineament patterns from images (e.g., Landsat images), since the number of Ts

between the observed fracture pattern and the larger area is unknown. This problem can be minimized if it can be determined that the largest fractal dimension calculated from a scanline or scangrid is similar to the dimension calculated from a larger scale of observation such as lineaments. Such is the case in western New York where the larger multifractal dimensions calculated from scanline data are close to those of lineaments and large-area scangrids (Xu and Jacobi, 1998).

6. Effects of image resolution and areal size on fractal dimension. Lineament patterns identified in topographic maps may display fairly large variations in D_2, both between adjacent quadrangles and between selected parts of individual quadrangles. In the first case, different series of 7.5′ topographic maps were contoured at different resolutions. The number of short lineaments is noticeably fewer in the images that were contoured at a lower resolution. This lack of lineaments, relative to the higher resolution maps, is translated into a lower fractal dimension. The second case, areal extent, is illustrated by the Fillmore 7.5′ topographic quadrangle (Fig. 14). The entire quadrangle has a D_2 value of 1.779, whereas the northern third of the quadrangle has a D_2 value of 1.685 (Appendix, Fig. A2), after truncation of the largest box size and the small box tail. This lower value, compared to 1.779 for all of the Fillmore 7.5′ topographic map, reflects the large area in the northwestern part of the quadrangle that has no lineaments. This area that lacks lineaments is propor-

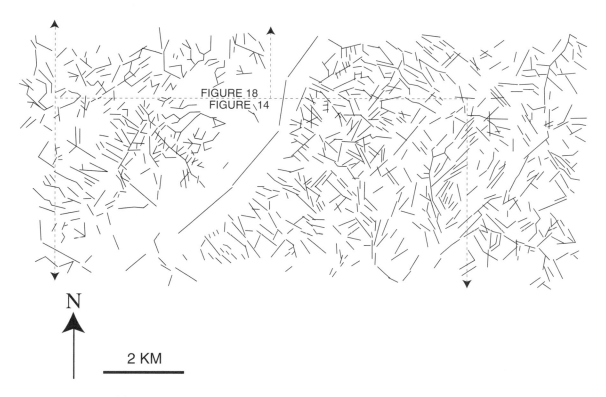

Figure 16. Topographic, vegetative and other tonal lineaments identified on air photos. Location of Figures 14 and 18 shown by dashed outlines. Lineaments after Wawrzynski and Jacobi (1992).

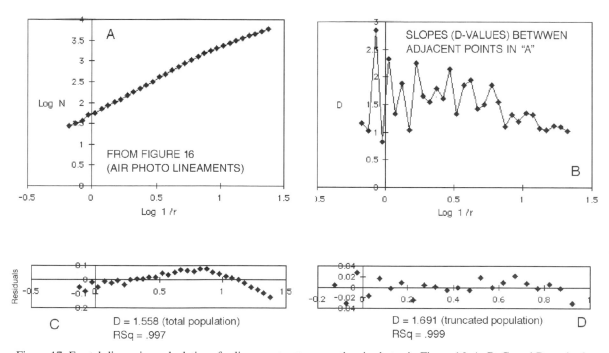

Figure 17. Fractal dimension calculations for lineament patterns on the air photos in Figure 16. A, B, C, and D are in the same formats as A–D in Figure 15. The fractal curve and D value are similar to those displayed in Appendix, Figure A1, of the topographic lineament pattern from the northern third of the Fillmore topographic map in Figure 14.

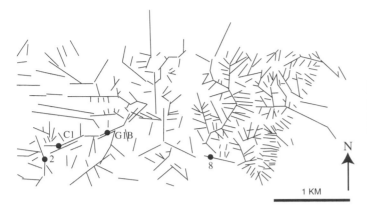

Figure 18. Lineaments identified in part of the Portageville 7.5′ topographic quadrangle map, western New York State. Annotated dots indicate location of scangrids in Figure 19 (western two sites) and Appendix
(eastern two sites). Lineaments after Wawrzynski and Jacobi (1992)

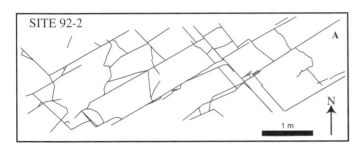

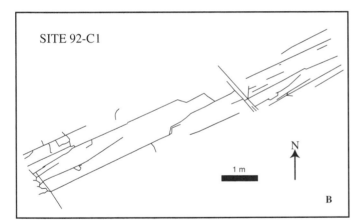

Figure 19. Scangrids of fractures in outcrop along Wiscoy Creek (see
Figure 18 for locations). These scangrids are from outcrop fracture
tracings with a plastic grid overlay. Scangrids from Jacobi and Fountain (1996). In Figure 19A the northwest-striking systematic fracture
on the right is master to the northeast set, whereas the central northwest-striking systematic fracture abuts the northeast set. Note the
poorly developed, non-systematic north-striking fractures in 19A. In
Figure 19B the northwest-striking fractures (on the right) are all masters to the northeast set.

Figure 20. Wiscoy Creek near site C1 (located on Figure 18), looking
east-northeast. Note that the master fractures control the orientation of
the stream.

tionally more important for the northern third of the quadrangle
fractal calculation than for the fractal calculation that involves the
entire quadrangle, thus resulting in the lower fractal dimension
for the northern third. The smoothing effect from increasing the
areal extent utilized in the fractal dimension calculation, as
demonstrated in this example, raises the question of how signifi-

cant a disparity or "agreement" in fractal dimensions is for large
area calculations.

7. FID fractal dimension. Fractal dimensions calculated
from a scangrid outside the boundaries of a FID cannot describe
the fracture pattern accurately within a FID (Jacobi and Xu,
1998). For example, in many areas of western New York, virtu-

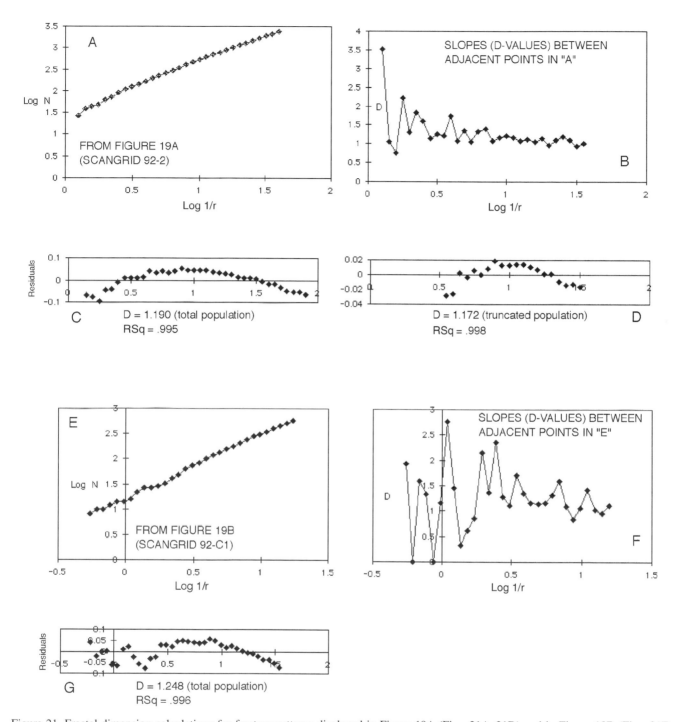

Figure 21. Fractal dimension calculations for fracture patterns displayed in Figure 19A (Figs. 21A–21D) and in Figure 19B (Figs. 21E and 21F). A, B, C, and D are in the same formats as Figures 15A–15D; E, F, and G are in the same formats as Figures 15A–15C.

ally no north-striking fractures exist (e.g., Jacobi and Fountain, 1996). The fractal dimension of the north-striking set is thus essentially 0.0 in these areas, but in north-striking FIDs, the fractal dimension of north-striking fractures can be quite high (up to 0.7 in 1-D space). A fractal dimension from an area outside FIDs will not predict the location of FIDs (and faults), and an outcrop in a FID will not result in a *D* value appropriate for fracture sites outside of a FID. However, construction of a FID base map that displays the fractal dimensions for various outcrops within and outside FIDs can promote (1) a demonstration of the degree of consistency of the FIDs along strike and among FID sets, and (2) a comparison among lineament patterns, lineament pattern *D* values, and the FID/non-FID zones and their *D* values. The latter consideration can aid in determining whether the origin of particular lineaments is founded in FIDs. Long et al. (1987) have also divided regions into subregions based on homogeneity of fracture spacing and length.

Fracture frequency and density

Introduction and operations. Fracture frequency, or its inverse, fracture spacing, is an important measure of rock integrity for mining, other engineering projects, weapon penetration, and in oil and gas production. In sedimentary rocks, except for FIDs, some researchers have suggested that fracture frequency is controlled by layer thickness (e.g., McQuillan, 1973; Price, 1979; Narr and Lerche, 1984; Narr and Suppe, 1991; Wu and Pollard, 1995; Gross et al., 1994), assuming corrections for scanline orientation, scanline terminations, fracture length effects, and scanline placement/length (e.g., La Pointe and Hudson, 1985; Long and Billaux, 1987; Long et al., 1987; Dershowitz and Herda, 1992; Mauldon, 1992, 1994; Kulatilake et al., 1993, 1996; Xu and Jacobi, 1998). In this scenario, for a given lithology, the relationship between bed thickness and fracture spacing is linear, and the slope of the regression line relating bed thickness to fracture spacing is defined as the fracture spacing index (FSI) (Narr and Lerche, 1984). For a single bed, the bedding thickness divided by the median-joint spacing is defined as the fracture spacing ratio (FSR) (Gross, 1993). Both of these quantities can be used to normalize fracture spacing in beds of similar lithology but differing thickness.

Others believe, however, that the controls on some fracture spacing are more complicated, and that bed thickness exerts little control on fracture spacing (e.g., McQuillan, 1974; Rawnsley et al., 1998). For example, Ladeira and Price (1981) demonstrated that graywacke beds thicker than 1 to 2 m (including those of McQuillan, 1973) have a constant fracture spacing, independent of bed thickness (although beds thinner than 1–2 m did show a linear relationship). In the Upper Devonian of western New York, Zhao and Jacobi (1994) found essentially no correlation between bed thickness and fracture spacing in thin siltstones and interbedded shales; only some relatively thick sandstone beds (approximately 0.25–2 m thick) displayed any consistent bed thickness/fracture spacing relationship. Rives et al. (1992) suggested that fracture spacing is at least as strongly a function of the stage of fracture growth as it is bed thickness. If fracture spacing is fractal, then the fracture spacing should vary inversely with the fracture length, consistent with the growth stage model of Rives et al. (1992).

In areas where radical variations in spacing of relatively long fractures occur in units of similar lithology and thickness, factors other than layer thickness must contribute to the control of fracture spacing. For example, the fracture frequency in FIDs is extremely high for the bed thickness and for the fracture height and length (Jacobi and Fountain, 1996; Jacobi and Xu, 1998). Although fracture clustering similar to that in FIDs could be

ascribed to continued random splitting of earlier fracture spacings (e.g., Long et al., 1987; Chiles, 1988), in western New York this excess number of fractures is related to observed faults, some of which extend through the entire Paleozoic section. Similarly, Gross et al. (1997) found that near a normal fault, the FSR values can be correlated to the amount of slip on a normal fault zone.

The problem with fracture spacing, FSR, and FSI is that these measures are only one-dimensional quantities. However, because many geological, military, and engineering problems are two- and three-dimensional, "fracture density" is used. The higher the fracture density, the more compromised the rock integrity is, assuming equal fracture healing, filling, and veining. The measures of fracture density are defined here (e.g., Xu, 1998).

$$\text{Fracture frequency:} \quad f = \frac{N}{L} \tag{4}$$

$$\text{Fracture density 1:} \quad D_{f1} = \frac{\sum_i^N l_i}{A} \tag{5}$$

$$\text{Fracture density 2:} \quad D_{f2} = \frac{\sum_i^N \left(\frac{l_2}{2}\right)^2}{A} \tag{6}$$

$$\text{Fracture density 3:} \quad D_{f3} = \frac{\sum_i^N (r_i)^3}{V} \tag{7}$$

where N is the total number of fractures, L is the cumulative orthogonal distance (length) between fracture pairs (or simply the scan line length if the scan line is orthogonal to the fractures), l_i is the length of fracture i, A is the sampling area, r_i is the average radius of fracture i and is approximated by $l_i/2$, and V is the sampling volume.

Note that common symbols used for these fracture densities are changed in this chapter to lessen confusion among dimensional, fractal, and density terms, all of which use "D."

Fracture frequency (f) and fracture density 1 (D_{f1}) have the same dimensional units: $1/L$, but fracture densities 2 and 3 (D_{f2} and D_{f3}) are dimensionless. Their scale-independent nature allows them to be applied to larger areas/volumes than the areas/volumes that were used in determining the densities. Renshaw (1997) found that D_{f2} of natural fracture patterns is in the range of 0.2 to 1.5. This narrow range is most likely the result of a reduction in the elastic continuity of the fractured medium as fracturing continues (e.g., Renshaw, 1997), i.e., preexisting fractures can accommodate large amounts of strain (e.g., Madden, 1983).

Unfortunately, the ability to collect the data in 2-D and 3-D commonly necessary for fracture density calculations is severely limited. For example, core and wireline logs generally yield only scanline (1-D) data, and in regions of heavy cover, outcrops may

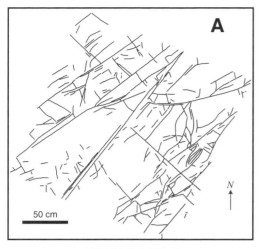

SITE 94-67-4

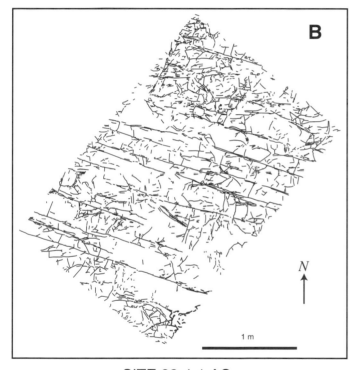

SITE 93-4-1 AG

Figure 22. Fracture pattern from photo scangrids. Location of Figure 22A shown on Figure 14, and location of Figure 22B is in the Houghton 7.5′ topographic quadrangle immediately west of the Fillmore Quadrangle. Scangrids from Jacobi and Fountain (1996).

be insufficient to allow 2-D and 3-D visualization of fractures, especially fracture length. Xu and Jacobi (1998) demonstrated that a stable relationship exists between fracture frequency, f, and D_{f1}, for a given area and a given method of data collection. Furthermore, by assuming that the fracture length distribution follows a power or exponential law, the dimensionless fracture

density D_{f2} can be calculated from D_{f1}; D_{f3} can then be calculated from D_{f2}. Thus 2-D and 3-D characterization of fracture intensity can be calculated from 1-D data, and theoretically can be extrapolated to denied areas in the same structural domain as the 1-D observed data.

In order to determine empirically the general relationship that might exist between f and D_{f1}, Xu and Jacobi (1998) calculated both f and D_{f1} for 37 fracture trace maps. The f values were calculated along synthetic scanlines drawn across the scangrids. The D_{f1} values were calculated for the same scangrids as the f values by determining in ARCINFO the arc lengths of the separate fracture sets (after fracture trace corrections), and then totaling the values from the various fracture sets. The fracture trace maps that were constructed from outcrops in western New York all have a similar resolution of 0.1 cm (Jacobi and Zhao, 1996a, 1996b), whereas the fracture trace maps from other sources, shown in Table 1, have variable resolutions. All 37 trace maps demonstrated a consistent relationship between f and D_{f1} (Table 1, Xu and Jacobi, 1998), however.

By comparing D_{f1} calculated from the equations in Table 1 to D_{f1} calculated from the fracture trace maps, Xu and Jacobi (1998) determined that the general equation has an estimated error of less than 11.5% for all regions and lithologies tested. If the locally derived equation is applied to a region outside the tectonic province, then the error can be as high as 40%, compared to the observed D_1. However, it appears that the relationship is stable across a single tectonic province (see the two local areas in the Appalachian Plateau, Table 1).

The problem with calculating D_{f2} and D_{f3} is that these quantities depend on the sum of the squared fracture half-lengths. This dependence on fracture half-length is a significant departure from D_{f1}, which depends on the total length of fractures in a given area—a sum easily calculated. In contrast, the fracture length distribution needed to calculate D_{f2} and D_{f3} is only poorly known in many cases. In small outcrops, the lengths of the master fractures are commonly unknown because the fractures have lengths greater than the outcrop. Furthermore, La Pointe and Hudson (1985) showed that longer fractures have a higher probability of being sampled along a scanline, no matter what the fracture length distribution is. Although these and other sampling problems can be partly corrected (e.g., La Pointe and Hudson, 1985; Long and Billaux, 1987; Long et al., 1987; Mauldon, 1992, 1994; Kulatilake et al., 1993, 1996; Xu and Jacobi, 1998), they probably have contributed to the diversity of views concerning the general fracture length distribution. For example, the fracture length distribution has been suggested to be exponential (e.g., Priest and Hudson, 1976, 1981; Segall and Pollard, 1983; La Pointe and Hudson, 1985; Kulatilake et al., 1993; Watterson et al., 1996), gamma (e.g., Kulatilake et al., 1993), lognormal (e.g., Rouleau and Gale, 1985; Long and Billaux, 1987; Renshaw and Pollard, 1994), normal (e.g., Wu and Pollard, 1992), or hyperbolic (e.g., Segall and Pollard, 1983). These different fracture length distributions may not be mutually exclusive; rather, different fracture length distributions may be representative of (1) different mechan-

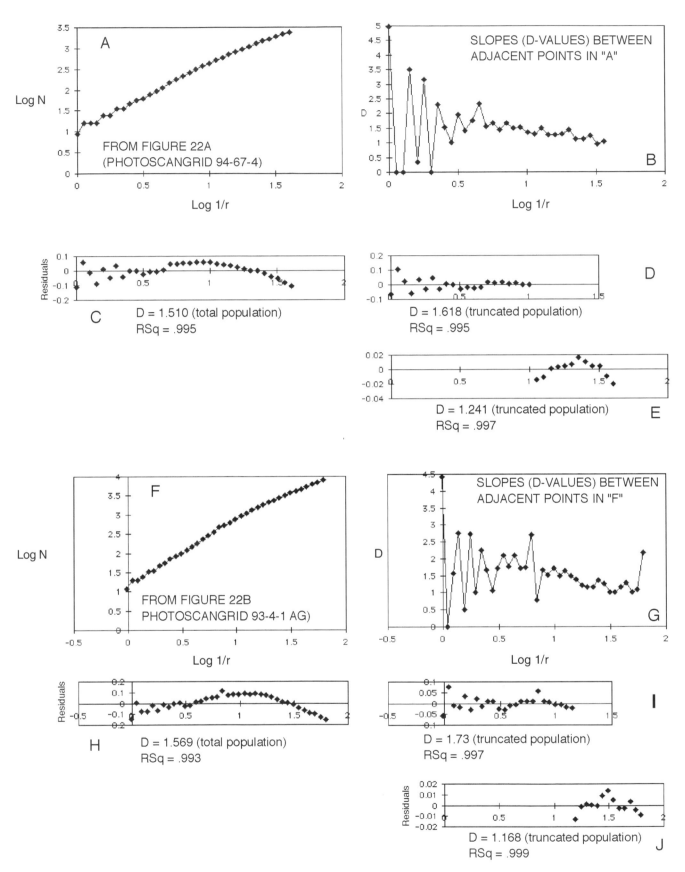

Figure 23. Fractal dimension calculations for fracture patterns displayed in Figure 22A (Figs. 23A–23E) and in Figure 22B (Figs. 23F–23J). Figures A, B, C, and D are in the same formats as Figure 15A–15D. D has the small-box tail truncated, whereas E has the large-box curve truncated. Figures F, G, H, and I are in the same formats as Figures 15A–15D. Figure 22I has the small-box tail truncated, whereas J has the large-box curve truncated.

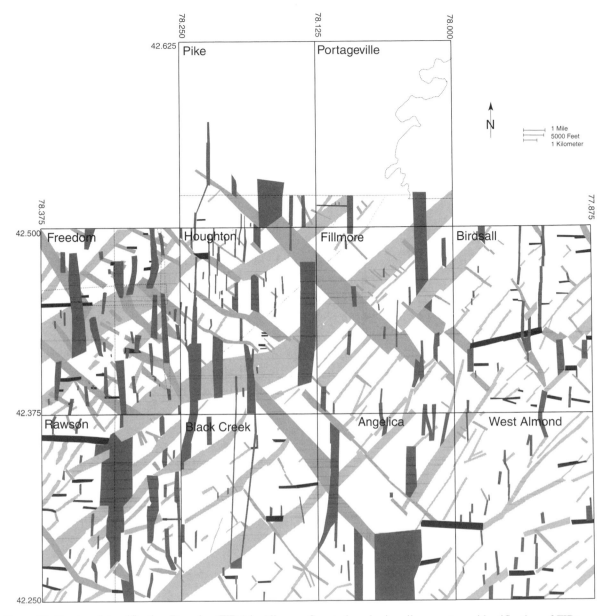

Figure 24. Fracture Intensification Domains (FIDs) in Allegany County based primarily on outcrop identification of FIDs and extrapolation of FIDs along lineaments. See Figure 13 for location. From Jacobi and Fountain (1996), Zack and Jacobi (1997), Peters and Jacobi (1997), and Smith et al. (1998).

ical processes (e.g., Dershowitz and Einstein, 1988), or (2) varying completeness of the data sets (Gillespie et al., 1993; Kulatilake et al., 1993). For example, Gillespie et al. (1993) showed that the 1-D distribution of natural fractures at a single outcrop can vary from a negative exponential distribution (if all fracture sets and fracture lengths are counted in the distribution) to a lognormal spacing population (if the spacing of all fracture lengths in only one fracture set was considered), and to a normal spacing distribution (if fractures with trace lengths < 5 m were excluded and fracture zones were represented by one long fracture).

Xu and Jacobi (1998) developed general equations (8) to (12) that related D_{f2} and D_{f3} to D_{f1}, assuming a general fracture length

distribution curve $f(x)$. They further developed specific equations (13) to (19) assuming the fracture length distribution follows either a power-law distribution or an exponential distribution.

$$D_{f1} = \frac{\int_0^N f(x)dx}{A} \qquad (8)$$

$$D_{f2} = \frac{\int_0^N \left(\frac{f(x)}{2}\right)^2 dx}{A} \qquad (9)$$

$$D_{f3} = \frac{\int_0^N \left(\frac{f(x)}{2}\right)^3 dx}{V} \tag{10}$$

therefore:

$$D_{f2}/D_{f1} = \frac{\int_0^N \left(\frac{f(x)}{2}\right)^2 dx}{\int_0^N f(x)dx} \tag{11}$$

$$D_{f3}/D_{f1} = \frac{\int_0^N \left(\frac{f(x)}{2}\right)^3 dx}{H\int_0^N f(x)dx} \tag{12}$$

where N is the total number of fractures, and H is the height of the sampling volume.

If the fracture length is power distributed on $[0, N]$, then

$$f(x) = cx^k \tag{13}$$

$$D_{f2}/D_{f1} = \frac{N^k c}{4} \frac{(k+1)}{(2k+1)} \tag{14}$$

If the fracture length is exponentially distributed, then

$$f(x) = ce^{kx} \tag{15}$$

$$D_{f2}/D_{f1} = \frac{c}{8}\left(1 + e^{Nk}\right) \tag{16}$$

$$D_{f3}/D_{f1} = \frac{\dfrac{c^3}{24k}\left(e^{3Nk}-1\right)}{H\dfrac{c}{k}\left(e^{Nk}-1\right)} = \frac{c^2}{24H}\left(e^{2Nk}+e^{Nk}+1\right) \tag{17}$$

$$D_{f3}/D_{f2} = \frac{\dfrac{c^3}{24k}\left(e^{3Nk}-1\right)}{H\dfrac{c^2}{8k}\left(e^{2Nk}-1\right)} = \frac{c}{3H}\left(\frac{e^{2Nk}}{e^{Nk}+1}+1\right) \tag{18}$$

where c and k are constants determined by curve-fitting the fracture length distribution with either power-law or exponential models, and H is the height of the sampling volume.

To test the validity of the derived D_{f1}/D_{f2} relationship, and to test which fracture distribution is more applicable to the 37 selected trace maps, Xu and Jacobi (1998) calculated D_{f2} from the

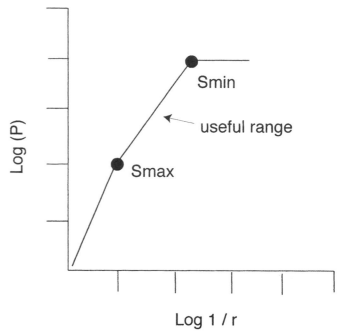

Figure 25. Useful range for calculating D values via the Cantor's Dust method (log P-log r). P = proportion of boxes that had at least one fracture, r = box size, S_{max} = maximum fracture spacing or map size, S_{min} = minimum fracture spacing (From Jacobi and Xu, 1998).

TABLE 1. EMPIRICAL RELATIONSHIPS BETWEEN D_{f1} AND f

D_{f1}= 1.29f + 0.10 (Livingston County, NY)
D_{f1}= 1.31f + 0.01 (Allegany County, NY)
D_{f1} = 1.52f + 0.02 (outside sources)
D_{f1}= 1.35f + 0.03 (general equation for all regions and all data collection methods)

Note: The equation for Livingston County is based on fracture trace maps from Xu and Jacobi (1998). The equation for Allegany County is based on fracture trace maps from Jacobi and Fountain (1996). The equation for "outside sources" is based on fracture trace maps from Kolb et al. (1970), Scott and Bonk (1984), La Pointe and Hudson (1985), Barton and Hsieh (1989), Olson and Pollard (1989), and Barton (1995). The relationship is from Xu and Jacobi (1998).

D_{f1}/D_{f2} equations (equations [14] and [16]), using both exponential and power-law curves that best fit the observed fracture length distribution (Table 2). These values are in general agreement with the range of D_{f2} (0.2 to 1.5) determined by Renshaw (1997).

Comparison between D_{f2} calculated directly from the scangrids and the D_{f2} values calculated from the D_{f1}/D_{f2} relationship showed that a power-law length distribution results in underestimated D_{f2} values. In all examples, the exponential length distribution resulted in a lower error than the power-law length distribution. The average error for 37 scangrids is 19.12% for exponential length distribution and 44.94% for power-law length distribution. However, D_{f2} calculated assuming either the power law or the exponential length distribution can have large errors compared to D_{f2} calculated directly from the scangrids (up to 68% for exponential and 78% for power-law distributions). These

TABLE 2. D_{f2} **VALUES CALCULATED ASSUMING AN EXPONENTIAL**
OR POWER LAW FRACTURE LENGTH DISTRIBUTION

Region	D_{f2} Exponential fracture distribution	D_{f2} Power law fracture distribution
Allegany County, western New York	0.567 to 2.005	0.300 to 2.048
Livingston County, western New York	0.228 to 2.298	0.175 to 0.714
Other regions	0.417 to 2.298	0.238 to 1.974

Note: Data sources are the same as in Table 1. Calculations from Xu and Jacobi (1998).

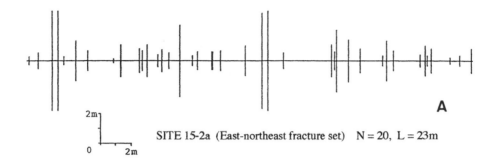

SITE 15-2a (East-northeast fracture set)   N = 20, L = 23m

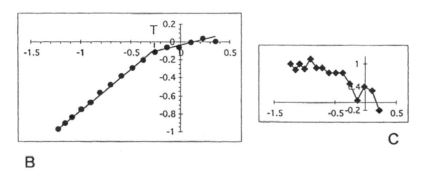

SITE 15-2a (East-northeast fracture set) $d_1 = 0.14$, $d_2 = 0.77$, $T_2 = 0.56$m

Figure 26. Example of a multi-fractal pattern (From Jacobi and Xu, 1998). A: Scanline with only east-northeast–striking fractures delineated, fractures centered on scanline to show length of fractures. B: Fractal calculation showing two slopes, implying a multifractal pattern of fracture spacing. C: Plot of slopes; note the two slopes with a break, T_2, at .56 m.

large errors can be reduced to acceptable errors by following the techniques discussed in the following section.

Fracture density problems and resolutions

1. Fracture length distribution. The primary problem for D_{f2} and D_{f3} is that they depend on the fracture length distribution, which is commonly not available and must therefore be estimated. Neither the power-law nor the exponential distribution of fracture lengths matches the observed fracture length distribution in the 37 scangrids tested. One solution to the problem is to use a higher order polynomial curve to match the fracture length distribution. For example, a third order polynomial function reduces the error of D_{f2} to 4.5%. However, higher order polyno-

mials will complicate the integration of the equations for D_{f1}/D_{f2}, resulting in inefficient calculations. Xu and Jacobi (1998) therefore developed two methods that reduce the error resulting from a poor fit of the exponential curve to the fracture length distribution. They first separated the fractures along the scanline into different sets based on orientation, and then matched an exponential curve to the fracture distribution of each fracture set. This method produced satisfactory best fit curves in most cases. If the exponential curve was still not a satisfactory best fit to the fracture length distribution, then fractures with lengths less than 10% of the maximum length were removed, and then the exponential curve was fit to the longer fractures. Because the fracture half-lengths are squared in the equation, removing the shortest fractures affects the D_{f2} calculation by less than 1%. D_{f2} values calculated from the D_{f1}/D_{f2} equation using these two methodologies have less than a 10% error with respect to D_{f2} calculated directly from the scangrids.

   2. FIDs. This method does not describe the location of FIDs. The denied area to which the fracture density is extrapolated must be within the same structural domain as the scanline, as deduced, for example, from lineament and fractal studies. If the scanline is between FIDs, the area for which D_2 may be extrapolated must also be between those FIDs, and conversely, if the scanline is located within a FID, then the density may be extrapolated only for the area covered by that FID.

   3. Expanding from 2-D to 3-D. The equations that relate D_{f3} to D_{f1} and D_{f2} ([17] and [18]) have been developed but not tested. Equations (17) and (18) are valid if the density is constant across the volume, and if the fractures found in 2-D space (such as in a scangrid on a bedding-parallel outcrop) are representative of all fractures in 3-D space. The primary problem with expanding from 2-D to 3-D is that fracture sets observed in 2-D do *not* typically represent all fractures in the third dimension. For example, bedding-parallel fractures are common, but are not observed at an outcrop on a bedding surface. In order to reduce the error due to undetected fractures, two mutually perpendicular scangrids, a horizontal and a vertical scangrid, or a single horizontal scangrid coupled with a borehole for the third-dimension data, are necessary to confirm that all the fractures in the volume are accounted for in the density calculation. For sedimentary rocks, the volume for the D_{f3} extrapolation should be restricted to a single mechanical layer comparable to the fracture height. If the vertical scangrid/scanline coverage demonstrates that the vertical fracture pattern is fractal, then the vertical dimension can be scaled beyond the height of the vertical scangrid/scanline, up to the height of the fractures.

Geostatistical analyses of fracture spacing and length

   Introduction and operations. Geostatistics, the application of the theory of regionalized variables (e.g., Matheron, 1963, 1971; Journel, 1974, 1986), can be used to analyze any spatially correlated data set. Geostatistical analyses can be applied to questions of how fracture attitude, frequency/spacing, or length vary over distance (e.g., Miller, 1979; La Pointe and Hudson, 1985; Hestir et al., 1987; Long and Billaux, 1987; Long et al., 1987; Chiles, 1988; Billaux et al., 1989; Villaescusa and Brown, 1990; Xu and Jacobi, 1998). Geostatistics can thus describe the variations associated with FIDs. Geostatistics can also provide a measure of the distance that fracture attributes can be reliably extrapolated away from the site of observation.

   Semivariograms are the geostatistical tool used to examine the similarity of two fractures as a function of distance between the fracture pairs. For a regionalized variable (e.g., spacing) $Z(x)$, the semivariogram function

$\gamma_\alpha(h)$, is defined as:

$$\gamma_\alpha(h) = \frac{1}{2}E\big[Z(x) - Z(x+h)\big]^2 \qquad (19)$$

where h is the distance between two locations in direction (called the "lag" distance), $Z(x)$ is the value at point x, and $Z(x+h)$ is the value at point $x+h$. The semivariogram is estimated by computing the differences between all pairs of samples in a region (Clark, 1979):

$$\gamma_\alpha(h) = \frac{1}{2N(h)} \sum_{i=1}^{N(h)} \big[Z(x_i) - Z(x_i + h)\big]^2 \qquad (20)$$

where h is the lag distance between two samples in direction α; $Z(x_i)$ is the sample value at point x_i; $Z(x+h)$ is the sample value at point x_i+h; and $N(h)$ is the number of sample pairs separated by distance h in direction α. A semivariogram is constructed by plotting $\gamma(h)$ against h for all sample pairs.

   Geostatistical analyses use many models to describe the resulting semivariograms. Among the most common models are spherical, Gaussian, pure nugget, and linear (e.g., La Pointe and Hudson, 1985; Long and Billaux, 1987; Xu and Jacobi, 1998; Fig. 27). Xu and Jacobi (1998) proposed two additional models that describe distributions of fracture spacing and length: the reversed spherical and polynomial models (Fig. 28).

   In the spherical model (Fig. 27A), fractures with a short lag distance, h, have a relatively high similarity, but as the lag distance increases, the similarity between fracture attributes decreases according to a spherical curve. At some lag distance, range α, the decrease in similarity reaches a plateau where further increases in lag distance do not result in further decreases in similarity, i.e., there is no correlation if h is greater than α. This plateau is called the sill, and indicates that extrapolation of fracture attributes at lag distances greater than a away from the observation site is unreliable. Like the spherical model, the Gaussian model also has a range value at which the curve reaches a sill, but the region of correlation is larger than that for the spherical model (Fig. 27B).

   In the pure nugget model (Fig. 27C) $\gamma(h)$, is independent of h, indicating that sample values are independent of lag distance. Such a model suggests a purely random pattern that is not predictable away from the site of observation. In the linear model, the similarity of a fracture attribute decreases linearly with increasing lag distance, but never reaches a sill (Fig. 27D). Fracture attributes that have a linear semivariogram can be extrapolated quite far from the observation site.

   The reversed spherical model (Fig. 28A) was developed to describe both fracture spacing and length distributions observed along scanlines in western New York (Xu and Jacobi, 1998). In this model, sample pairs with small lag distances have a low similarity, whereas increasing lag distances increases the similarity between sample pairs.

   A second order polynomial model describes periodic variation in similarity. In one case, a concave-downward curve indicates that sample pairs with similar attributes occur at small and large lag distances (Figs. 28B and 29A). This type of sample pair

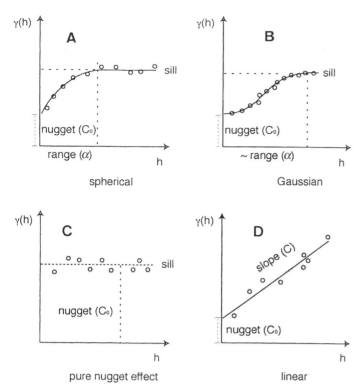

Figure 27. Common types of semivariogram models.

distribution is apparent, but not described, in other data sets (e.g., Long and Billaux, 1987; Billaux et al., 1989). A different semivariogram can be described by a concave-upward curve (Fig. 29B). In this case the sample pairs with small and large lag distances have the lowest similarity.

These periodic semivariograms are consistent with the clustering observed in Cantor's Dust fractal analyses (e.g., Velde et al., 1991, 1993). The concave downward periodic function suggests that fracture-pair similarities can be extrapolated periodically away from the sample site at intervals equal to the periodicity of the polynomial. For example, in the case of Figure 28B, similarities in length of fracture pairs spaced between about 11 and 16 m apart can be extrapolated in increments of about 11 to 16 m.

Xu and Jacobi (1998) analyzed 28 scanlines from the Appalachian Plateau in Livingston County, western New York, using a FORTRAN 77 code, "GEO" (Xu, 1998) and a standard geostatistical program, GSLIB (Deutsch and Journel, 1992). GEO prepares fracture spacing and length data collected from scanlines for input to GSLIB. Xu and Jacobi (1998) found that fracture spacing and length are described generally by spherical, reversed spherical, and polynomial models (Table 3). The spacing and length of some fracture sets can be extrapolated more than 16 m away from the observation site (Table 3). These values are generally lower than, but the same order as, values found for the number of fractures and fracture density in a mine drift penetrating a granite massif (Long and Billaux, 1987). There, ranges of frac-

ture number and density for various fracture sets vary from about 10 m to about 40 m, with most ranges between 20 m and 40 m.

If some fracture sets can truly be described by periodic polynomial semivariograms (Table 3), then the range for the periodic attributes of these fracture sets may be extended from certain sites far beyond the range of ~16 m indicated by the observed data set. For example, fracture length variation in Figure 28B and fracture spacing variation in Figure 29A both appear to be periodic, with a wavelength of about 16 m. Thus, the length of fractures 16 m apart may be extrapolated in increments of 16 m away from site 15-2a (Figs. 28B and 28C) and the fracture spacing may be extrapolated similarly from site 36-6 (Figs. 29A and 29C).

Baudo and Jacobi (1999) have measured fractures along a scanline over 2 km long to determine whether the periodic semivariograms can be recognized in larger data sets. Preliminary results suggest that some fracture sets with periodic polynomial semivariograms do demonstrate repeated similar characteristics over the scale of the scanline. Scanline and scangrid data and fractal analyses suggest that the master fracture set, and to a lesser extent, other systematic fracture sets, have quasiperiodic spacing outside of fracture intensification domains. This periodic function is not surprising, given the regular fracture spacing observed by several researchers (e.g., Narr and Lerche, 1984).

An advantage of semivariograms is that they can describe the presence of narrow FIDs. The semivariograms for the fracture set that defines the FID should display distinct semivariogram characteristics, assuming that the FID has closely spaced, relatively long fractures (since the FID fractures are predominately masters). If the scanline, on which the semivariogram is based, is longer than the width of the FID, then the semivariogram for length should exhibit a concave-upward curve (e.g., Fig. 29B) or a reversed spherical curve. The length of relatively closely spaced fractures will be highly variable, depending on whether the pair is within the FID (and both are therefore long) or outside the FID, compared to fracture pairs spaced somewhat wider than the FID that will not exhibit the variability between FID and non-FID fractures (e.g., Fig. 29B).

Geostatistical sampling problems and resolutions

1. Sampling. Problems with the semivariogram method are linked primarily to sampling, i.e., outcrop/scanline size. In order to nullify the inherent dependence between sample value and sample location, a sample size must be at least four times greater than the mean lag distance (Miller, 1979). For closely spaced fracture sets, such a sample size is easily collected, but for widely spaced fractures, such as the master northwest-striking set in western New York, most outcrops are not large enough to record a sufficient sample size. For example, none of the 27 scanlines analyzed by Xu and Jacobi (1998) is large enough to analyze the widely spaced northwest-striking set.

Another problem related to scanline length is that, in practice, the maximum lag distance of a semivariogram can be only about one-half the length of the scanline. Thus, extrapolations away from

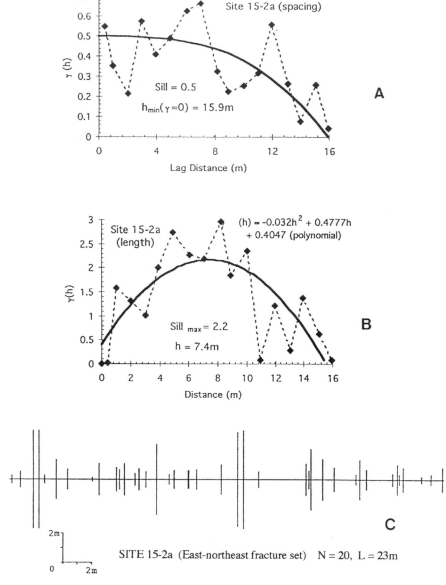

Figure 28. Semivariograms from scanlines at Site 15-2a in Livingston County, central New York State (Xu and Jacobi, 1998). A: Inverse spherical semivariogram of the spacing of east-northeast-striking fractures. B: Concave downward polynomial semivariogram of the length of east-north-east-striking fractures. C: Scanline with only east-northeast-striking fractures, fractures centered on scanline to show length of fractures.

the site involving distances greater than one-half the scanline length can only be assumed, based on the semivariogram curve established over the lag distances. Rigorous extrapolation can be accomplished only for relatively short distances away from a typical scanline if the semivariogram curve is spherical, nugget, linear, or Gaussian. If, however, a second order polynomial function describes the semivariogram, then it is probable that more distant extrapolations are possible within the same structural domain as the scanline. The problem is the common inability to establish a sufficiently long scanline to recognize a potential second order polynomial function. For example, in Figure 29, it is clear that if only a short scanline with lag distances of <8 m had been available, the semivariogram would have been identified as spherical. However, the longer scanline allows determination of larger lag distances, which can reveal the second order polynomial function.

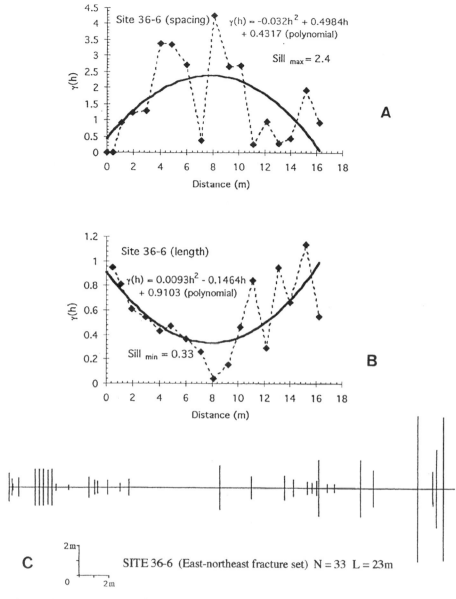

Figure 29. Semivariograms from scanlines at Site 36-6 in Livingston County, central New York State (Xu and Jacobi, 1998). A: Concave downward polynomial semivariogram for the spacing of east-northeast–striking fractures. B: Convex downward polynomial semivariogram for the length of east-northeast–striking fractures. C: Scanline with only east-northeast–striking fractures, fractures centered on scanline to show length of fractures.

CONCLUSIONS

Military utilization of cutting-edge technology is shrinking the globe in space and time, necessitating a redefinition of global battlefields. In an attempt to maximize uncertainty on the part of one's enemy, and to hide both capability and intent to wage war, potential and real aggressor countries are increasingly building military facilities underground, away from the eyes and ears of free-world remote sensing systems. In light of the ever-increasing use of bedrock for military operations, it is imperative that we hone our ability to effectively neutralize such underground facilities. We must understand the disposition of fractures in areas where these underground facilities are the target because we know that fracture orientation can determine the final trajectory of earth-penetrating weapons. Furthermore, we know that rock integrity is largely dependent upon fracture density, but fracture density and distribution are commonly unknown in denied areas targeted for attack. In this chapter, we reviewed several methods designed to

TABLE 3. SEMIVARIOGRAM MODELS FOR FRACTURE SPACING AND LENGTH IN WESTERN NEW YORK

Fracture set	Semivariogram model	Spacing range (m)	Length range (m)
Northeast-striking	Spherical and polynomial	10.5 to > 16.0	4.5 to 15.0
East-northeast–striking	Spherical, reversed spherical, and polynomial	5.0 to > 15.9	4.8 to > 15.8
North-striking and north-northeast–striking	Spherical, reversed spherical, and polynomial	8.9 to > 16.8	> 15.4 to > 18.0

Note: Calculations from Xu and Jacobi (1998).

help estimate the fracture distribution and character in denied areas. These methods are based on a knowledge of fractures in localities near the denied areas, coupled with remotely sensed images.

One method that can aid in identifying the fracture pattern in a denied area employs fractal analysis. Fractal analysis can confirm whether a lineament pattern, identified using remotely sensed data, could be related to fractures. In the simplest case, if both the lineament pattern and the fracture pattern in outcrops from the area of the lineaments are fractal and have similar fractal dimensions, then the lineament pattern may indicate that the fracture pattern characterizes the area defined by the lineament pattern. Although this method has potential, there are problems with (1) calculating the fractal dimension, (2) determining which patterns are actually fractal, (3) implications of multifractal dimensions for a given pattern, and (4) inability to predict either Fracture Intensification Domain (FID) locations or FID fracture pattern character, unless comparison outcrops are located both within and outside of variously oriented FIDs.

FIDs can be best identified by recognition of long lineaments that have a fractal dimension and orientation similar to fractures observed in a FID outcrop. In the Appalachian Plateau of western New York, virtually every relatively long lineament (~ >1.0 km) marks a FID. FIDs have a high probability of being associated with faults.

A second method to characterize fracture distribution in a denied area is to calculate the fracture density. We developed relationships that allow D_{f2}, a dimensionless quantity in 2-D space, to be calculated from D_{f1}, a dimensional quantity in 1-D space. D_{f1} is calculated from fracture spacing along a scanline. It is possible, therefore, to predict in denied areas the density of fractures from a scanline outside the area if the structural domains of the scanline and the denied area are judged to be similar. Fractal analysis and comparison of lineament and fracture orientations could be used to determine whether the scanline and denied areas are located in similar structural domains. Problems with calculating fracture density D_{f2} are that the fracture length distribution is generally poorly known, and that the calculated density applies only to the same structural domain in which the scanline was located. Thus, this method does not predict the location of FIDs or the fracture character of a FID unless the scanline is located in a FID.

The third method to estimate fracture patterns in denied areas is to utilize semivariograms in the characterization of fractures. Semivariograms allow one to estimate the distance to which frac-

ture attributes may be extrapolated away from the site of observation. We found that fracture length and spacing can be predicted, based on some semivariogram patterns, to a distance of at least 15 m. A recent 2 km scanline suggests much more distant extrapolations are possible. The semivariogram method does allow for the recognition of FIDs. Problems are related primarily to the large size of the sample needed.

These three methods all have advantages and drawbacks, but in a combined program utilizing all the techniques for analyses of both remotely sensed data and outcrop/borehole data, we can make a very good approximation of the character of the fractures in a denied area. As we refine these techniques, the underground military environment will become more vulnerable, and the military UGF will not continue to be a bastion of impunity.

ACKNOWLEDGMENTS

We thank John Fountain for his always insightful and enthusiastic participation in discussions. We thank Andy Baudo, Tricia Kleise, Alison Lagowski, and Valerie Jill Podet for assistance in data reduction and manuscript preparation. We thank two anonymous reviewers and Judy Ehlen for helpful comments.

APPENDIX

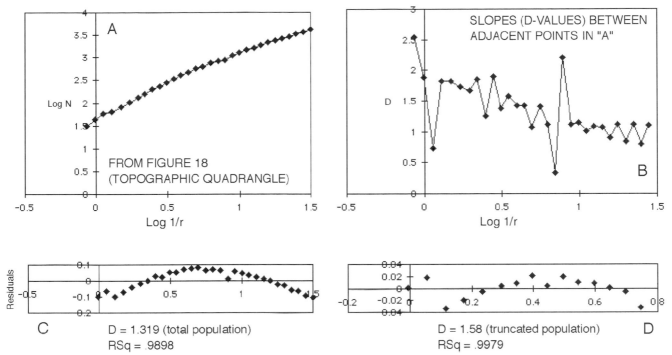

Figure A1. Fractal dimension calculations for lineament patterns in the portion of the Portageville 7.5′ topographic quadrangle shown in Figure 18. A: A *log N/log 1/r* plot of the lineament pattern. B: Slopes (*D* values) between adjacent points in "A". C: Residual values after a least squares linear regression line has been fitted to curve in "A", with a *D* value (slope) and correlation coefficient annotated below. D: Residual values after a least squares linear regression line has been fitted to a truncated curve of "A", with a *D* value (slope) and correlation coefficient annotated below. In all fractal calculations the dimension of the counting box size varies from about half the narrow dimension of the map analyzed to a minimum size equal to the distance between the closest line element pairs.

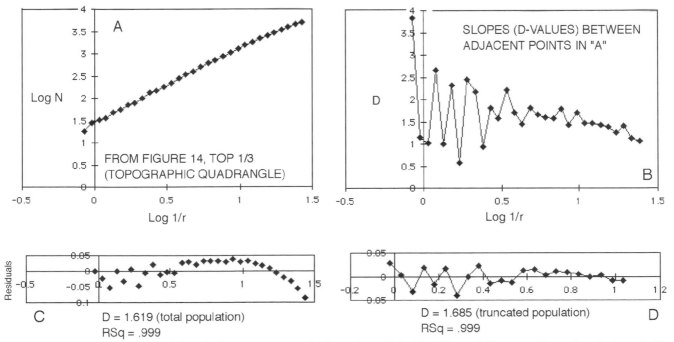

Figure A2. Fractal dimension calculations for lineament patterns for the northern third of the Fillmore 7.5′ topographic quadrangle shown in Figure 14. A, B, C, and D have the same format as A, B, C, and D in Appendix, Figure A1. This portion of the topographic map corresponds to the area of the air photo lineaments in Figure 16. The fractal curve and *D* value are similar to the air photo fractal curve and *D* value in Figure 17.

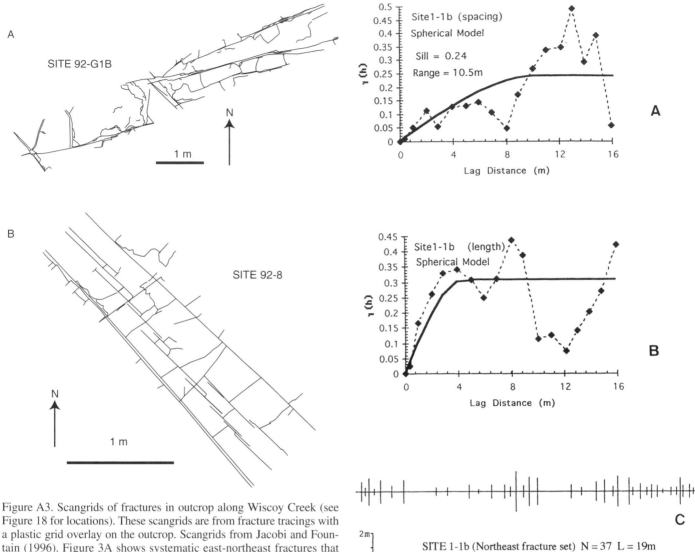

Figure A3. Scangrids of fractures in outcrop along Wiscoy Creek (see Figure 18 for locations). These scangrids are from fracture tracings with a plastic grid overlay on the outcrop. Scangrids from Jacobi and Fountain (1996). Figure 3A shows systematic east-northeast fractures that intersect the northwest set; both sets are mutually abutting in the central part of the scangrid. Note the north-striking fractures that abut the east-northeast set. Figure 3B displays well-developed cross joints, as well as a right-step, northwest-striking fracture (the central northwest-striking fracture). This fracture apparently formed later than the other northwest-striking fractures (to the left and right), and indicates a counterclockwise rotation of the stress field (Zhao and Jacobi, 1977).

Figure A4. Semivariograms for northeast-striking fractures along a scanline at Site 1-1b in Livingston County, central New York State (Xu and Jacobi, 1998). A: Spherical or concave downward polynomial semivariogram for the spacing of northeast-striking fractures. B: Spherical or concave downward polynomial semivariogram for the length of northeast-striking fractures. C: Scanline with only northeast-striking fractures, fractures centered on scanline to show length of fractures.

REFERENCES CITED

Austin, C.F., Whelan, J.A., and Eastler, T.E., 1982, Projectile penetration into thin layered rock: China Lake, California, Naval Weapons Center, NWC TP-6344, 23 p.

Barton, C.C., 1995, Fractal analysis of scaling and spatial clustering of fractures, *in* Barton, C.C., and La Pointe, P.R., eds., Fractals in the earth sciences: New York, Plenum Press, p. 141–178.

Barton, C., and Hsieh, P.A., 1989, Physical and hydrologic-flow properties of fractures, *in* International Geological Congress, 28th, Field Trip Guide book T385: Washington, D.C., American Geophysical Union, 36 p.

Barton, C.C., and La Pointe, P.R., eds., 1995a, Fractals in the earth sciences: New York, Plenum Press, 265 p.

Barton, C.C., and La Pointe, P.R., eds., 1995b, Fractals in petroleum geology and earth processes: New York, Plenum Press, 317 p.

Barton, C.C., and Larsen, E., 1985, Fractal geometry of two-dimensional fracture networks at Yucca Mountain, southwest Nevada, *in* Stephannson, O., ed., Proceedings, International Symposium on Fundamentals of Rock Joints, Bjorkliden, Lapland, Sweden: Lulea, Sweden, Centek Publishers, p. 74–84.

Barton, C.C., Gott, C.B., and Montgomery, J.R., 1986, Fractal scaling of fracture and fault maps at Yucca Mountain, southwest Nevada [abs.]: Eos (Transactions, American Geophysical Union), v. 67, p. 870.

Barton, C., Schutter, T., and Samuel, J., 1989, DIMENSION—A computer program that computes the fractal dimension of lines or points in a plane: U.S. Geological Survey Open-File Report 89-111, 10 p.

Bashilov, V.I., and Kuprin, B.F., 1995, Relationship of oil and gas fields and shows to faults in the Timan-Pechora Basin: Otechestvennaya Geologiya, n. 2, p. 16–21.

Baudo, A., and Jacobi, R.D., 1999, Fracture patterns along a 2.3 km scanline in the Appalachian Plateau, Cattaraugus County, western NY: Statistical analysis and implications for fault activity: Geological Society of America Abstracts with Programs, v. 31, n. 2, p. A3.

Berkowitz, B., and Hadad, A., 1997, Fractal and multifractal measures of natural and synthetic fracture networks: Journal of Geophysical Research, v. 102, p. 12205–12218.

Billaux, D., Chiles, J.P., Hestir, K., and Long, J., 1989, Three-dimensional statistical modelling of a fractured rock mass: An example from the Fanay-Augeres mine, *in* Cornet, F.H., ed., International workshop on forced fluid flow through fractured rock masses: International Journal of Rock Mechanics and Mining Sciences & Geomechanics Abstracts, v. 26, p. 281–299.

Brown, S.R., 1987, A note on the description of surface roughness using fractal dimension: Geophysical Research Letters, v. 14, p. 1095–1098.

Brown, S.R., and Sholtz, S.H., 1985, Broad bandwidth study of the topography of natural rock surfaces: Journal of Geophysical Research, v. 90, p. 12575–12582.

Chiles, J.P., 1988, Fractal and geostatistical methods for modeling of a fracture network: Mathematical Geology, v. 20, p. 631–654.

Clark, I., 1979, Practical geostatistics: London, Applied Science Publishers, 129 p.

Cowie, P.A., Knipe, R.J., and Main, I.G., 1996, Scaling laws for fault and fracture population: Analyses and applications: Journal of Structural Geology, Special Issue, v. 18, p. v–xi.

Cowie, P.A., Sornette, D., and Vanneste, C., 1995, Multifractal scaling properties of a growing fault population: Geophysics Journal International, v. 122, p. 457–469.

Department of the Air Force, 1954, Photographic interpretation keys, underground installations: Washington, D.C., Air Force Manual 200-35, p. 83.

Dershowitz, W.S., and Einstein, H.H., 1988, Characterizing rock joint geometry with joint system models: Rock Mechanics and Rock Engineering, v. 21, p. 21–51.

Dershowitz, W.S., and Herda, H.H., 1992, Interpretation of fracture spacing and intensity, *in* Tillerson, J.R., and Wawersik, W.R., eds., Rock mechanics: Rotterdam, A.A. Balkema, p. 757–766.

Deutsch, C.V., and Journel, A.G., 1992, GSLIB—Geostatistical software library and user's guide: New York, Oxford Press, 369 p. and 1 disk.

Doe, T.W., Dershowitz, W.S., and La Pointe, P.R., 1993, Identifying conductive features for fracture network models: Geological Society of America Abstracts with Programs, v. 25, n. 6, p. 426.

Dubuc, B., Quiniou, J., Roques-Carmes, C., Tricot, C., and Zucker, S.W., 1989, Evaluating the fractal dimension of profiles: Physics Review, v. A30, p. 1500–1512.

Eastler, T., 1985, Post-penetration geologic evaluation of Wilson Canyon site, Naval Weapons Center, China Lake, California: Albuquerque, New Mexico, Sandia National Laboratory, Unpublished research note, 8 p.

Eastler, T., and Andersen, J.A., 1988, Post-test evaluation of HTEPW II, a hard rock weapon penetrator test: Albuquerque, New Mexico, Sandia National Laboratory, Unpublished research note, 50 p.

Ehlen, J., 1998, A proposed method for characterizing fracture patterns in denied areas, *in* Underwood, J.R., Jr., and Guth, P.L., eds., Military geology in war and peace: Geological Society of America, Reviews in Engineering Geology, v. 13, p. 151–163.

Engelder, T., 1985, Loading paths to joint propagation during a tectonic cycle: An example from the Appalachian Plateau, U.S.A.: Journal of Structural Geology, v. 7, p. 459–476.

Engelder, T., and Geiser, P.A., 1980, On the use of regional joint sets as trajectories of paleo-stress fields during the development of the Appalachian Plateau, New York: Journal of Geophysical Research, v. 85, p. 6319–6341.

Feder, J., 1988, Fractals: New York, Plenum Press, 282 p.

Gillespie, P.A., Howard, C.B., Walsh, J.J., and Watterson, J., 1993, Measurement and characterization of spatial distributions of fractures: Tectonophysics, v. 226, p. 113–141.

Gross, M.R., 1993, The origin and spacing of cross joints: Examples from the Monterey Formation, Santa Barbara coastline, California: Journal of Structural Geology, v. 15, p. 737–751.

Gross, M.R., Bahat, D., and Beacker, A., 1997, Relations between jointing and faulting based on fracture-spacing ratios and fault-slip profiles: A new method to estimate strain in layered rocks: Geology, v. 25, p. 887–890.

Gross, M.R., Fischer, M.P., Engelder, T., and Greenfield, R.J., 1994, Factors controlling joint spacing in mechanically layered rocks: Integrating numerical models with field observations from the Monterey Formation, California: Geological Society of America Abstracts with Programs, v. 26, n. 7, p. 211.

Guo, G., 1997, FRAC-EXPLORE: A new computer software for locating oil and gas reservoirs using remote sensing data and surface fracture analysis: Proceedings, Thematic Conference on Geologic Remote Sensing, Bartlesville, Oklahoma, BDM Petroleum Technologies, v. 12, n. 2, 117 p.

Hardcastle, K.C., 1995, Photolineament factor: A new computer-aided method for remotely sensing the degree to which bedrock is fractured: Photogrammetric Engineering and Remote Sensing, v. 61, p. 739–747.

Hestir, K., Chiles, J-P., Long, J., and Billaux, D., 1987, Three dimensional modeling of fractures in rock: From data to a regionalized parent-daughter model, *in* Evans, D.D., and Nicholson, T.J., eds., Flow and transport through unsaturated fractured bedrock: American Geophysical Union Geophysical Monographs, v. 42, p. 133–140.

Jacobi, R.D., and Fountain, J.C., 1991, Evidence for the continuation of the Clarendon-Linden Fault System into central Allegany County, New York: Toronto, Ontario, Canada, Geological Association of Canada, Mineralogical Association of Canada, Canadian Geophysical Union, Joint Annual Meeting, Abstract, v. 16, p. 60.

Jacobi, R.D., and Fountain, J.C., 1996, Determination of the seismic potential of the Clarendon-Linden Fault System in Allegany County, final report: Albany, New York State Energy Resources Development Agency, 2106 p.

Jacobi, R.D., and Xu, J., 1998, Fracture intensification domains as fault indicators: Geological Society of America Abstracts with Programs, v. 30, n. 7, p. A63.

Jacobi, R.D., and Zhao, M., 1996a, Digital imaging and analyses of fractures: Evidence for Appalachian style tectonics in the Appalachian Plateau of western New York: Geological Society of America Abstracts with Programs, v. 28, n. 3, p. 67.

Jacobi, R.D., and Zhao, M., 1996b, Rapid and rigorous outcrop fracture trace mapping and analysis: Part 4 of a short course on contaminant hydrogeology of fractured bedrock: Buffalo, New York, Northeastern Section of the Geological Society of America, IV-1–IV-19.

Journel, A.G., 1974, Geostatistics for conditional simulation of ore bodies: Economic Geology, v. 69, p. 673–687.

Journel, A.G., 1986, Geostatistics: Models and tools for the Earth sciences: Mathematical Geology, v. 18, p. 119–141.

Kulatilake, P.H.S.W., Chen, J., Teng, J., Shufang, X., and Pan, G., 1996, Discontinuity geometry characterization in a tunnel close to the proposed permanent shiplock area of the Three Gorges Dam site in China: International Journal of Rock Mechanics and Mining Sciences & Geomechanics Abstracts, v. 33, n. 3, p. 255–277.

Kulatilake, P.H.S.W., Wathugala, D.N., and Stephansson, O., 1993, Joint network modelling with a validation exercise in Stripa Mine: Sweden, International Journal of Rock Mechanics and Mining Sciences & Geomechanics Abstracts, v. 30, n. 5, p. 503–526.

Ladeira, F.L., and Price, N.J., 1981, Relationship between fracture spacing and bed thickness: Journal of Structural Geology, v. 3, p. 179–183.

Langberg, H., and Davis, L.K., 1993, Attack of deep underground target entrances with penetrating warheads: Literature analysis: Vicksburg, Mississippi, U.S. Army Corps of Engineers Waterways Experiment Station, Technical Report SL-93-18, 56 p.

La Pointe, P.R., 1989, A method to characterize fracture density and connectivity through fractal geometry: International Journal of Rock Mechanics and Mining Sciences & Geomechanics, Abstracts, v. 26, p. 421–429.

La Pointe, P.R., and Hudson, J.A., 1985, Characterization and interpretation of rock mass joint patterns: Geological Society of America Special Paper 199, 37 p.

Long, J.C.S., and Billaux, D., 1987, From field data to fracture network modeling: An example incorporating spatial structure: Water Resources Research, v. 3, p. 1201–1216.

Long, J.C.S., Billaux, D., Hestir, K., and Chiles, J-P., 1987, Some geostatistical tools for incorporating spatial structure in fracture network modeling, *in* Proceedings, International Congress of the International Society for Rock Mechanics, 6th: Boston, A.A. Balkema, p. 171–176.

Lottman-Craig, L., and Malone, P., 1991, Fracture analysis: Methods and applications to coal-bed methane and Devonian shale: American Association of Petroleum Geologists Bulletin, v. 75, p. 1386–1387.

Mabee, S.B., Hardcastle, K.C., and Wise, D.U., 1994, A method of collecting and analyzing lineaments for regional-scale fractured-bedrock aquifer studies: Ground Water, v. 32, p. 884–894.

Madden, T.R., 1983, Microcrack connectivity in rocks: A renormalization group approach to the critical phenomena of conduction and failure in crystalline rocks: Journal of Geophysical Research, v. 88, p. 585–592.

Mandelbrot, B.B., 1967, How long is the coast of Britain? Statistical self-similarity and fractional dimension: Science, v. 156, p. 636–638.

Mandelbrot, B.B., 1975, Stochastic models for the Earth's relief, the shape and the fractal dimension of the coastlines, and the number-area rule for islands: National Academy of Sciences Proceedings, v. 72, p. 3825–3828.

Mandelbrot, B.B., 1983, The fractal geometry of nature: San Francisco, Freeman, 468 pp.

Matheron, G., 1963, Principles of geostatistics: Economic Geology, v. 58, p. 1246–1266.

Matheron, G., 1971, The theory of regionalized variables and its applications: Fontainebleau, France, Centre de Geostatistique, 137 p.

Mauldon, M., 1992, Relative probabilities of joint intersections, *in* Tillerson, J.R., and Wawersik, W.R., eds., Rock mechanics: Rotterdam, A.A. Balkema, p. 767–774.

Mauldon, M., 1994, Intersection probabilities of impersistent joints: International Journal of Rock Mechanics and Mining Sciences & Geomechanics, Abstracts, v. 31, p. 107–115.

McQuillan, H., 1973, Small-scale fracture density in Asmari Formation of southwest Iran and its relation to bed thickness and structural setting: American Association of Petroleum Geologists Bulletin, v. 57, p. 2367–2385.

McQuillan, H., 1974, Fracture patterns on Kuh-e Asmari Anticline, southwest Iran: American Association of Petroleum Geologists Bulletin, v. 58, p. 236–246.

Miller, S.M., 1979, Geostatistical analysis for evaluating spatial dependence in fracture set characteristics, *in* APCOM Symposium on Application of Computers and Operations Research in the Mineral Industry, 16th, New York, Society of Mining Engineers, AIME, p. 537–545.

Narr, W., and Lerche, I., 1984, A method for estimating subsurface fracture density in core: American Association of Petroleum Geologists Bulletin, v. 66, p. 1231–1247.

Narr, W., and Suppe, J., 1991, Joint spacing in sedimentary rocks: Journal of Structural Geology, v. 13, p. 1037–1048.

Olson, J., and Pollard, D.D., 1989, Inferring paleostress from natural fracture patterns: A new method: Geology, v. 17, p. 345–348.

Peters, T.W., and Jacobi, R.D., 1997, Geology of the Rawson 7.5 minute quadrangle, in New York State: Upper Devonian tempestites and multiple fault systems: Geological Society of America Abstracts with Programs, v. 29, n. 1, p. 72.

Price, N.J., 1979, Fractures in the crust [abs.]: Eos (Transactions, American Geophysical Union), v. 60, p. 752.

Priest, S.D., and Hudson, J., 1976, Estimation of discontinuity spacing and trace length using scanline surveys: International Journal of Rock Mechanics and Mining Sciences & Geomechanics Abstracts, v. 13, p. 135–148.

Priest, S.D., and Hudson, J., 1981, Estimation of discontinuity spacing and trace length using scanline surveys: International Journal of Rock Mechanics and Mining Sciences & Geomechanics Abstracts, v. 18, p. 183–198.

Pruess, S.A., 1995, Some remarks on the numerical estimation of fractal dimension, *in* Barton, C.C., and La Pointe, P.R., eds., Fractals in the earth sciences: New York, Plenum Press, p. 65–75.

Rawnsley, K.D., Peacock, D.C.P., Rives, T., and Petit, J-P., 1998, Joints in the Mesozoic sediments around the Bristol Channel Basin: Journal of Structural Geology, v. 20, p. 1641–1661.

Renshaw, C.E.,1997, Mechanical controls on the spatial density of open-mode fracture networks: Geology, v. 25, p. 923–926.

Renshaw, C.E., and Pollard, D.D., 1994, Numerical simulation of fracture set formation: A fracture mechanics model consistent with experimental observations: Journal of Geophysical Research, v. 99, p. 9359–9372.

Rives, T., Razack, M., Petit, J-P., and Rawnsley, K.D., 1992, Joint spacing: Analogue and numerical simulations: Journal of Structural Geology, v. 14, p. 925–937.

Rouleau, A., and Gale, J.E., 1985, Statistical characterization of the fracture system in the Stripa Granite, Sweden: International Journal of Rock Mechanics and Mining Sciences and Geomechanics Abstracts, v. 10, p. A52.

Scott, R.B., and Bonk, J., 1984, Preliminary geologic map of Yucca Mountain, Nye County, Nevada with geologic sections: U.S. Geological Survey Open-File Report, OF 84-0494, 10 p.

Segall, P., and Pollard, D.D., 1983, Joint formation in granitic rock of the Sierra Nevada: Geological Society of America Bulletin, v. 94, p. 563–579.

Smalley, R.F., Shatelain, J.L., Turcotte, D.L., and Prevot, R., 1987, A fractal approach to the clustering of earthquakes: Applications to the seismicity of the New Hebrides: Bulletin of the Seismological Society of America, v. 77, p. 1368–1381.

Smith, G.J., Jacobi, R.D., Peters, T.W., Reay, M.L., Zack, D.L., and Zhao, M., 1998, Stratigraphic and structural analyses of 7.5' topographic quadrangles in western New York State: Geological Society of America Abstracts with Programs, v. 30, n. 1, p. 85.

Turcotte, D., 1986a, Fractals and fragmentation: Journal of Geophysical Research, v. 91, p. 1921–1926.

Turcotte, D., 1986b, A fractal model for crustal deformation: Tectonophysics, v. 132, p. 261–269.

Turcotte, D., 1986c, A fractal approach to the relationship between ore grade and tonnage: Economic Geology, v. 81, p. 1528–1532.

Turcotte, D., 1989a, Fractals in geology and geophysics: Pure and Applied Geophysics, v. 131, p. 171–196.

Turcotte, D., 1989b, A fractal approach to probabilistic seismic hazard assessment: Tectonophysics, v. 167, p. 171–177.

Turcotte, D., 1992, Fractal and chaos in geology and geophysics: Cambridge, Cambridge University Press, 221 p.

Van Tyne, A.M., 1975, Clarendon-Linden structure, western New York: Albany, New York, New York State Geological Survey Open-File Report No. 10, 12 p.

Van Tyne, A.M., Kamakaris, D.G., and Corbo, S., 1980, Structure contours on the base of the Dunkirk: New York State Museum and Science Service, Geological Survey, Alfred Oil and Gas Office, Morgantown Energy Technology Center/Eastern Gas Shales Project series 111, 1 map, scale 1:250 000.

Velde, B., Dubois, J., Moore, D.E., and Touchard, G.,1991, Fractal patterns of fractures in granites: Earth and Planetary Science Letters, v. 104, p. 25–35.

Velde, B., Dubois, J., Touchard, G., and Badri, A., 1993, Fractal analysis of fractures in rocks: The Cantor's Dust method: Tectonophysics, v. 179, p. 345–352.

Villaescusa, R., and Brown, E.T., 1990, Characterizing joint spatial correlation using geostatistical methods, *in* Barton, C.C., and Stephansson, O., eds., Rock joints: Loen, Norway, International Symposium on Rock Joints, p. 115–122.

Walsh, J.J., and Watterson, J., 1993, Fractal analysis of fracture pattern using the standard box-counting technique: Valid and invalid methodologies: Journal of Structural Geology, v. 15, p. 1509–1512.

Watterson, J., Walsh, J.J., Gillespie, P.A., and Easton, S., 1996, Scaling systematics of fault sizes on a large-scale range fault map: Journal of Structural Geology, Special Issue, v. 18, p. 199–214.

Wawrzynski, A.L., and Jacobi, R.D., 1992, Remote sensing in the Clarendon-Linden Fault System in Allegany County, New York: Geological Society of America Abstracts with Programs, v. 24, n. 3, p. 83.

Wilson, T.H., 1999, Non-fractal size-scaling attributes of fracture trace and active fault networks with examples from the central Appalachians and Japan; Geological Society of America Abstracts with Programs, v. 31, n. 7, p. A-112.

Wilson, T.H., and Dominic, J., 1998, Fractal interrelationships between topography and structure: Earth Surface Processes and Landforms, v. 23, p. 509–525.

Wu, H., and Pollard, D.D., 1992, Propagation of a set of opening-mode fractures in layered brittle materials under uniaxial strain cycling: Journal of Geophysical Research, v. 97, p. 3381–3396.

Wu, H., and Pollard, D.D., 1995, An experimental study of the relationship between joint spacing and layer thickness: Journal of Structural Geology, v. 17, p. 887–905.

Xu, J., 1998, Geometrical characterization of fracture networks: Core and borehole fracture surveys, density calculation, and spatial structure analyses [Ph.D. thesis]: Buffalo, State University of New York, 262 p.

Xu, J., and Jacobi, R.D., 1998, Characterizing natural fracture networks: Density calculation and spatial structure analyses: Geological Society of America Abstracts with Programs, v. 30, n. 7, p. A224.

Zack, D., and Jacobi, R.D., 1997, Geologic mapping of the Freedom Quadrangle in Allegany and Cattaraugus Counties, New York: Evidence for multiple fault systems in the Appalachian Plateau: Geological Society of America Abstracts with Programs, v. 29, n. 1, p. 91.

Zhao, M., and Jacobi, R.D., 1993, Fractal and more conventional analyses of fracture systems in the Appalachian Plateau, Allegany County, New York: Geological Society of America Abstracts with Programs, v. 25, n. 3, p. 91.

Zhao, M., and Jacobi, R.D., 1994, Further fractal and more conventional analyses of fracture systems in the Appalachian Plateau, Allegany County, New York: Geological Society of America Abstracts with Programs, v. 26, n. 3, p. 82.

Zhao, M., and Jacobi, R.D., 1997, Formation of cross-fold joints in the northern Appalachian Plateau: Journal of Structural Geology, v. 19, p. 817–834.

Zhao, M., Jacobi, R.D., and Xu, J., 1994, Fractal features of extensional fracture sets: An insight from a mechanically based fracture-pattern generation: Geological Society of America Abstracts with Programs, v. 26, n. 3, p. 82.

MANUSCRIPT ACCEPTED BY THE SOCIETY OCTOBER 27, 2000

Geological Society of America
Reviews in Engineering Geology, Volume XIV
2001

Predicting fracture properties in weathered granite in denied areas

Judy Ehlen

U.S. Army Engineer Research and Development Center, 7701 Telegraph Road, Alexandria, VA 22315-3864, USA

ABSTRACT

This chapter describes a model developed to predict fracture properties of weathered granite in denied areas, predictions made using imagery, and a test undertaken to determine prediction accuracy. This project is part of a geotechnical characterization of weathered granites that will be used to predict weapons effects at denied sites. Joint spacings, orientations, and trace lengths were measured in four field areas near the denied sites. Three-dimensional models of field measurements from an analogue area and lineation data derived from imagery over this area and over two denied sites were sampled to determine mean joint spacings in simulated horizontal and vertical boreholes, mean joint trace length, joint intensity, termination percent, mean rock block width and volume, and RQD (Rock Quality Designation) at the denied sites. The simulated data were regressed against scale in log-log space and the equations for the best fit were used to calculate the predictions.

The predictions made for the denied sites are realistic compared to measurements made in the four field areas. They are within the standard deviations of field measurements and generally fall within the range of measurements made in the four field areas. Most predictions are within 25% of field measurements in the analogue area. The accuracy of the predictions was assessed by selecting one of the field areas as a denied area, and then using the same procedures to make predictions for the same set of variables. These predictions are very similar to the field measurements; most lie within 10-15%, indicating that predictions made using these procedures are accurate as well as realistic.

INTRODUCTION

This effort is part of a geotechnical characterization of weathered granites for use by the military in predicting weapons effects (e.g., penetrability, ground shock, cratering) at denied sites. The purpose of geotechnical site characterization is to define the mechanical properties and the state of the rock mass. This involves determining the strength and deformation characteristics of the rock mass, the geometric and mechanical properties of pervasive joints, and the location and description of other discrete structural features (Brady and Brown, 1993).

Jointing is the most common, and usually the most significant, structural feature in a rock mass. The joint properties of most importance in a geotechnical/geomechanical context are orientation, spacing, surface roughness, persistence, aperture, and fillings (Brady and Brown, 1993). Joint properties, particularly spacing and size (persistence), are especially important with respect to weapons effects and penetrability (Eastler et al., 1998; Jacobi et al., this volume). For example, for a hard rock target, the closer the joint spacing, the more penetrable the rock. Accurate information about joint spacing is, therefore, crucial to choice of weapon and fusing. In addition, penetration may be increased if the weapon enters along longer joints with preferred orientations parallel to the line of entry: Increased depth of penetration is directly related to increased damage.

Denied areas are those to which one does not have access. A region can be "denied," for example, if it is underground, if it is politically or militarily sensitive, or if it is inaccessible for some

Ehlen, J., 2001, Predicting fracture properties in weathered granite in denied areas, *in* Ehlen, J., and Harmon, R.S., eds., The Environmental Legacy of Military Operations: Boulder, Colorado, Geological Society of America Reviews in Engineering Geology, v. XIV, p. 61–73.

other reason. Examples are, respectively, a proposed site for an underground power plant; Camp David, the U.S. presidential retreat in Maryland; part of a military base where live firing occurs; and a mountaintop in a remote wilderness area. Under such access conditions, estimates based on data from accessible sites with properties thought to be similar to those at the denied site (analogue area concept), from the literature, or from remotely sensed imagery are often the only sources of information. Estimates from such data sources are usually descriptive or given as ranges, and uncertainties are unknown. Development of a method to gain quantitative information about joint properties in denied areas is thus of importance.

The first phase of this work is described in Ehlen (1998a), in which the relationships between field measurements of joint properties and lineation data derived from imagery were examined. Fracture/lineation properties were found to exhibit power law distributions, to be scale independent, and to have similar fractal dimensions. This chapter describes the second phase, in which a model developed to predict quantitative fracture properties in weathered granite in denied areas using remotely sensed imagery is presented and evaluated. The model is based on a combination of field measurements from an area with similar geologic characteristics (an analogue area) and lineation data derived from imagery of the analogue area and the denied sites. Details of the procedure used to make the predictions are described in Ehlen (1996); this chapter discusses the modeling process, the predictions that were made using these procedures, and a test done to determine the accuracy of the predictions.

DATA COLLECTION

Field data

Field data were collected in accessible areas with geology thought to be similar to that at the denied sites. Joint spacing, orientation, and trace length were measured at thirteen sample sites in granite using an areal sampling scheme. In addition, termination percent (i.e., the percentage of "T" intersections) was estimated for the majority of joint sets at most sample sites. Nine road cuts, two excavated faces, and the walls of two tunnels were examined. Observations also were made at each outcrop with respect to rock texture (grain size characteristics and relations), joint fillings, whether the joints were open or closed, and the location of shearing, if present. Finally, the granites were separated into the standard six weathering grades using a U.S. Army Corps of Engineers rock material classification (Murphy, 1985; Table 1). The rocks were classified by field observation; no engineering tests were employed. Although most outcrops consisted of more than one weathering grade, each was classified according to the predominant grade (Ehlen, 1999). Three outcrops were classified as fresh, one as slightly weathered, three as moderately weathered, five as highly weathered, and one as completely weathered. Combinations of moderately and highly weathered rock were typical at many outcrops. The thickness of weathered granite typically ranged from 10 to 20 m, and soil cover was usually less than 0.5 m. Figure 1 shows examples of moderately and highly weathered outcrops.

Lineation data

Lineations were delineated on multiple scales of imagery over the two denied sites and the four field areas (Table 2). Large-scale imagery (e.g., 1:2700), particularly over the denied sites, was considered especially important with respect to prediction accuracy. Large- and small-scale lineations delineated manually from air photos were digitized and then geographically registered using ARC/INFO (Fig. 2). Additional small-scale lineations were digitized directly on digital orthographic SPOT (Satellite Probatoire d'Observation de la Terre) imagery, also using ARC/INFO. Lineation strikes and trace lengths were determined from the sets of x_1y_1, x_2y_2 coordinates for each lineation using purpose-written code.

MODELING

Three-dimensional models of the fracture and lineation patterns were generated for each field area and for each lineation overlay, i.e., those over the field areas and those over the denied sites. The three-dimensional models were generated using *FracMan* (version 2.52), an interactive, discrete feature data analysis, geometric modeling, and exploration simulation software package of Golder Associates, Inc. (Dershowitz et al., 1995). An analogue area model was selected from among the four field areas as the source for data required for three-dimensional modeling of the denied sites that could not be obtained from imagery (i.e., lineation dips; see below). Simulated data derived from the three-dimensional models provided the input for predictions of ground-level fracture properties at the denied sites.

Only joint sets in weathered granite were used to generate the three-dimensional models. Fresh granite is not exposed at the surface in the field areas, so it was assumed it would not be exposed at the denied sites. Previous work (Ehlen, 1999) has shown that: (1) there are no statistically significant differences for joint properties among the different grades of weathered granite (i.e., the joint properties were not statistically significantly different in moderately, highly and completely weathered rock); and (2) that joint properties in weathered granite (moderately, highly and completely weathered) are significantly different from those in fresh granite, so lumping the different grades of weathered granite together was acceptable.

Model input

FracMan generates a three-dimensional model, joint set by joint set. Input for each model consists of pole trend and plunge, mean radius and standard deviation, intensity, and termination percent for each joint set. These parameters were determined from the field data for the field area models, and from a combination of

TABLE 1. CLASSIFICATION OF WEATHERED ROCKS (FROM MURPHY, 1985)

Weathering grade	Description
Fresh	No visible signs of weathering. Rock is fresh. Crystals are bright.
Slightly weathered	Discontinuities are stained or discolored and may contain a thin filling of altered material. Discoloration may extend into the rock from the discontinuity to a distance of 20% of the discontinuity spacing.
Moderately weathered	Slight discoloration extends from discontinuity planes for a distance of more than 20% of the discontinuity spacing. Discontinuities may contain filling of altered material. Partial opening of grain boundaries observed.
Highly weathered	Discoloration extends throughout the rock, and the rock material is partly friable. The original texture of the rock has mainly been preserved, but separation of the grains has occurred.
Completely weathered	The rock is totally discolored and decomposed and in friable condition. The external appearance is that of a soil. Internally, the rock texture is partly preserved, but the grains have been completely separated.
Residual soil	Not included.

Figure 1. Moderately (A) and highly (B) weathered outcrops.

field data and two-dimensional analysis of the lineation patterns using *FracMan* for the lineation models. Pole trend and plunge for the field area models were calculated from field measurements of strike and dip. Strikes and dips measured in the analogue area were used to generate the lineation models.

Mean radius is a first approximation of mean joint trace length for each joint set and is defined as $0.3\ L + s$, where L is mean trace length and s is the standard deviation about this mean.

Joint intensity is defined as nL/WH, where n is the number of joints, L is mean trace length, W is the sampling area width, and H is the sampling area height for each joint set (Dershowitz and Herda, 1992). This value was then weighted based on the proportion of the outcrop occupied by the particular joint set (Ehlen, 1998b). Intensity is additive, so field area intensities were determined by summing the intensities for the individual joint sets at each sample site within each field area. For example, if the intensities for three joint sets at site 1 in Area X, which consists of two sites, were 1.03, 0.79 and 1.45, the site intensity would be 3.27. If intensities at Site 2 were 1.17, 0.92, and 0.57, the site intensity would be 2.66. The intensity for Area A would thus be 5.93.

Termination percent was estimated in the field at most outcrops for each joint set, and is entered directly into the *FracMan* program. Termination percent was entered as zero for the lineation models.

The models

The sizes of the three-dimensional models that were generated vary with intensity (both field area and lineation models) as well as with image scale (for lineation models). The higher the intensity, the smaller the model had to be, and the smaller the image scale, the larger the model could be. For example, some of the models for field areas with high intensities (i.e., large numbers of fractures) took six to eight hours to generate: Model-generation times depend upon the number of fractures being generated and the speed of the computer used (in this case a 90 MHz PC). Field area models were 10 m to 20 m on a side. Lineation models were typically generated within a few minutes, although physically much larger than the field area models. This is because there are fewer lineations—and thus lower intensities—on imagery than there are joints in an outcrop for a given area. Lineation models were in the range of 50 m to 300 m on a side for imagery larger than 1:10 000 scale, and 1000 m to 1500 m on a side for imagery 1:40 000 scale or smaller.

Three levels of three-dimensional models were generated for each field area: (1) sample site models, (2) field area models, and (3) lineation models for each image scale. Lineation models were also generated for each image scale over the denied sites. Examples of a field area model and a lineation model are shown in Figure 3.

Sampling

Three-dimensional models were generated first for each sample site. Each model was compared to the field data by sampling. This involved cutting the model with a vertical plane oriented in the same direction as the line of measurement in the field (Fig. 4). Statistical analysis of the vertical plane provided mean simulated trace length and simulated termination percent. Joint trace lengths and termination percent were determined for the vertical plane because this plane is comparable to an outcrop face, thus facilitating comparisons with field measurements and simulated data from the analogue area model.

In addition, nine or ten simulated boreholes were positioned throughout the model perpendicular and parallel to the "ground surface" to determine simulated mean joint spacings (Fig. 5). Mean joint spacing in simulated horizontal boreholes is equivalent to vertical joint spacing, whereas mean joint spacing in simulated vertical boreholes is roughly equivalent to inclined, not horizontal, joint spacing. This is because horizontal joints are not discernible in most cases on imagery, so only vertical and inclined joint sets were generated in the three-dimensional lineation models.

This simulated borehole sampling procedure also determines RQD (Rock Quality Designation) for each borehole. RQD is defined as " … a modified core recovery percentage in which all the pieces of <u>sound</u> core over four inches long (100 mm) are summed and divided by the length of the <u>core run</u>" (Deere and Deere, 1989). The concept of RQD was developed using NX-size core, which is 2.155 in (54.7 mm) in diameter. It is an indirect measure of fracture spacing: The higher the RQD, the fewer the joints and the better the rock quality. RQD was determined for simulated horizontal, not vertical, boreholes to facilitate comparisons with field measurements made in the vertical plane. RQD also can be estimated from joint spacings measured in the field, but the results do not necessarily correlate well with RQD determined from core (Deere and Deere, 1989). Estimated RQDs for the field data were calculated using the equation given by Priest and Hudson (1976). RQD was included because it is a key parameter for estimating penetrability of rock in many prediction codes.

Simulated mean rock block width and volume were determined using a separate program within *FracMan*. Statistics for rock blocks provide information on the sizes of rock fragments that may be produced when a penetrating weapon fractures rock. Block size is indirectly related to joint spacing. *FracMan* determines block size by passing a set of rays through the model, which are initiated at points chosen at random within the model (Dershowitz et al., 1995). The distance between the point of origin of the ray and the first fracture is measured. This distance is

TABLE 2. AIR PHOTO AND SPOT IMAGE SCALES

	Panchromatic air photos	SPOT
Field areas		
A	1:3500	1:50 000
	1:6600	
B	1:40 000	1:160 000
C		1:50 000
D	1:5200	1:53 000
	1:8300	
Denied sites		
1	1:2700	
	1:40 000	
2	1:2200	
	1:40 000	

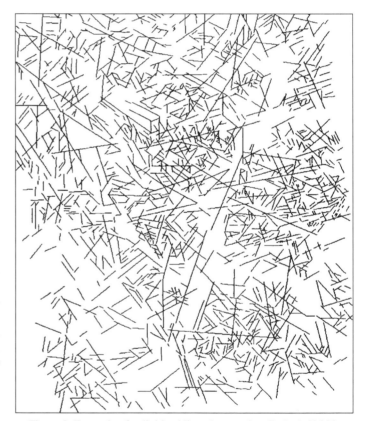

Figure 2. Example of a digitized lineation overlay. Scale 1:40 000.

well correlated with block surface area and dimensions in real fracture patterns (Dershowitz et al., 1995). The number of rays is user specified, as is the number of blocks to be compiled. In this study, mean block widths and volumes were determined for 100 blocks in each three-dimensional model.

Analogue area selection

As noted above, analysis of two-dimensional lineation patterns does not provide all the information required to generate three-dimensional models for lineations; specifically, information

A

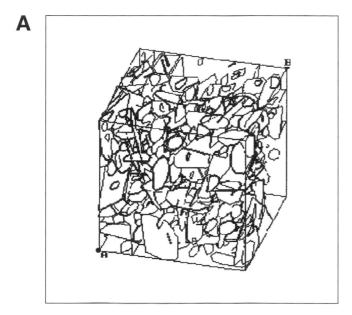

B

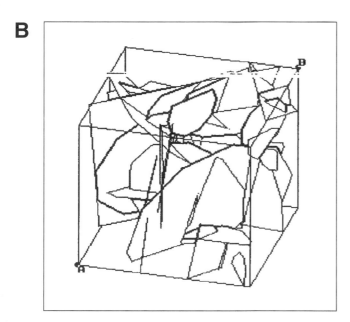

Figure 3. Three-dimensional models of a field area (A) and a lineation overlay (B). The field area model is 15 m on a side, and the lineation model is 1500 m on a side. Ten percent of the total number of fractures generated are shown.

on lineation dips is missing. Dips could be assigned randomly from a distribution, but a more reasonable approach is to substitute measured dips from joint sets with identical strikes in similar, nearby rocks that have undergone a similar stress history. For this reason, it was necessary to identify an analogue area to serve as the source for the missing data in the lineation models. The analogue area was chosen from among the four field areas containing weathered granite based on two criteria: (1) minimum statistical

variation, and (2) a good match between the simulated model data and the field measurements. The field data and the simulated data for the four field areas are shown in Table 3. The standard deviations for the six variables for which standard deviations could be determined tend to be smallest for Area D. In addition to having variables with the lowest standard deviations, Area D is in the same pluton as the denied sites, unlike the other field areas. Although mainly moderately weathered granite, Area D also contains significant amounts of highly weathered granite and is representative of the majority of outcrops in the field areas. Therefore, it is highly likely to be representative of the denied sites as well. Consequently, Area D was selected as the analogue area. The three-dimensional model for Area D is shown in Figure 3A.

Model quality

The simulated data were compared to the field measurements for each sample site following the procedures described by Ehlen (1998b). If necessary, the input parameters were adjusted and the model was regenerated until a good match with the field data was obtained via sampling (Ehlen, 1998b). Changing one input parameter affects all simulated output, so multiple regenerations were often required. When the results were satisfactory for each sample site within a field area, the sample site data were combined to produce a field area model.

Intensity. Intensity was the primary factor used for matching the field data to the simulated data for each three-dimensional sample site model. More often than not, initial intensities were too high, which resulted in predicted joint spacings at the denied sites that were too small, and predicted joint trace lengths that were too long (Ehlen, 1998b). Early predictions for mean joint spacing in simulated horizontal boreholes, for example, were less than half the closest mean vertical joint spacings measured at the sample sites, which was not acceptable. This may have resulted in part from different methods of "measurement"—field measurements, as noted previously, were made perpendicular to joint strike, whereas mean simulated spacings from the simulated boreholes were calculated from the number of fracture intersections and the length of the borehole regardless of strike. The Terzaghi correction for bias (Terzaghi, 1965) was not used. Consequently, the input data for the three-dimensional field area models were reevaluated. Success was achieved by weighting joint intensities for each joint set according to the proportion of the outcrop occupied by that set. A comparison between initial and final intensities for one field area is shown in Figure 6.

Generation order. The order in which the joint sets were generated was also adjusted. Initially, the joint sets were generated arbitrarily in the order in which measurements were made in the field. Review of the sampling results suggested that generation in order of increasing termination percent would be more realistic. This ordering, which helped bring the simulated data closer to field measurements, better reflects the likely sequence in which the joint sets were formed (Ehlen, 1998b).

Trace length. In early models, mean simulated trace lengths and predicted mean trace lengths were significantly greater than field measurements. As a result, the approximation used to calculate mean joint radius from mean measured trace length was reevaluated. Initially, one-half mean measured trace length plus standard deviation (0.5 L + s) was used to estimate mean joint radius on the recommendation of W.S. Dershowitz (Golder Associates, Inc., personal commun., 1995). But because both mean simulated and mean predicted trace lengths were too long, the field area models were regenerated using three-tenths mean measured trace length plus standard deviation (0.3 L + s). This measure produced mean simulated trace lengths much more akin to the means for the field measurements. Using the smaller mean joint radius also resulted in increased mean simulated and predicted joint spacings for both simulated horizontal and vertical boreholes, which better matched the field data.

These changes resulted in better quality sample site, field area, and lineation models, and consequently, in significantly improved predictions for the two denied sites. Variables in addition to intensity, spacing, and trace length also changed as a result of these adjustments, but not consistently from field area to field area. Standard deviations were decreased (improved) for all simulated variables and the R^2 values for the least-squares fits improved as well as a result of these modifications.

DENIED AREA PREDICTIONS

The natural logs of the simulated data for each variable at each image scale for the analogue area and the two denied sites were plotted with the natural logs of the simulated data from the analogue area model (y-axis) against the natural logs of scale (x-axis) using regression analysis. Natural logs were used because of the large-scale range among the data sets (1:1 to 1:50 000). The equation for the best-fit line, most often a linear model (indicating a power law distribution and scale independence between variables), was used to calculate the prediction for each variable at the ground surface at each denied site ($x = 0$ in the regression equation). The 95% confidence limits also were determined for each prediction. Predictions of ground level fracture properties for each denied site were made for mean joint spacings in simulated horizontal and vertical boreholes, mean joint trace length, joint intensity, termination percent, mean rock block width and volume, and RQD.

The simulated data from the three-dimensional model for Area D; from the 1:5 200, 1:8 300, and 1:53 000 scale lineation model for Area D; and from the 1:40 000 and 1:2700 or 1:2200 scale lineation models for the two denied sites (Sites 1 and 2, respectively) were plotted for each variable. The best-fit models for each variable in the analog area three-dimensional model were used for the predictions at the denied sites. Linear models produced the best fits for all variables except for joint trace length and RQD. Figures 7 and 8 show examples of the regressions in log-log space for mean "horizontal" and vertical joint spacings, and for mean trace lengths at Denied Sites 1 and 2, respectively.

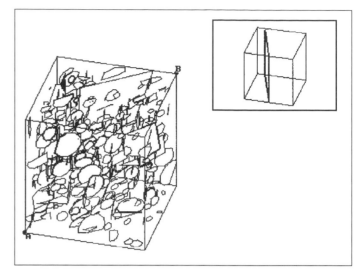

Figure 4. Three-dimensional model and orientation of simulated vertical trace plane. The three-dimensional model is oriented with a 345 degree angle of view, and the trace plane in the upper right corner is parallel to the line of measurement in the field.

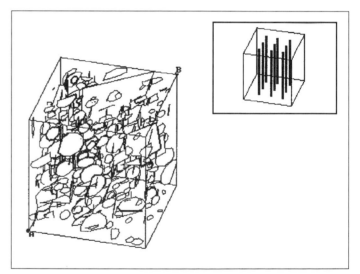

Figure 5. Three-dimensional model and simulated vertical boreholes through the model.

Table 4 shows the equation for the best-fit model for each variable at the two denied sites with the 95% confidence limits, and Table 5 shows the predictions for each variable at each denied site. There is very little difference between the predictions for the two denied sites, but this was expected because they are located about 300 m apart. Table 6 compares the predictions with the field data from Area D and with the range in field measurements for the three other field areas.

The predictions for the denied sites were compared with the field data, particularly that from Area D, to determine their reasonableness (Table 6). Although joint properties can vary widely

TABLE 3. FIELD DATA AND SIMULATED RESULTS FOR FIELD AREA MODELS

Field	Area A	Area B	Area C	Area D
Model size (m)	20x20x20	15x15x15	15x15x15	15x15x15
Mean joint spacing (m)				
Horizontal joints				
Field measurement	N.D.	N.D.	0.23	0.27
Standard deviation	N.D.	N.D.	0.35	0.50
Simulation (vertical boreholes)	0.87	0.65	0.26	0.33
Standard deviation	0.22	0.10	0.02	0.03
Vertical joints				
Field measurement	0.22	0.16	0.31	0.24
Standard deviation	0.26	0.28	0.74	0.49
Simulation (horizontal boreholes)	0.27	0.15	0.25	0.24
Standard deviation	0.04	0.02	0.06	0.06
Mean trace length (m) - vertical plane				
Field measurement	2.41	0.92	1.46	1.02
Standard deviation	1.54	0.91	1.26	1.19
Simulation	2.67	1.49	1.97	1.19
Standard deviation	2.95	1.44	1.61	1.03
Joint intensity				
Calculation from field data	5.59	8.84	7.62	6.66
Simulation	5.59	8.84	7.54	6.66
Termination % - vertical plane				
Field estimate	22.80	32.50	24.17	13.30
Simulation	15.49	11.90	21.10	15.90
RQD (%)				
Calculation from field data	92.5	87.2	92.9	91.5
Simulation (horizontal boreholes)	94.6	87.1	93.9	92.0
Standard deviation	2.5	5.3	4.2	3.9
Mean block size				
Simulated width (m)	0.505	0.270	0.355	0.265
Standard deviation	0.316	0.171	0.244	0.143
Simulated volume (m³)	0.244	0.037	0.124	0.032
Standard deviation	0.534	0.080	0.478	0.055

from outcrop to outcrop, predictions for the denied sites should be similar to measurements made in the four field areas because all sites, including the denied sites, are located in plutons of the same age that have undergone similar stress histories and consist of similar material (hence the analogue concept).

The relations between the predictions for each variable for the two denied sites, the range in field measurements for the four field areas, and field measurements at Area D are summarized as follows:

Predicted mean joint spacings in simulated vertical boreholes ("horizontal" joint spacing) are at the lower end of the range measured in the field areas, and are about 10% less than field measurements at Area D.

Mean predicted joint spacings in simulated horizontal boreholes (vertical joint spacing) are at the lower end of the range of field measurements. They are about 25% less than mean measured vertical joint spacings at Area D.

Mean predicted trace lengths are within the range of field measurements, but are about 13% greater than mean measured trace length at Area D.

Predicted joint intensities are 5% to 7% greater than the calculated intensities for the field areas. They are more than 40% higher than the intensity at Area D.

Predicted termination percentages are in the lower half of the range of the field estimates, but are about 25% greater than field estimates at Area D.

Predictions for RQD are within the range of the estimated RQDs calculated from the field data. They are about 5% greater than the RQD calculated for Area D.

Block size was not measured in the field, but comparisons can be made with simulated block size data from the field area models: predicted mean block widths are less than the range for the field area simulations (see Table 3), and are about 25 to 30% less than simulated block width at Area D.

Predicted mean block volumes are significantly less than the range for the field area simulations (see Table 3). Predicted mean block volumes for the two sites are more than 60% smaller than simulated mean block volume for Area D.

This comparison of predicted values for Denied Sites 1 and 2 with measured values for the field areas, particularly the analogue area, Area D, indicates that the predictions are realistic. All predictions are within the standard deviations of field measurements, where standard deviations could be determined and, with the exception of joint intensity, are within the range of the field measurements. Most predictions are within 25% of measurements made at the analogue area.

PREDICTION ACCURACIES

Field data could not be collected at either denied site, so to better understand how accurate the predictions are using these procedures, one of the field areas (Area A) was selected as a "denied area." The procedures described above were repeated using Area D as the analogue area to predict the fracture properties at Area A. These predictions were then compared directly to the field data collected in Area A. It should be noted that, unlike the two denied sites, Area A is in a different granite pluton than Area D. Furthermore, Area A consists of moderately, highly, and completely weathered granite, whereas the Area D model is based only on moderately and highly weathered granite. The relative amounts of moderately and highly weathered granite are similar, however, in the two areas.

Table 7 shows the best-fit regression equations with the 95% confidence limits for each variable. Again, linear models usually provided the best fits, suggesting power law distributions and scale independence for most variables. Table 8 shows the field measurements and the predictions made for Area A. The predictions are in very good agreement with the field data: Most are within 10 to 15% of field measurements at Area A. Selected regressions in log-log space for mean joint spacings in simulated vertical and horizontal boreholes, and for trace length, are shown in Figure 9.

The relations between the predictions for each variable at Area A using the Area D model and field measurements made in Area A are summarized as follows:

Predicted mean joint spacing in simulated horizontal boreholes (vertical joint spacing) is about 5% less than the mean for the field measurements at Area A.

No horizontal joint spacings were measured at Area A, so no direct comparison can be made. However, predicted mean joint spacing in simulated vertical boreholes ("horizontal" joint spacing) is about 10% greater than the mean horizontal joint spacings measured in the other three field areas.

Mean predicted trace length is about 10% less than mean measured trace length at Area A.

Predicted joint intensity is about 40% higher than joint intensity at Area A. Joint intensity at Area D is about 15% greater than that at Area A, which may, in part, explain why predicted intensity is too high.

Predicted termination percent is about 30% less than the termination percent estimated in the field at Area A. The estimated termination percent for Area D, however, is much lower (about 70%) than that for Area A.

Predicted RQD is virtually the same as the RQD calculated from the field data at Area A.

The high degree of similarity between the predictions and the measurements indicates that the procedures used to make the predictions are realistic and that accurate predictions can be made. These results also suggest that Area D provides an acceptable analogue area model for fracture patterns in the weathered granites of nearby areas.

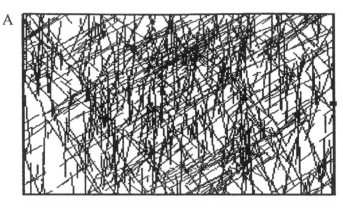

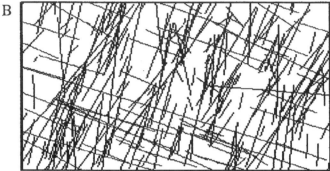

Figure 6. Initial (A) and final (B) intensities for the Area A field model.

DISCUSSION

Joint spacings

Simulated vertical boreholes provide spacings for horizontal joints, and simulated horizontal boreholes, spacings for vertical and dipping joints. In the field, horizontal joints were defined as those dipping 25 degrees or less; vertical joints as those dipping 70 degrees or more. Inclined joints are those with dips between 26 and 69 degrees. It is highly likely that inclined joints were intersected by the simulated vertical boreholes as well as by the simulated horizontal boreholes, so the relations between measured and simulated horizontal joint spacings in these models are not as clear as one would like. The predicted joint spacings in simulated vertical boreholes at the denied sites are within 20% of the mean measured horizontal joint spacings for the two field areas in which horizontal joint spacings were measured. It is inconvenient that Area A is one of the field areas in which horizontal joint spacings were not measured, so no direct comparison can be made.

It also should be emphasized that horizontal joint sets were not included in the three-dimensional lineation models. These joints are usually not observable on imagery and accordingly were not included in the models. In fact, joints dipping less than 50 degrees were excluded from the lineation models. This means that the spacings in simulated vertical boreholes for these models are actually for inclined, not horizontal, joints. Work in granitic

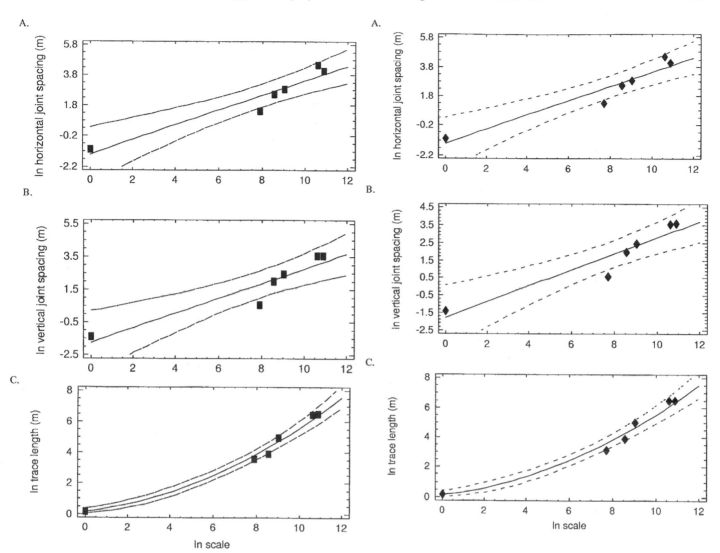

Figure 7. Sample regressions for the predictions at Denied Site 1. The outer lines are the upper and lower 95% confidence limits. A: "Horizontal" joint spacings. B: Vertical joint spacings. C: Joint trace length.

Figure 8. Sample regressions for the predictions at Denied Site 2. The outer lines are the upper and lower 95% confidence limits. A: "Horizontal" joint spacings. B: Vertical joint spacings. C: Joint trace length.

plutons in Montana (Ehlen and Zen, 1992, and unpublished data) and general observations in granites elsewhere indicated that inclined joints tend to be more widely spaced than either horizontal or vertical joints, so the predictions for mean joint spacings in simulated vertical boreholes at the denied sites may be greater than horizontal joint spacings measured in the field at those sites.

RQD

As noted above, RQD is an indirect measure of joint spacing. RQDs were determined for simulated horizontal boreholes, which reflect vertical joint spacing, so that comparisons could be made more easily with the field measurements made in the vertical plane, which consisted primarily of vertical joint spacings.

Vertical boreholes were drilled at two of the field areas (Ehlen, 1999). RQDs determined from these boreholes were compared to RQDs calculated from the field data collected near the boreholes (Paul Fisher, UTD, Inc., personal commun., 1996). The RQDs calculated from the field data are significantly higher (i.e., indicating much better quality rock) than those determined from the two boreholes, although they are consistent with the joint spacing measurements made in the field. The simulated RQDs from the three-dimensional models also are significantly higher than RQDs determined from the two boreholes, but again, are consistent with RQDs calculated from the field data. These differences were expected. First, they result in part because RQD and joint spacing cannot be directly related (Deere and Deere, 1989). Second, field measurements were made only on the major joint sets in each outcrop. As a result, all joints were not included in the cal-

TABLE 4. EQUATIONS FOR PREDICTIONS AT DENIED SITES 1 AND 2

	Equation	Model	R^2
Denied Site 1			
Mean joint spacing (m)			
Horizontal joints	lny = -1.4216 + 0.4847*lnx	linear	91.32
Vertical joints	lny = -1.7660 + 0.4536*lnx	linear	88.49
Mean trace length (m) - vertical plane	lny = (0.3899 + 0.1971*lnx)^2	square root-y	99.24
Joint intensity	lny = 2.2492 - 0.4596*lnx	linear	88.82
Termination % - vertical plane	lny = 2.8677 - 0.0945*lnx	linear	78.09
RQD (%) - horizontal boreholes	lny = 4.5160 + 0.0297*sqrt(lnx)	square root-x	97.20
Mean block size			
Width (m)	lny = -1.6260 + 0.5225*lnx	linear	93.73
Volume (m^3)	lny = -4.4171 + 1.6138*lnx	linear	92.91
Denied Site 2			
Mean joint spacing (m)			
Horizontal joints	lny = -1.4382 + 0.4873*lnx	linear	91.56
Vertical joints	lny = -1.7725 + 0.4566*lnx	linear	89.82
Mean trace length (m) - vertical plane	lny = exp(0.3752 + 0.1974*lnx)	exponential	98.80
Joint intensity	lny = 2.2732 - 0.4627*lnx	linear	89.95
Termination % - vertical plane	lny = 2.7452-0.0941*lnx	linear	65.12
RQD (%) - horizontal boreholes	lny = 4.5153 + 0.0294*sqrt(lnx)	square root-x	98.87
Mean block size			
Width (m)	lny = -1.6751 + 0.5241*lnx	linear	92.42
Volume (m^3)	lny = -4.5244 + 1.6218*lnx	linear	92.29

TABLE 5. PREDICTIONS AND 95% CONFIDENCE LEVELS FOR DENIED SITES 1 AND 2

	Denied Site 1			Denied Site 2		
	Prediction	95% confidence limits		Prediction	95% confidence limits	
		Lower	Upper		Lower	Upper
Mean joint spacing (m)						
Horizontal joints	0.24	0.04	1.45	1.45	0.04	1.39
Vertical joints	0.17	0.02	1.22	0.17	0.03	1.07
Mean tr. length (m) - vertical plane	1.16	1.03	1.43	1.15	1.01	1.50
Joint intensity	9.48	1.34	66.98	9.71	1.38	68.18
Termination % - vertical plane	17.60	9.65	32.07	15.57	6.84	35.45
RQD (%) - horizontal boreholes	91.47	89.70	93.27	91.40	90.30	9.52
Mean block size						
Width (m)	0.197	0.04	0.99	0.187	0.031	1.129
Volume (m^3)	0.012	0.00	2.53	0.011	0.00	2.93

TABLE 6. PREDICTIONS FOR DENIED SITES COMPARED WITH FIELD DATA FROM AREA D (THE ANALOGUE AREA) AND THE RANGE IN FIELD MEASUREMENTS FOR THE FOUR FIELD AREAS

	Predictions for denied sites		Area D (field data)	Range in field measurements (all field areas)
	Site 1	Site 2		
Mean joint spacing (m)				
Horizontal joints	0.24	0.24	0.27	0.23–0.27
Vertical joints	0.17	0.17	0.24	0.16–0.31
Mean trace length (m) - vertical plane	1.16	1.15	1.02	0.92–2.41
Joint intensity	9.48	9.71	6.66*	5.59–8.84*
Termination % - vertical plane	17.6	15.8	13.30	13.3–32.5
RQD (%) - horizontal boreholes	91.5	91.4	91.5*	91.3–99.1*
Mean block size				
Width (m)	0.197	0.187	N.D.	N.D.
Volume (m^3)	0.012	0.011	N.D.	N.D.

* Calculated from raw field data.

TABLE 7. EQUATIONS FOR PREDICTIONS AT AREA A

	Equation	Model	R^2
Mean joint spacing (m)			
Horizontal joints	lny = -1.2171 + 0.4863*lnx	linear	97.43
Vertical joints	lny = -1.5834 + 0.4511*lnx	linear	97.88
Mean trace length (m) - vertical plane	lny = (0.4164 + 0.1985*lnx)^2	square root-y	99.02
Joint intensity	lny = 2.0773 + 0.4614*lnx	linear	97.08
Termination % - vertical plane	lny = 2.7595 - 0.0718*lnx	linear	72.86
RQD (%) - horizontal boreholes	lny = 4.5159 + 0.0291*sqrt(lnx)	square root-x	97.88
Mean block size			
Width (m)	lny = -1.5132 + 0.5287*lnx	linear	97.21
Volume (m³)	lny = -4.0444 + 1.6436*lnx	linear	96.34

**TABLE 8. PREDICTIONS AND 95% CONFIDENCE LEVELS FOR AREA A
COMPARED WITH FIELD MEASUREMENTS**

	Prediction	95% confidence limits		Field measurement
		Lower	Upper	
Mean joint spacing (m)				
Horizontal joints	0.30	0.13	0.65	N.D.
Vertical joints	0.21	0.11	0.40	0.22
Mean trace length (m) - vertical plane	1.19	1.05	1.46	2.41
Joint intensity	7.98	3.58	17.82	5.59*
Termination % - vertical plan	15.79	10.17	24.53	22.86
RQD (%) - horizontal boreholes	91.46	90.18	92.76	92.5*
Mean block size				
Width (m)	0.220	0.09	0.53	N.D.
Volume (m³)	0.018	0.00	0.44	N.D.

* Calculated from raw field data.

culation, as they would be in a borehole: The greater the number of joints, the greater the proportion of small pieces of core, and the lower the RQD. Third, there are other planes of weakness in rock (discontinuities) along which core would break, which are not joints, e.g., mineral alignments. Finally, RQD values based on core are undoubtedly affected by the drilling, coring, and core handling procedures, whereas RQDs calculated from joint spacing measurements are not.

Joint trace lengths

Although of importance to site characterization and penetrability in terms of persistence and of most importance for model generation in the *FracMan* program, joint trace length was the least important variable measured in the field with respect to matching the simulated data to the field data. This is because most trace length data are biased in natural rock outcrops (Baecher and Lanney, 1978), such that the relationship between measured trace lengths and true joint size is unknown (Jacobi et al., this volume). Assuming a three-dimensional joint is a disk, one cannot determine from the typical outcrop whether one is measuring a minimum, maximum, or intermediate distance across the disk. For this reason, less emphasis was placed on matching mean simulated trace length to mean measured trace length than on matching mean joint spacings and joint intensity. Numerous corrections for these

biases have been identified (e.g., Baecher et al., 1977; Priest and Hudson, 1981; Kulatilake et al., 1993), but because it is virtually impossible to know exactly what is being measured, and because the field data represent only a small sample of trace lengths for each joint set (about 23% of the joint spacing measurements), no corrections were applied to the trace length data.

Fractal geometry

Both Ehlen (1998a) and Jacobi et al. (this volume) suggest that the fractal nature of fracture properties could form the basis for a predictive model of fracture properties in denied areas based on a combination of field measurements and lineation data. The work described here substantiates this hypothesis in several ways. First, most variables exhibit power law distributions (i.e., linear regression models provide the best fits in log-log space). Second, the lineation patterns are scale independent. The work of others (e.g., Barton et al., 1988; Kojima et al., 1989; Barton et al., 1991; Velde et al., 1991; Ehlen, 1992, 1993; Broadu and Long, 1994) has suggested that fracture spacing, fracture and lineation length, and fracture trace maps (two-dimensional depictions, such as lineation overlays and maps of fracture patterns from rock pavements) can be fractal, although some recent research has suggested otherwise (e.g., Gillespie et al., 1993; Walsh and Watterson, 1993). La Pointe (1988), Poulton et al. (1990), and Broadu and

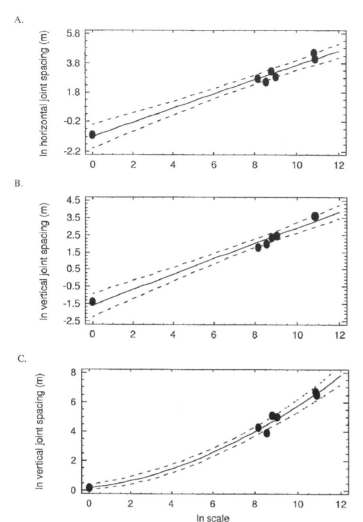

Figure 9. Sample regressions for the predictions at Area A. The outer lines are the upper and lower 95% confidence limits. A: "Horizontal" joint spacings. B: Vertical joint spacings. C: Joint trace length.

Long (1994) suggest that block size and RQD can be fractal as well. Further work is required to validate a fractal model for joint properties and their prediction and, if successful, to facilitate the application of such a model in the future.

CONCLUSIONS

The predictions made for mean joint spacings in simulated horizontal and vertical boreholes, mean joint trace length, joint intensity, termination percent, mean rock block width and volume, and RQD in weathered granite at the two denied sites are realistic. This statement is based on comparisons with mean measured and simulated values for each variable from the four field areas, particularly Area D, the "analogue area." The predictions are within the standard deviations of means for field measurements and are generally within the range of mean field measure-

ments at the four field areas. Most predictions are within 25% of field measurements at Area D.

Realistic predictions are one thing; accurate predictions are another. In order to assess the accuracy of the predictions, Area A was defined as "denied," and the same procedures were used to make predictions for joint properties here. The predictions made for Area A are within 10–15% of the field measurements. This suggests that the predictions are accurate for the denied sites as well as realistic, and that the procedures developed are viable. These results also suggest that Area D is a good field area model, at least for fracture patterns in the weathered granites of nearby areas. It remains to be seen if the Area D model can serve in a similar way in denied areas elsewhere, where quantitative information about joint properties is needed.

ACKNOWLEDGMENTS

This work was partly funded by the Defense Threat Reduction Agency (DTRA; previously Defense Special Weapons Agency). The project was a multi-agency effort involving personnel from the DTRA, the U.S. Geological Survey, and the U.S. Army Corps of Engineers. Other personnel from universities and private industry were under contract to support this effort. Thanks are also due to Edward L. Tremba, DTRA, for his thorough review of an early version of this chapter; Douglas Caldwell, U.S. Army Topographic Engineering Center (TEC), for his guidance and assistance with ARC/INFO, and to Jim Shine, TEC, for his advice on matters statistical. Citation of commercial product brand names does not constitute an official endorsement or approval of the use of such commercial products by the Army.

REFERENCES CITED

Baecher, G.B., and Lanney, N.A., 1978, Trace length biases in joint surveys, *in* Proceedings, U.S. Symposium on Rock Mechanics, 19th, Reno, Nevada: Reno, University of Nevada, p. 56–65.

Baecher, G.B., Lanney, N.A., and Einstein, H.H., 1977, Statistical description of rock properties and sampling, *in* Proceedings, U.S. Symposium on Rock Mechanics, 18th: Keystone, Colorado, Johnson Publishing Company, p. 5C1-1–5C1-8.

Barton, C.C., La Pointe, P.R., and Malinverno, A., 1991, Fractals and their use in Earth sciences: Short course manual: San Diego, California, Geological Society of America Annual Meeting, 312 p.

Barton, C.C., Samuel, J.K., and Page, W.R., 1988, Fractal scaling of fracture networks, trace lengths, and apertures: Geological Society of America Abstracts with Programs, v. 20, p. A299.

Brady, B.H.G., and Brown, E.T., 1993, Rock mechanics for underground mining: London, Chapman and Hall, 571 p.

Broadu, F.K., and Long, L.T., 1994, The fractal character of fracture spacing and RQD: International Journal of Rock Mechanics and Mining Sciences & Geomechanics Abstracts, v. 31, p. 127–134.

Deere, D.U., and Deere, D.W., 1989, Rock Quality Designation (RQD) after twenty years: Vicksburg, Mississippi, U.S. Army Corps of Engineers Waterways Experiment Station, 67 p.

Dershowitz, W.S., and Herda, H.H., 1992, Interpretation of fracture spacing and intensity, *in* Proceedings, U.S. Symposium on Rock Mechanics, 33rd: Rotterdam, A.A. Balkema, p. 756–766.

Dershowitz, W., Lee, G., Geier, J., Hitchcock, S., and La Pointe, P., 1995, *Frac-Man*, Interactive discrete feature data analysis, geometric modeling, and exploration simulation, user documentation, Version 2.42: Seattle, Washington, Golder Associates, Inc., 171 p.

Eastler, T.E., Percious, D.J., and Fisher, P.R., 1998, Role of geology in assessing vulnerability of underground fortifications to conventional weapons attack, *in* Underwood, J.R., Jr., and Guth, P.L., eds., Military geology in war and peace: Geological Society of America, Reviews in Engineering Geology, v. 13, p. 173–187.

Ehlen, J., 1992, Comparison of air photo lineations and joint patterns, Dartmoor, southwest England: Fort Belvoir, Virginia, U.S. Army Topographic Engineering Center, TEC-0006, 18 p.

Ehlen, J., 1993, Joint control of drainage patterns and tor locations, Dartmoor, southwest England: Hamilton, Ontario, Canada, McMaster University, International Conference on Geomorphology, 3rd, Programme with Abstracts, p. 134.

Ehlen, J., 1996, Predicting fracture characteristics using three-dimensional modeling, *in* Proceedings, International Conference on GeoComputation, 1st: Leeds, England, University of Leeds, v. 1, p. 227–247.

Ehlen, J., 1998a, A proposed method for characterizing fracture patterns in denied areas, *in* Underwood, J.R., Jr., and Guth, P.L., eds., Military geology in war and peace:, Geological Society of America, Reviews in Engineering Geology, v. 13, p. 151–163.

Ehlen, J., 1998b, Matching simulated fracture data with field measurements using joint intensity: International Journal of Rock Mechanics and Mining Sciences, v. 35, CD-Rom, Paper No. 010.

Ehlen, J., 1999, Fracture characteristics in weathered granite: Geomorphology, v. 31, p. 29–45.

Ehlen, J., and Zen, E., 1992, The effects of valley glaciation on jointing, East Pioneer Mts. MT: Geological Society of America Abstracts with Programs, v. 24, n. 7, p. A315.

Gillespie, P.A., Howard, C.B., Walsh, J.J., and Watterson, J., 1993, Measurement and characterisation of fractures: Tectonophysics, v. 226, p. 113–141.

Kojima, K., Tosaka, H., and Ohno, H., 1989, An approach to wide-ranging correlation of fracture distributions using the concept of fractal, *in* Khair, K., ed., Rock mechanics as a guide for efficient utilization of natural resources: Rotterdam, A.A. Balkema, p. 211–218.

Kulatilake, P.H.S.W., Wathugala, D.N., and Stephansson, O., 1993, Joint network modeling with a validation exercise in Stripa mine, Sweden: International Journal of Rock Mechanics and Mining Sciences & Geomechanics Abstracts, v. 30, p. 503–526.

La Pointe, P.R., 1988, A method to characterize fracture density and connectivity through fractal geometry: International Journal of Rock Mechanics and Mining Sciences & Geomechanics Abstracts, v. 25, p. 421–429.

Murphy, W.L., 1985, Geotechnical descriptions of rock and rock masses: Vicksburg, Mississippi, U.S. Army Corps of Engineers Waterways Experiment Station, Technical Report GL-85-3, 49 p.

Poulton, M.M., Mojatabai, N., and Farmer, I.W., 1990, Scale invariant behavior of massive and fragmented rock: International Journal of Rock Mechanics and Mining Sciences & Geomechanics Abstracts, v. 27, p. 219–221.

Priest, S.D., and Hudson, J.A., 1976, Discontinuity spacings in rock: International Journal of Rock Mechanics and Mining Sciences & Geomechanics Abstracts, v. 13, p. 135–148.

Priest, S.D., and Hudson, J.A., 1981, Estimation of discontinuity spacing and trace length using scan-line surveys: International Journal of Rock Mechanics and Mining Sciences & Geomechanics Abstracts, v. 18, p. 183–197.

Terzaghi, R.D., 1965, Sources of error in joint surveys: Geotechnique, v. 15, p. 287–304.

Velde, B., Dubois, J., Moore, D., and Touchard, G., 1991, Fractal patterns of fractures in granites: Earth and Planetary Science Letters, v. 104, p. 25–35.

Walsh, J.J., and Watterson, J., 1993, Fractal analysis of fracture patterns using the standard box-counting technique: Valid and invalid methodology: Journal of Structural Geology, v. 15, p. 1509–1512.

MANUSCRIPT ACCEPTED BY THE SOCIETY OCTOBER 27, 2000

Geological Society of America
Reviews in Engineering Geology, Volume XIV
2001

Battlefield terrain and engineering geology in the eastern Chorwon Valley, central Korean Peninsula

C.P. Cameron
Department of Geology, Box 5044, University of Southern Mississippi, Hattiesburg MS, 39406, USA

ABSTRACT

The terrain of the eastern Chorwon Valley is geologically complex, controlled by spatial relationships between Precambrian metamorphic rocks, Mesozoic granite, and locally intense structural deformations within and adjacent to major faults. Fundamental controls of terrain are overprinted by cycles of deep weathering and erosion during Pleistocene sea-level fluctuations, as well as by accelerated human impacts during the twentieth century. Geological characterization, terrain analysis, and Korean War history here provide significant lessons in the use of battlefield terrain.

Military access, mobility, and the orientation of attack corridors in this area are predominantly a function of major tectonic faults, and (to a lesser extent) lithology. Severely tectonized granite rock mass extends outward for 300 m to 2 km from major fault zones. Erosion of highly weathered granite in some of these zones forms elongate valleys. The easily-ripped saprolite by-products of granite weathering provide in situ construction materials (sand and gravel), soft foundations prone to boggy conditions in some areas, reasonable groundwater supplies near the fault zones, and an overall situation suitable for staging and military infrastructure. Resistant Precambrian metamorphic rocks form rugged terrain suitable for defensive positions. These hard lithologies support steep ridges and towering hills in and around the eastern Chorwon Valley in the Kumhwa vicinity. The (often) strongly magnetic character of some of the metamorphic rocks complicates the location of mines and unexploded ordnance in this sector of the Korean Demilitarized Zone (DMZ).

INTRODUCTION

Geology, the fourth dimension of terrain
—James E. Wilson (1946, p. 49)

Major (Retired) James E. Wilson stated in his *Military Review* article (1946) that subsurface geology is a "fourth dimension of terrain." This concept emphasizes the importance of geology in predicting battlefield terrain conditions. Wilson, a geological engineer, has a veteran's appreciation of the use of terrain in warfare, having waded ashore at Omaha Beach on D+6. By the time he was wounded during the Saint-Lo breakout, he had also noted that commanders of ground forces seldom used good, well-compiled geological information in the field. Concep-

tually robust and timeless in its application, the phrase "Geology, the fourth dimension of terrain" aptly conveys the major goal of this chapter, to document the geologic elements that control terrain in the eastern Chorwon Valley of central Korea. In particular, this chapter will discuss terrain aspects of the Kumhwa area that directly influenced the outcome of a major Korean War battle fought there during the fall of 1952 (Fig. 1).

The broad physiographic patterns shown in Figure 1 illustrate the strategic significance of the Chorwon Valley and its eastern margins. The Korean terms displayed on detailed topographic maps of the central peninsula to describe common terrain features are used herein to insure an appropriate level of consistency. Hence use of the suffixes "-sanmaek" (mountain range), "-san" (mountain), and "gang" (river or stream). The

Cameron, C.P., 2001, Battlefield terrain and engineering geology in the eastern Chorwon Valley, central Korean Peninsula, *in* Ehlen, J., and Harmon, R.S., eds., The Environmental Legacy of Military Operations: Boulder, Colorado, Geological Society of America Reviews in Engineering Geology, v. XIV, p. 75–93.

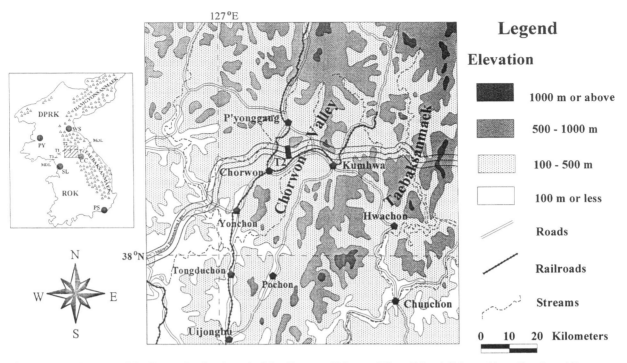

Figure 1. Location map of the Korean Peninsula and of the Chorwon Valley and "Iron Triangle" formed by rail and road lines connecting P'yonggang, Chorwon, and Kumhwa. Abbreviations: ROK—Republic of Korea; DPRK—Democratic People's Republic of Korea; SL—Seoul; CC—Ch'unchon; PS—Pusan; PY—Pyongyang; WS—Wonson; T1, T2, T3, and T4—Clandestine Tunnels 1–4, respectively; MDL—military demarcation line.

terms "West Sea of Korea" and "East Sea of Korea" are used in deference to Korean sensibilities while an absolutely neutral stance is maintained by providing (parenthetically) the alternate terms "Yellow Sea" and "Sea of Japan," respectively. To the east of this region, the terrain is dominated by the T'aebaeksanmaek, a north-northwest trending range of mountains that controls the east coast of the peninsula as far north as the Wonson area. The elevations of the T'aebaeksanmaek rise sharply east of Kumhwa. Local relief increases as the terrain becomes very rugged and incised. Mountain barriers that are breached only by steep and narrow stream valleys limit mechanized access and mobility. The stream valleys are often dammed, the impounded reservoirs forming as difficult a barrier to mechanized access as the towering ridgelines (Cameron, 1998a). The Chorwon Valley is part of the only major north-south access route connecting Seoul, and its nearby port of Inchon on the West Sea of Korea (Yellow Sea), to the port of Wonson on the East Sea of Korea (Sea of Japan). In central Korea, elements of the Wonson-Seoul fault system control elongate connecting valleys that link P'yonggang, Chorwon, and Kumhwa, the "Iron Triangle" (Fig. 1). A term coined by the allied media during the Korean War, the "Iron Triangle" described the steel rail lines flanking the road system that connected Chorwon, P'yonggang, and Kumhwa. Military forces, supplies, and materials moved along the Wonson-Seoul corridor must transit the Iron Triangle. Low terrain in and around this hub provides strategic access to the Chorwon Valley. At the same time, the high terrain around P'yonggang guards the northern

and northwestern portals of the valley while that around Kumhwa overlooks valleys providing access from the northeast and east. Similarly, terrain to the northwest and south of Chorwon overlooks access to the valley from the west. Kumhwa, an important regional hub consisting of a city and a score of nearby villages, was the eastern apex of the Iron Triangle. Like most of the population centers in this region, Kumhwa and its nearby hamlets were completely destroyed, along with road and railroad infrastructure, during the Korean War. Kumhwa, because of its location on the Demilitarized Zone (DMZ), was never rebuilt, unlike Chorwon and P'yonggang. As defined herein, the "Kumhwa area" is contained on the "Gimhwa" and "Jeoggeunsan" 1:25 000 scale Defense Mapping Agency map sheets, DMA 3222 IV SE and DMA 3222 1 SW, respectively.

The valleys of the Iron Triangle provided the North Korean People's Army (NKPA or "Inmun Gun") primary transit and staging areas from which they launched their three-pronged invasion of central South Korea, toward Seoul and Ch'unchon, in 1950. The Iron Triangle was contested during several stages of the Korean War and particularly severe fighting took place here during the closing year of the conflict (Hermes, 1966). Military use of terrain is particularly complicated in the Kumhwa area; rocks of differing geotechnical properties being juxtaposed by igneous intrusion and faulting. Deep weathering and erosion of variably resistant lithologies are responses to these primary bedrock controls. However, human impacts during the past 3500 years significantly overprint some of these natural controls.

The geologic development of this terrain is linked to the relatively late formation of Korea as a peninsula. Separation and eastward movement of terrains now part of Japan occurred during the Late Cretaceous (Paek et al., 1993a). Subduction and back-arc spreading during the Oligocene and Miocene more fully developed the East Sea of Korea (Tamaki, 1995). Tectonic uplift of as much as 200 m along the T'aebaeksanmaek on the east coast during the Miocene and Pliocene tilted Korean terrain to the west and established current drainage patterns. Severe dissection of the elevated regions followed, erosion being particularly severe along rock mass discontinuities weakened by structural dislocation or in rock predisposed to deep weathering by virtue of original chemical composition and hydrothermal alteration (e.g., some granite). Particularly important to the evolution of the Korean terrain is the fact that the peninsula was not glaciated during the Pleistocene. The otherwise wet climate produced deep chemical weathering of Mesozoic granites particularly where major fault zones disrupt them. Major lowstands of Pleistocene sea level significantly increased hydraulic energy in stream systems already incised along structural and lithological avenues of erosion. In summary, tectonic uplift and renewed dissection of an ancient metamorphic shield and selective erosion of the deeply weathered granite plutons combined to produce a terrain of alternately hard and soft rocks, generally high and steep in the east, low and rolling in the west.

GEOLOGY

The central Korean Peninsula is part of an Archean and Proterozoic polymetamorphic shield in northeastern Asia. Crystalline basement gneiss and schist of igneous and sedimentary origin were formed during (at least) three Precambrian orogenies. This terrain was further uplifted and intruded by granitic rocks of batholithic dimension during orogenic episodes of the Mesozoic (Triassic Songrim disturbance, Jurassic Daebo Event, and Cretaceous Bulgugsa Event). These plutonic rocks have diverse compositions. Unless otherwise stated, the term "granite" is used herein in its broadest generic sense, i.e., a generally medium- to coarse-grained plutonic igneous rock in the granite to diorite compositional range. Following extensive erosion during the Tertiary, basaltic volcanic rocks that outcrop sporadically in the Chorwon Valley and lower Imjin River were extruded along portions of the Wonson-Seoul fault system (Chugaryeong Rift Valley) during a Quaternary-rifting pulse. Cameron (1998a) summarizes the regional geology of the central Korean Peninsula, citing as major references the thorough treatises of Lee, D.-S. (1987) and Paek et al. (1993a).

Magmatic and tectonic setting

Examination of the geology of the study area, as illustrated by the map and cross section in Figures 2 and 3, respectively, reveals a significant juxtaposition of stratigraphic units. The Mesozoic granite *directly* intrudes rocks of the Neoproterozoic

Sadang-u Series. Boreholes drilled northeast of Kumhwa, on the southwestern flank of Kyeungsan, verified this relationship. These boreholes penetrated the thermal contact between the granite and the Sadang-u calc-silicate schist. The Kyônggi Basement Gneiss complex is missing in the Kumhwa area directly under Kyeungsan and immediately adjacent hill masses (Fig. 3). However, across the granite-floored, gentle valleys to the east and south, the Kyônggi Gneiss Complex forms a steep and rugged terrain, its northern boundary intruded by similar Mesozoic granite.

A scenario used by the Republic of Korea (ROK) Institute of Energy Resources (KIER) geologists explains similar stratigraphic juxtapositions in other regions of the ROK. This interpretation suggests that the regional unconformity that separates the Archean basement from the Neoproterozoic metasediments locally served as an avenue of intrusion for Mesozoic granite. In the Kumhwa area the intrusion assumed the form of a lopolith that accompanied regional uplift and tilting of the entire section (Fig. 3). High-angle fault displacements along local portions of the Wonson-Seoul fault system helped preserve the Sangwon System under Kyeungsan and immediately adjacent hill masses to the east and northeast. The calc-silicate Sadang-u metasediments forming Kyeungsan apparently represent a relatively shallow roof pendant of the intrusive mass.

Lithology

Kyônggi Gneiss Basement Complex. From the standpoint of the military geology of the eastern Chorwon Valley, the Kyônggi Gneiss Basement Complex forms a steep and rugged boundary terrain, the western margin of the T'aebaeksanmaek (Cameron, 1998a). Elevations and local relief rise sharply immediately to the east and south of Kumhwa. This an important consideration from the standpoint of positioning artillery that can cover the Kumhwa sector of the Iron Triangle. The steep and rugged Kyônggi terrain affords artillery concealed within the mountain front optimal protection with respect to counter-battery fire directed from the north. These artillery positions can cover the advance of forces seeking to move north along the eastern Chorwon Valley or, alternatively, target an enemy attempting to mount a southerly attack. The metamorphic basement to the south and east of Kumhwa was not mapped in detail as part of the author's work in the eastern Chorwon Valley and will be treated only in a general sense in this chapter.

Sangwon System metasediments. The terrain in the immediate vicinity of Kumhwa consists of Middle and Upper Proterozoic metasediments (Sangwon System) intruded by a Mesozoic granite mass of batholithic dimensions. The assigned age is based on an isotopic age date of 853 Ma on glauconite from quartzite in the Sangwon System sampled in the Amnok (Yalu) River valley (Kim and Na, 1987). Most of the metasediments exposed in the areas south of the Military Demarcation Line (MDL) in the Kumhwa area fit published descriptions of the

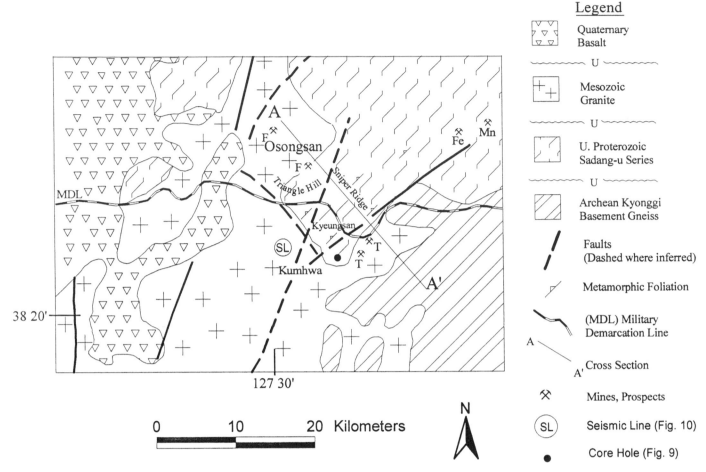

Figure 2. Generalized geologic map of the Kumhwa area, eastern Chorwon Valley. Abbreviations: F—fluorite; Mn—manganese; Fe—iron; T—talc; MDL—military demarcation line.

Sadang-u Series, a middle calcareous facies of the Sangwon System. The metasediments of the Sadang-u Series originated as deposits of impure dolomite, sandy and argillaceous limestone, calcareous sandstone and graywacke, and thin beds of calcareous shale. The carbonates hosted various types of algal mats (stromatolites) including collenia.

In the study area, the Sadang-u Series sedimentary succession underwent considerable thermal metamorphism during the invasion of granitic batholiths during the Mesozoic Era. Near Kumhwa high-temperature, low-pressure metamorphism produced calc-silicate hornfels assemblages that include quartz-epidote-actinolite-magnetite skarn; calc-silicate–magnetite schist; thin-bedded, banded, calc-silicate gneiss; biotite schist and amphibolite; spotted magnetite-garnet schist; and meta-arenite. Petrographic examination revealed that most of the rocks in the contact aureole were metamorphosed under the conditions of the hornblende hornfels facies of contact metamorphism. Locally, however, some rocks reached the pyroxene hornfels facies (Cameron et al., 1995). The contact calc-silicate suite gives way to metasediment and to greenschists with increasing distance from intrusive contacts.

Granite. This intrusive mass is very extensive. Granite and granodiorite south and west of Kyeungsan, as well as the adjacent terrain to the east, underlie low rolling hills and cultivated valleys. The Mesozoic intrusive mass is overall a coarse-grained porphyritic granodiorite that exhibits the compositional and textural diversity seen commonly in complex batholiths. Sudden shifts in rock mass composition and texture occur as a function of multiple intrusion and differentiation, proximity to intrusive margins, and tectonism of the rock mass along regional and local fault zones. In some Kumhwa outcrops, the granite is very similar to that at NKPA Clandestine Tunnel-2, (T-2, Fig. 1). Intrusive rock mass compositions, based on petrographic analyses of intact, relatively unweathered specimens collected at Kumhwa and Tunnel-2, are shown in Table 1.

Faulting

Several major fault systems cut central Korea. Most of these faults display characteristic "Korean" (north and north-northwest) or "Sinian" (north-northeast and northeast) directions (Fig. 2). The Wonson-Seoul fault system, which exhibits the "Sinian"

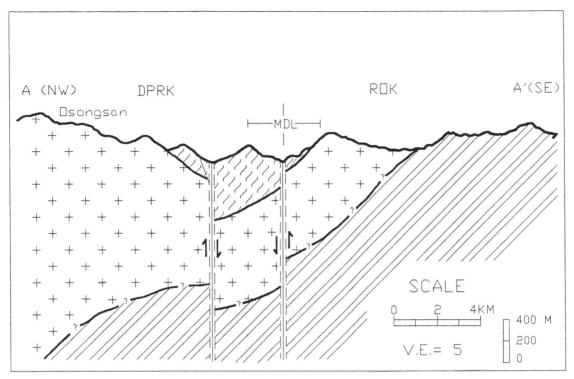

Figure 3. Generalized subsurface geology of the Kumhwa area, eastern Chorwon Valley. Abbreviations: ROK—Republic of Korea; DPRK—Democratic People's Republic of Korea; MDL—military demarcation line. See Figure 2 for lithologic symbols.

trend, controls the valleys of the Iron Triangle, in general, and the eastern Chorwon Valley in particular.

Relatively small splays of this fault system cause disruption of the uniform foliation that is characteristic of the Sadang-u metasediments that form the slopes of Kyeungsan and immediately adjacent hill masses. Faults, and fault-controlled veins and dikes that transect or dilate the foliation in the metasediments, show pronounced northeast-southwest and east-northeast–south-southwest (Sinian) trends, paralleling some of the regional faults of the Wonson-Seoul system. Fault gouge materials are generally rich in clays, mica, and graphite. These low-strength materials form a weak matrix for broken, crushed, and macerated rock and minerals. The fault zones are easily weathered to form steeply incised small draws and valleys.

Severely tectonized rock extends outward for 300 m to 2 km from fault zones that control low-lying areas in the granite terrain around Kumhwa. Here the granite is mylonitized, the fabric disrupted, and the rock reduced to quartz-clay-mica mixtures (saprolite). Weathering is extensive in these zones and saprolite thickness of 80 m is common. Evidence from boreholes suggests that highly and moderately weathered rocks exist to depths of 150 m along portions of these fault zones.

Terrain development and rock mass weathering

The development and character of terrain features in central Korea are largely a function of magmatic and tectonic history,

Pleistocene sea-level change, and (to a lesser extent) human impacts. A dynamic geologic history spanning 2.8 to 3.4 billion years resulted in the development of a polymetamorphic shield formed during multiple orogenies, the most recent of which involved large-scale uplift and intrusion. These major events provided ground preparation for terrain development as follows: (1) creation of rocks of variable compositions, textures, and hardness; (2) zones of hydrothermal alteration in granite plutons proximal to contact metamorphic effects; and (3) rock mass discontinuities that provided avenues for differential weathering and erosion. Finally, changes in base level during Pleistocene glaciation resulted in appreciable changes in the amounts of hydraulic energy available for downcutting and erosion along stream courses. Groundwater levels fluctuated as a function of changing base level, controlling the depth of penetration and volume of meteoric waters, which acted as a major weathering agent in the metamorphic and granitic terrain.

Metamorphic rock mass. Most of the metamorphic rock mass exposed in this area is moderately to slightly weathered. Completely weathered and highly weathered rocks occur only in fault and shear zones. The hard metamorphic rock mass outside of these zones is resistant to weathering relative to the softer granite and tends to form rugged hill masses. The hard calc-silicate metasediments of the Sadang-u Series, for example, form the ridges, peaks, and slopes of Kyeungsan (Fig. 4). Differential erosion of slightly weathered calc-silicate gneiss and more highly weathered biotite schist is reflected in narrow, elongate, sharp-

TABLE 1. PETROGRAPHIC ANALYSES OF FRESH GRANITE FROM KUMHWA AND TUNNEL 2

Modal Composition (est. %)	Kumhwa 36A	Kumhwa 36B	Kumhwa SL-7A	Kumhwa SL-7B	Kumhwa SL-7C	Kumhwa SL-7D	Tunnel 2 75 m
Quartz	10	10	20	25	35	20	30
K-feldspar (microcline)	55	25	40	10	5	10	30
Plagioclase	25	50	20	25	45	60	30
Biotite	5	10	15	35	15	10	5
Muscovite							5
Accessories							
Magnetite	5	5	4	4	Tr		
Ilmenite	2					Tr	
Pyrite					Tr	Tr	
Apatite			1	1	Tr	Tr	Tr
Zircon			Tr	Tr			
Texture	Coarse	Very coarse	Coarse	Coarse	Coarse	Coarse	Medium
Alteration	Limonite after magnetite	Limonite after magnetite		Saussurite after plagioclase			
Classification	Quartz-biotite monzonite	Granite-quartz monzonite	Quartz-biotite monzonite	Granite	Granodiorite-tonalite	Granodiorite-tonalite	Granite

Note: The term "granite" is used herein in its broadest generic sense, i.e., a generally medium to coarse grained plutonic igneous rock in the compositional range granite–diorite. Tr—traces.

crested ridges that connect the hill masses. Regional jointing and the intersection of major joint sets with foliation planes, coupled with diminished joint spacing due to shearing along foliation planes in the more schistose lithologies, commonly control steep, narrow draws that are oriented transverse to major ridgelines. Where these discontinuities intersect the major crests, they form saddles separating higher strength, relatively unweathered lithologies. This results in a hummocky terrain often seen on major ridge line spurs.

Granite rock mass. The granites have relatively homogeneous composition, and are generally deeply weathered. The terrain produced by these rocks is most often subdued, gentle, and rolling in sharp contrast to the steep and broken hills and ridges underlain by metamorphic rocks (Fig 5). There is one important exception to this generalization in the Kumhwa area: Osongsan. Situated approximately 7.5 km north of Kumhwa, Osongsan is a dominant rugged rock mass mapped by NPRK geologists as Daebo granite. This peak has a summit elevation of 1062 m, almost twice that of any hill mass in the Iron Triangle (Fig. 6). The reason for the anomalous topographic expression of Osongsan is not clear. Its situation in the Democratic People's Republic of Korea (DPRK) proximal to the Demilitarized Zone (DMZ) makes it unlikely that detailed investigation of its lithology and erosional expression has been conducted. However, this granite hill mass is bounded on its southwest and northwest flanks by faulting, and the northeast and southeast margins are in direct intrusive contact with Sadang-u calc-silicates. It is possible that Osongsan is part of the large down-dropped block shown in Figure 3. The main mass of this block is not crossed by the faults that produced extensive shearing and mylonitization of surrounding granite. Also, the occurrence of hydrothermal mineral deposits (fluorite) on the southern intrusive margin raises the possibility that silicification of portions of the granite strengthened its resistance to weathering.

ROCK MASS PROPERTIES AND STRUCTURE

Murphy (1985) and Bieniawski (1989) describe rock mass properties considered important from the standpoint of surface and underground construction projects, rock mass stability, foundation and support requirements, and groundwater characterization. The most important of these properties are rock type and strength, structural discontinuity (foliation, jointing, faults, veins, and dikes), condition of discontinuity, weathering, and groundwater condition. Condition of discontinuity refers to the width of discontinuity aperture separations and their fillings (if any). Water movement in the rock mass indicated by stained, damp, wet, dripping, or flowing discontinuities is recorded as groundwater condition. The geotechnical descriptors used herein are those recommended by Murphy (1985), unless otherwise noted.

We lack laboratory strength tests of the rocks in this area. Intact rock strength was estimated in the field using the Rock Hardness Classification scheme of the Core Logging Committee, South African Section (in Murphy, 1985). Seismic refraction surveys in the Kumhwa granite terrain produced in situ compressional wave velocities of weathered and sub-weathered rocks. The wave velocities are an indirect measurement of in situ rock strength.

The concept(s) of Rock Mass Rating (RMR) is fully developed by Bieniawski (1989). RMR combines the above properties to develop quantitative estimates of in situ rock mass quality. Rock Quality Designation (RQD), the percentage of intact core longer than 10 cm in length in a given core-drilling run, can be correlated to rock quality (Deere and Deere, 1989). RQD was compiled by the author from lithologic logs of cores recovered in calc-silicate schist and gneiss on the southern flank of Kyeungsan by the U.S. Army Corps of Engineers Far East District. Because this core had been removed from the drilling site, the logged data represent minimum RQD values given that some breakage is inevitable in transport.

Figure 4. Resistant calc-silicates form the steep ridges of Kyeungsan (view to east).

Sangwon system metasediments

Intact strength. The metasedimentary rock mass of the Sangwon system and, in particular, the facies described herein as the Sadang-u Series, exhibits a considerable range of intact strengths depending on the specific rock type. Overall the rock mass exhibits intact strengths in the range soft to very hard (3–200 Mpa). Rocks described in the field as quartz-epidote-actinolite-magnetite skarn are hard and very hard rock in fresh surface exposures such as those produced in road cuts excavated by blasting. These rocks are thick-bedded and massive; intact compressive strength is estimated to range from 25 to 200 Mpa. Magnetic calc-silicate schist and gneiss, spotted magnetite-garnet schist, and biotite schist are moderately and slightly weathered in the surface environment and exhibit intact strengths in the medium-hard to very-hard range. These rocks exhibit pronounced strength anisotropy due to well-developed metamorphic foliation and thinly spaced, often-contorted planes, which divide the rock along relict bedding planes. As indicated by coring on the southern flank of Kyeungsan, below depths of 27 m the rock mass probably exhibits hard and very hard compressive strength in the plane perpendicular to metamorphic foliation. These rocks (particularly biotite schist) have less strength and are prone to splitting in the foliation plane.

Quartzite and meta-arenite are hard rock masses with compressive strengths above 25 Mpa. Amphibolite is soft to medium hard in surface exposures with estimated compressive strengths in the range 3 to 25 Mpa.

Structural discontinuities. Structural discontinuities in the Sadang-u Series metasediments include planes of metamorphic foliation, joints, faults, and veins that serve to divide the rock mass into blocks, slabs, and small (cm scale) rock fragments. These metasediments have a remarkably uniform and predictable foliation. Foliation dictates to a large degree the size of blocks produced by weathering, mass wasting, pick and shovel excavation, ripping, and blasting. The foliation "thickness" is a product of original bedding. The hard skarn and calc-silicate shist and gneiss are usually thick (60–120 cm) and very thick bedded (> 120 cm). Block sizes range up to 1 m in diameter. Biotite schist and amphibolite are generally thin and very thin bedded, 5–60 cm and 1–5 cm, respectively. These rocks tend to produce blocks less than 10 cm in diameter.

Foliation trend in the rock mass underlying Kyeungsan is approximately northeast-southwest with moderate (30–50°) dips to the northwest (Fig. 4). This trend is distorted only in tectonic and/or igneous contact zones. Aperture separations are generally very tight and tight, 0.1–0.5 mm, usually rough, stained, and dry, along foliation planes in the skarn and calc-silicate gneiss. However, where these planes are dilated by foliation-plane shear, aperture separation increases to moderately open and open, 0.5–10 mm. In the latter situation, fillings of clay, soils, and finely divided rock fragments are often washed out. Apertures dilated by foliation plane shear or the effects of unloading and weathering are most common in biotite schist where separation is commonly open, 0.5–2.5 mm, slightly rough, and filled with a fine, sandy gouge made of crushed rock fragments, inactive clays, chlorite, or graphite.

Jointing in the Sadang-u Series reflects well-established regional stress patterns including the Korean (north-northwest–south-southeast), Sinian (northeast-southwest), and Yodong (Liaotung) (east-west) directional trends (Fig. 7). Most joint sets are moderately and steeply dipping. Joint spacing is close, 5–30 cm, in and around faults and sheared joints, but is most often moderately close to wide, 0.5–2.5 m, away from these disruptive features. Joint apertures are tight to open, 0.1–10 mm, in most outcrops studied. However, very tight apertures are not uncommon and probably increase in frequency with depth. Apertures are generally rough but are occasionally smooth with

Figure 5. Gently sloping hills and valleys form the granitic terrane to the west of Kyeungsan from which this photo was taken. Faulting and intrusive contact between granite and calc-silicate schist control the valley. Kumhwa occupied part of the area on the left-hand side of the photo. The cleared fence line on the right-hand side is the southern margin of the DMZ.

Figure 6. Osongsan, on the left background, towers above the Triangle Hill complex shown in the right center of the photo. This was the scene faced by troops of the 3rd Battalion (31st Regiment, U.S. 7th Division) as they commenced their attack on the Triangle Hill complex on 14 October 1952.

chlorite-coated slickensides in zones of shearing and faulting. Joint fillings, often partially washed out in the near-surface environment, include soils, moss, crushed rock fragments in a sandy gouge, chlorite, and other inactive clays.

The metasediments host quartz, quartz-epidote, and quartz-epidote-magnetite veins, particularly near intrusive contacts. Clots of manganese are not uncommon in these veins. Veining is particularly common along dilated foliation planes. "Pinch and swell" veins are commonly pod- or lens-shaped with dimensions that range up to 3 m (length) × 2 m (width) × 1 m (thickness). The foliation planes probably dilated during differential displacements along the major regional faults that bound Kyeungsan to the east and west. Sigmoidal open-space vein fillings were precipitated during these events. The mineral paragenesis of the veins indicates that at least some of these displacements occurred during the waning stages of thermal metamorphism associated with emplacement of the Mesozoic granite. Some veins mapped in the

immediate vicinity of the DMZ follow or fill fault planes. These veins commonly are surrounded by low shear strength phyllonite comprised of low friction metamorphic minerals such as chlorite and graphite, other inactive clays, macerated rock fragments often healed by quartz veinlets, and spidery networks of quartz-chlorite-sulfide veinlets.

The Kumhwa area was intensively prospected for mineral deposit, (talc, magnetite, fluorite, fluorite-lead) during the era of Japanese occupation (Fig. 3). Sporadic mineralization occurs in the calc-silicate metamorphic aureole along the contact between granite and the Sadang-u Series. During fierce fighting that raged in the southeastern Iron Triangle in the fall of 1952, Chinese Communist Forces (CCF) used abandoned prospect shafts and tunnels on the southern flanks of Osongsan for both concealment and staging.

Most discontinuities examined in the exposed section on the flanks of Kyeungsan are dry to damp during the spring and early summer. All are stained. Fillings are occasionally washed out or partially so. Following the classification suggested by the International Society for Rock Mechanics (in Murphy, 1985), groundwater seepage rating is estimated at III–V (stained, damp, occasional seepage) and is somewhat dependent on seasonal precipitation cycle. Groundwater condition probably changes during and immediately after the monsoon rains that saturate the region during the summer and during times of rapid snow melt in the late winter and early spring. Zones of relatively high permeability (where some wet and occasionally dripping conditions were encountered) occur in some exposed fault zones or along sheared and dilated foliation planes. These probably diminish with depth except in the major steep, well-developed fault systems that disrupt the metasedimentary sequence.

Rock Quality Designation (RQD) and Rock Mass Rating (RMR). The compiled RQD values for two cores (DDH1 and DDH2) drilled on the southern flank of Kyeungsan are shown in Figure 8. These holes were drilled vertically through calc-silicate schist and gneiss and biotite schist. The foliation dips moderately to the northwest at approximately 40° at this location. The holes were drilled approximately 20 m apart, nearly parallel to foliation strike. The "box-and-whisker" plots in Figure 8 show overall RQD. Median RQDs are 56% and 66% for DDH1 and DDH2, respectively, corresponding to "fair" rock quality. Below depths of 25–30 m, the rock mass generally exhibits fair to excellent quality. Exceptions occur in a relatively wide shear zone intersected by both cores at 45–52 m. The rock mass quality is less predictable at shallow depths. Colluvium and moderately weathered rock cover the slope to depths of 10 m in DDH1 and 15 m in DDH2. The difference in rock quality between the two holes in the interval 10–30 m is due to a change of lithology and differences in thermal metamorphic effects. Highly fractured, slightly weathered biotite schist in DDH1 gives way to biotite gneiss, very fine-grained calc-silicate rock, and interbedded biotite schist in DDH2.

The metasedimentary calc-silicate rocks that underlie Kyeungsan have overall RMR of "good" and "very good" below depths of 10 to 15 m. This rock mass requires blasting in excavations below 10 m in covered ground. Outcropping rock mass requires excavation by drill and blast methods. The combined data indicate that small diameter tunnels (2–3 m) and underground facilities of small dimension can be built in this rock mass with a minimum of support requirements except where major faults are crossed. This estimation is in agreement with the empirical record of mining and the extensive use of underground space by NKPA and CFF forces in this area during the Korean War.

Granite

Intact strength. The diverse composition of the granite is shown in Table 1. This rock mass is deeply weathered. Saprolite accumulations tens of meters thick (or greater) are common in the major fault zones that occupy the eastern Chorwon Valley. Generally, well-developed grus and sandy soil are developed over much of the area underlain by granite. Notable exceptions occur where military and civil construction have stripped or scraped the surface. These soils, easily ripped and excavated, provide the material for hundreds of thousands of sandbags used to fortify the DMZ.

Seismic refraction surveys provide evidence of the average depth of weathering on gently sloping granite terrain in the eastern Chorwon Valley. The refraction surveys show that the average thickness of weathered rock mass is on the order of 17 to 20 m in the Kumhwa area (Fig. 9). Most of the hill slopes accessible for testing in the Kumhwa area are missing 1–3 m of completely weathered and highly weathered saprolite commonly found in areas less impacted by human activity. Total weathered thickness was probably on the order of 23 m in this area prior to the extensive deforestation during Japanese occupation and the extensive environmental impacts of the Korean War and its aftermath. Results of the surveys suggest that, as in other granitic terrain in Korea, a layered weathered granite model is generally appropriate. Average seismic velocities and thickness are 0.7 km/s and 6 m, respectively, for the uppermost layer. This material corresponds to highly weathered and moderately weathered granite. An intermediate zone ranges in velocity from 1.3–1.8 km/s depending on position on the slope and is about 11–14 m thick. This zone appears to represent mostly moderately weathered material. A high-speed layer with velocities in the 2.9–4.3 km/s range underlies the intermediate zone and appears to represent slightly weathered and fresh granite. The zone between saturated and unsaturated rock corresponds to a substantial change in seismic velocity in these weathered granites. The position of the water table, low under the ridge crests and high in the valley, corresponds to a concomitant shift in layer velocities, from 2.9 km/s to 1.8 km/s, respectively (Fig. 9). There is some suggestion in the data that the water table position corresponds (roughly) to a shift in weathering grade in the granite, from slightly weathered and fresh at water tables under the ridgelines to moderately weathered where water tables are situated under the toe of slopes or under adjacent stream valleys.

In terms of the total thickness of weathered granite, the Kumhwa seismic surveys produced similar results to those obtained at other sites in the ROK (e.g., Lee, S.G., 1987). In most cases, the shift in weathering from highly and moderately weathered to fresh and slightly weathered granite is abrupt rather than transitional. Not unexpectedly, the thickness of the weathered zone diminishes toward valley floors. These changes probably relate, respectively, to net groundwater fluctuation and change in valley profiles due to erosion during lowstands of Pleistocene sea level.

The seismic velocity data indicate that below the effects of weathering, the granite is a hard and very hard rock with outstanding foundation and stability engineering properties. The layer immediately above this zone, however, is diverse, alternating between moderately hard ground and soft material. The uppermost layer is very soft and will not support significant loads (concrete block structures of one or two stories) on steep (greater than 20–25°) slopes when saturated.

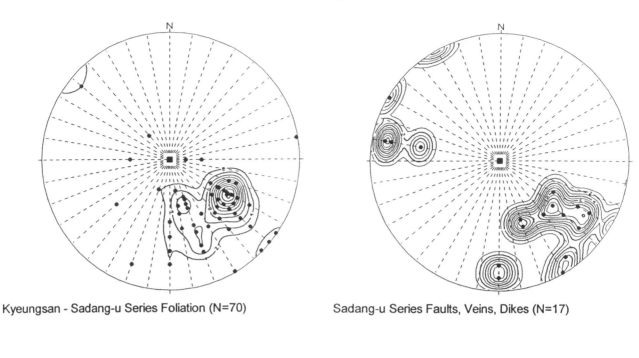

Kyeungsan - Sadang-u Series Foliation (N=70)

Sadang-u Series Faults, Veins, Dikes (N=17)

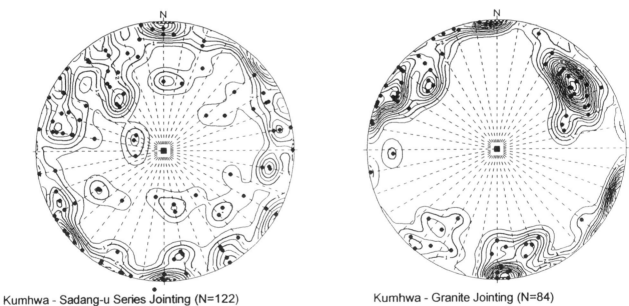

Kumhwa - Sadang-u Series Jointing (N=122)

Kumhwa - Granite Jointing (N=84)

Figure 7. Equal area (Schmidt) stereonet plot of rock mass discontinuities in metasediments and granite near Kumhwa. Contours (in percent of total points) on the stereonet depict lines of equal point density generated by Gaussian density gridding with a search value of 5%. Abbreviation: N - sample population.

Structural discontinuities. Joint orientation measurements made where the granite is exposed along road cuts and in shallow underground fortifications generally mirror the directional and dip patterns displayed by jointing in the Sadang-u Series described previously. Joint spacing in the granite is highly variable. Most of the granite in the vicinity of Kumhwa has been disrupted by tectonism along various splays of the Wonson-Seoul fault zone. At many sites spacing is close, 5–30 cm, and mean spacing is reported to be 18 cm (personal commun., J. Ehlen, 1999). How-

ever, where the granite is not proximal to faults and shear zones, or where deformation within fault blocks is minimal, joint spacing commonly ranges up to 2.5 m (wide).

Even where the major joint sets are widely spaced the granite is often deeply weathered. Weathering in the granite rock mass is controlled not only by the major joint sets but also by extensive networks of microfractures, hydrothermal alteration that predisposed portions of the rock mass to accelerated chemical weathering, and groundwater level fluctuations during Pleistocene base level changes. In slightly weathered rock, iron staining along microfractures is indicative of slow infiltration of meteoric waters. Substantial portions of this rock mass exhibit evidence of both tectonism and hydrothermal alteration. Petrographic studies show that plagioclase is altered in some of the monzonitic and granodioritic rocks; the original feldspar is partially replaced by mosaics of epidote, clay, and calcite. Regional patterns of granite-associated gold mineralization suggest that hydrothermal alteration probably took place during late stage emplacement of the granite batholith under mesothermal conditions of temperature and pressure.

Joint apertures are tight (0.1–0.5 mm) and moderately open (0.5–2.5 mm), except where dilated by shear. Apertures are rough and stained, and are often filled with clay or sandy gouge. Near shear zones, slickensides are common on clay coats, indicating small displacement(s) along joint planes. Groundwater condition is generally damp along joints in fresh granite. The weathered rock mass is uniformly damp in most places.

In the Kumhwa area veining in the granite is comparatively uncommon except at very small (cm and mm) scales. Contact metamorphism of calcareous sediments favored vein formation in the Sadang-u Series rather than in the intruding granite.

MILITARY GEOLOGY

The key elements of military geology in the eastern Chorwon Valley are shown in Figure 10. These elements form essential requirements in warfare and military occupation of terrain. While these are certainly not unique to this region, it is somewhat uncommon to find them all of considerable import to military operations in one relatively small area. For the sake of simplicity, each element will be discussed individually. However, the six key areas are interrelated through integrated terrain analysis conducted on the basis of robust geologic data sets and, most important, correct geologic interpretation(s). These interpretations must be made against a background of significant terrain alterations during Japanese occupation, the Korean War, and post-war activities as described below.

Attack corridors

On the early morning of 25 June 1950, soldiers of the NKPA 2nd, 3rd, and 4th Infantry Divisions (ID), and the 105 Armored Brigade, left their lines of departure and hurtled south from staging areas in the Iron Triangle to start the Korean War (Fig. 11). The 3rd and 4th Divisions raced down the long open valleys that form the eastern and western margins of the Chorwon Valley to slam across the 38th parallel in a two-pronged attack on Uijongbu and Seoul. On their eastern flank the NKPA 2nd ID moved with equal determination down a similar corridor to strike at Ch'unchon. During the next year, campaigns involving rapid advances and retreats of giant armies would take place along these corridors. During the fall of 1951, however, the fluid mobility of these forces ground to a halt. Final large-scale maneuvers in central

Korea ended where they began, along the southern base of the Iron Triangle.

Cameron (1998a) compared lineations created by rock-mass discontinuities (faults, joints, metamorphic foliation) with trends of the road and rail network of eastern and central Korea, to demonstrate that only minor statistical differences exist between the data sets. Major access routes historically used to attack the major centers of commerce and engineering infrastructure in central Korea are controlled by rock-mass discontinuity. The Chorwon Valley was included in this study, which includes Landsat lineations and ground measurements from surface and underground rock exposures. Booth (1999) shows that the same results pertain for topographic lineations; the orientations of these natural linear features are controlled by rock mass discontinuities.

In the eastern Chorwon Valley, faulting and the occurrence of large masses of granite combine to produce a soft, generally low, terrain suitable for staging, mobilization, and attack along the branching corridors. In wet weather some of the soils in the Chorwon and Kumhwa areas may saturate and produce boggy conditions unsuitable for heavy transport. Part of this problem is related to the clay derived from volcanic ash interbedded with Quaternary basalt. Most of the corridors leading from these areas are composed of relatively hard ground, the lowstands of Pleistocene seas having provided hydraulic energy adequate for the removal of most alluvial sediments from the valley floors.

Defensive positions

Hills and mountains composed of metamorphic rock provide the best defensive positions along attack corridors, particularly when changes in geology result in mobility restrictions where valleys narrow to perilously confined space. The latter situation is a particularly good example of the fourth dimension control on terrain. Because a conventional attacking force is generally confined to the long valley complexes, defenders can position their fighting positions and artillery on high ground to saturate those zones where the terrain is constricted and lateral movement by the enemy is restricted. That this was unsuccessful during the defense of Uijongbu on 25–26 June 1950 is due to the fact that a high percentage of the ROK 7th Division had weekend passes (Appleman, 1961). Quite the opposite situation prevailed in the center at Ch'unchon during the same time period where well-prepared defenders of the ROK 6th Division successfully stopped the advance of the NK 2nd Division for three days using the defensive battlefield techniques described above (Cameron, 1998a).

Flanking large hills and ridgelines provide outstanding fire control capability to their occupants, enabling them to decimate large forces moving in the relatively narrow attack corridors of the eastern Chorwon Valley. In the Kumhwa area, good examples of such positions include Osongsan and Kyeungsan, as well as the Taebaeksan front to the south and east. These prominent features embody the old military adage, "You don't have to occupy some terrain in order to control it." During the historic battle for the Triangle Hill complex and Sniper Ridge in the fall of 1952,

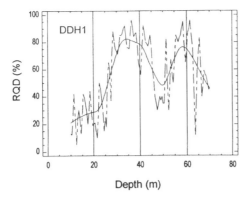

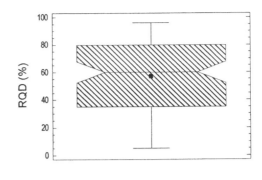

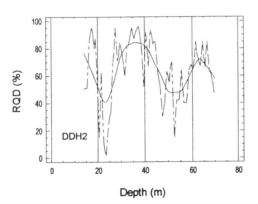

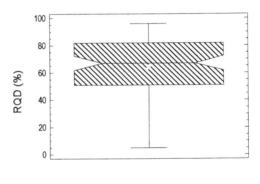

Figure 8. Variation in RQD values in core recovered on the southern flank of Kyeungsan. The solid lines on the left-hand graphs are locally weighted regression lines calculated with a 25% smoothing function. The box-and-whisker plots on the right show the median RQD values (box indents), the mean RQD value (solid black dot), and the first quartiles which contain 50% of the RQD values (vertical box limits).

the CCF held the vital strongpoint of Osongsan to the north of the contested ground. To the south, United Nations (UN) forces maintained equally important positions on Kyeungsan and within the mountain front. With little exception, this situation was repeated all along the Korean War front lines of 1952. With Communist and Allied forces occupying strategic mountaintops on either side of "no man's land," little wonder that the Korean War ended in a military stalemate.

The hummocky terrain forming Kyeungsan and the adjacent hills and ridges of Triangle Hill and Sniper Ridge deserves special mention here. The elevation difference between hummocks and adjacent lower ground often exceeds "military height" (this is the height of natural or engineered features behind which infantry can stand out of sight or direct line of fire from enemy positions), but is generally less than the resolution of the 20 m contours on topographic maps of the area. Thus, this terrain has the potential to conceal and protect infantry seeking to gain a summit position, and defenders must take special care to deny hummocky ground to an aggressor force. Allied planners in the campaign for the Triangle Hill and Sniper Ridge complex apparently underestimated this aspect of terrain.

Underground facilities

Cameron (1998a) describes the effective use of the underground for concealment and staging of men and materials by the CCF and the NKPA "Inmun Gun" in the T'aebaeksan during the Korean War. The more recent NKPA construction of deep tunnels as infiltration conveyances is discussed in the same volume (Cameron, 1998b). NKPA Clandestine Tunnel-2, discovered in 1975, amply demonstrates the suitability of the granite of the Chorwon Valley to host deep clandestine tunnels. In this context it is notable that the granite of the Kumhwa area does not differ substantially from that of the Tunnel-2 area. The threat of clandestine tunnel operations will remain as long as the southern boundary of the DMZ remains as a fixed and strongly fortified defensive line.

Construction of small underground fortifications in the weathered granite during the Korean War and its aftermath was not uncommon in the eastern Chorwon Valley. Used for protection and concealment, these underground spaces have remarkable stand-up time given the moderately and highly weathered nature of the rock. Built largely by pick and shovel excavation with

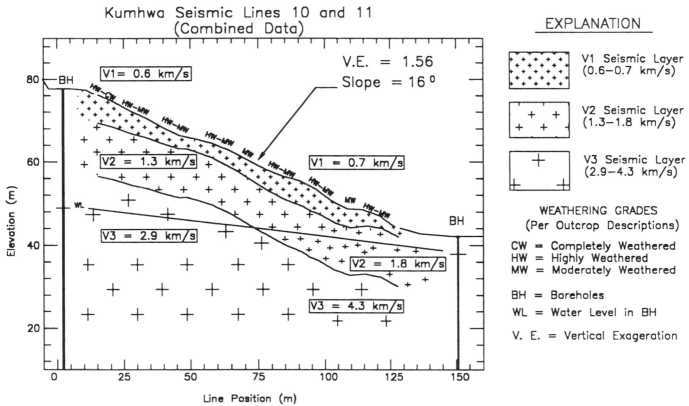

Figure 9. Compiled seismic refraction section from the Kumhwa area showing average velocity and thickness of weathered granite rock mass layers on hillsides.

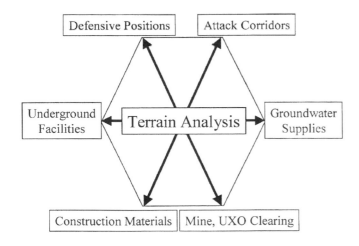

Figure 10. Key elements of military geology in the eastern Chorwon Valley of central Korea.

U-shaped configurations, these spaces commonly have two entrances with total longitudinal dimension in the 10–20 m range. Widths are generally in the 2 m range with (weapons) galleries opened to 6 m. Overhead height is in the range 1.5–3.0 m. The stand-up time is a function of slow movement of water in the weathered rock mass that increases surface tension between grains over time. Cohesion of the entire weathered rock mass is thereby increased. These spaces remain open for decades. The builders had a good sense of the potential utility of these easily built structures. At the very least they offer protection from the elements. They can be completely camouflaged with local materials and vegetation and sited in ambush positions. Although not sufficiently robust to withstand direct hits or near misses from large caliber artillery or bombs, particularly in the portal areas, these underground spaces offer protection from proximity-fused ordnance and from nearby mortar impacts. In this regard they are superior to trenches and foxholes.

Groundwater supplies

Surface water supplies in the broad valleys are dammed and provide adequate water supplies for resident military garrisons, nearby villages, and crop production. Drilling has established that the groundwater volume in the weathered granites underlying the low valley terrain is appreciable, especially in major fault zones. However, the high clay content of the saprolite inhibits flow and supplies are thus quite limited. Water stands as high as 1 m from the surface in some of these boreholes but they pump down quickly and refill slowly, over several hours. The groundwater situation in the calc-silicate schist and gneiss is similar to that in other metamorphic terrain in Korea. The military forces

C.P. Cameron

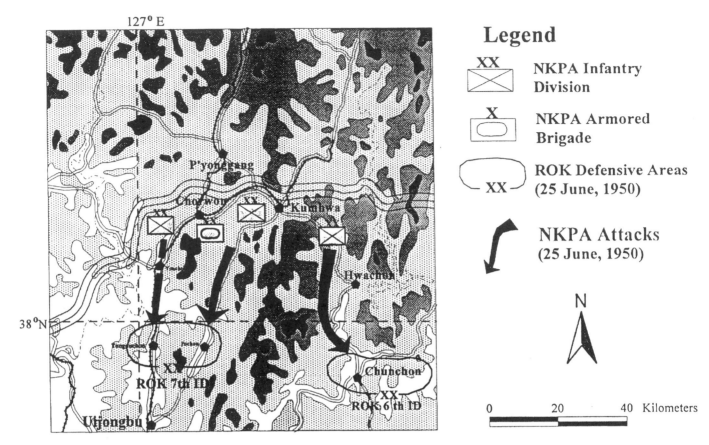

Figure 11. Lines of attack (arrows) used by NKPA forces to invade the Republic of South Korea on 25 June 1950.

manning high ground must rely on water pumped uphill from local catchments at lower elevations or on water tankers that laboriously climb steep, narrow, and precipitous roads to reach summits like Kyeungsan.

Construction materials

Part of the human impact on terrain described herein derives from the use of weathered granite "grus" as a major source of sand and gravel. Soldiers filling sandbags with grus is a very common sight along the DMZ sector; millions of these bags have been used as the basic material of military fortifications. Because most streams are small and largely devoid of accumulation of sand and finer sediment, the granites provide an acceptable source for sand and gravel for unpaved road construction and repair, and concrete and concrete block fabrication. Hard schist and gneiss are also locally quarried for road metal and used as building stone. Virtually all other construction materials, including cement (the ROK has few dry limestone deposits), have to be brought in from other areas, many imported from overseas.

Mines and unexploded ordnance (UXO)

Korea is a beautiful land but is also a crowded country. Scarce land now in the hands of soldiers will not sit vacant and

nonproductive once returned to the civilian sector. Some day, after reunification of Korea, a decision will be made to clear important sectors of the DMZ terrain of land mines and UXO. These areas will be valuable as commercial corridors, potential farmland, or tourist sites. This will be a huge and dangerous job. Terrain in and around the DMZ is heavily sown with mines laid over a period of fifty years. In addition, large amounts of UXO are buried in shallow soils and colluvium. Both mines and UXO mobilize easily and great care must be taken when bulldozing new roads or improving embankments; explosive munitions often roll or slide out of new road cuts.

Not all of the ordnance fell as bombs or artillery rounds. At the end of the war the troops that manned the ridge line bunkers and trench lines wanted to rotate out of those positions—and the faster the better! They were in no mood to lug crates of rifle and machine gun ammunition, "pineapple" grenades, anti-personnel and tank mines, and mortar and recoilless rifle rounds to the rear. So they left these implements of war in their fortifications. The ROK Army made use of some, and engineers covered the rest with shallow soil and rock, an impermanent solution at best.

The locations of many of the Korean War minefields are speculative and searching is required. Normally this is an uncomplicated operation. Mines of this vintage generally respond well to magnetic or electromagnetic methods of detection. Some of the terrain near Kumhwa, however, is not suitable for this geophysical

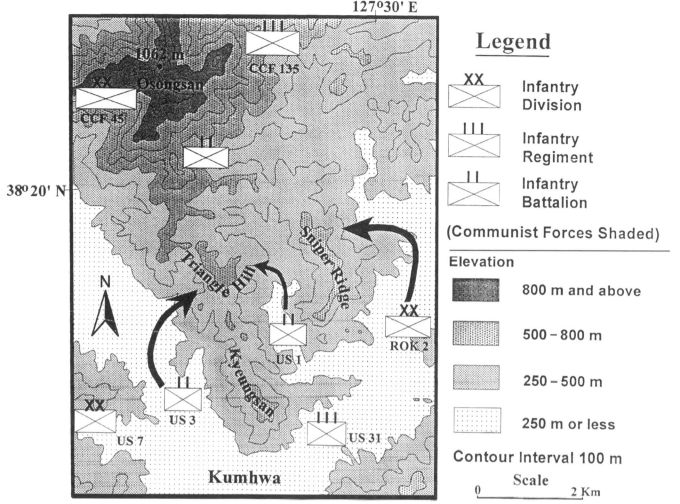

Figure 12. Lines of attack (arrows) used by U.S. and ROK Army infantry assaults on Triangle Hill and Sniper Ridge during Operation Showdown, October and November 1952

method. The Sadang-u calc-silicate schist and skarn are magnetic. Magnetite comprises 1–15% of the rock mass, a range that will produce variable magnetic effect. The outlook is for magnetic and electromagnetic prospecting to yield an unacceptable level of false anomalies. The situation will require a lot of study; the first step is to map and investigate the extent and distribution of magnetic calc-silicates in the Sadang-u Series.

THE BATTLE

War in Korea is a critical exercise in the correct interpretation and use of terrain. The decisive campaigns fought in 1951 to gain control of advantageous terrain in the T'aebaeksanmaek, east of the Chorwon Valley, reflect the decisions of commanders, particularly Eighth Army Commander General James Van Fleet, who correctly assessed terrain conditions and initiated costly but successful operations. The victorious battles for commanding heights in the eastern sector won UN forces the defendable terrain that flanks major invasion corridors to the west (Cameron, 1998a).

A campaign conducted a year later in the eastern Chorwon Valley at Kumhwa demonstrated that terrain analysis and its application to military operations were not always well conceived, however. Poor interpretation and use of terrain on the part of U.S. Army military planners at the Corps level, combined with just the opposite on the part of the CCF, resulted in dire consequences for an operation named *Showdown*.

Stabilization of the front along lines that approximate the current position of the DMZ followed the campaign for advantageous terrain in the fall of 1951. By the summer of 1952, the war had developed into a high-attrition struggle waged from fixed positions along front lines that resembled the trench-line fortifications of World War I (Hastings, 1987). The enemy became increasingly aggressive, attempting to gain negotiating position and "face" at slow-moving truce talks at Panmunjon. During the early fall, UN positions manned by the ROK Army 9th Division northwest of Chorwon came under such intense enemy pressure that Van Fleet determined to initiate small offensive actions in order to relieve pressure on his left and to put the enemy on the defensive.

The UN Commander, General Mark Clark, was under strict orders not to initiate major new offensives. It had been decided that the war was to end at the negotiating table if at all possible (Fehrenbach, 1963). Eighth Army Commander Van Fleet had a definite ceiling to the scope of his offensive activities. Nevertheless, Clark approved *Operation Showdown*, an operation limited in scope and objectives planned by US IX Corps to improve defensive lines north of Kumhwa and relieve enemy pressure on the left flank in the western Chorwon Valley (Hermes, 1966).

The operation sought to push the enemy into a new defensive posture on Osongsan by driving him off the Triangle Hill and Sniper Ridge complex. The front in this area had closed to within a few hundred yards between US 7th ID positions on Kyeungsan and those of the enemy. Casualties were correspondingly high. The operation was planned as a joint U.S. and ROK Army mission. Two battalions, the 1st and the 3rd of the 31st Regiment (US 7th ID), were to take Triangle Hill. The ROK 2nd ID was to attack enemy positions on Sniper Ridge and occupy that terrain to secure the right flank of the 31st Regiment's battalions (Fig. 12). The operation was anticipated to take five days and incur an estimated 200 casualties. A planned five days of air strikes and artillery barrage were reduced to two because of demands arising from enemy pressure on IX Corps' left flank and ammunition shortages. After two days of artillery barrages and air strikes on the enemy positions, the joint attack commenced on 14 October 1952 (Hermes, 1966).

Six weeks later the US 7th Infantry Division had committed eight of its nine battalions in what had become a bloodbath that no one had foreseen. Its soldiers fought well and never quit, but in fighting over unfamiliar terrain, decimating casualties occurred on a daily basis. The ROK 2nd ID fought its way into history with its courageous fight for Sniper Ridge. Here they engaged in a colossal battle in which portions of the ridge were won and lost daily for a month. The ROK 2nd ID, while still engaged on Sniper Ridge, actually took over the 7th ID positions on Triangle Hill at the end of October. All of the CCF's 45th Division of the elite CCF 15th Army (encamped on the north side of Osongsan) had engaged and was liberally reinforced by replacements from other units. United States and ROK forces suffered 9000 casualties, the CCF an estimated 19 000. Terrain gained by the US 7th and ROK 2nd IDs after six weeks of bitter struggle was insignificant and the operation was finally halted. Flawed terrain analysis in this region, a lack of appreciation of the underground workings in enemy hands, and underestimation of the enemy's determination to yield no further led to disaster.

The enemy's use of terrain was excellent in this sector. Well dug in, with a good supply situation, they appear to have been very well led. Osongsan is barely mentioned in the U.S. Army's five-volume history of the Korean War. This is a strange omission. The ROK Army has full appreciation of the critical role played by this imposing terrain, of the defiladed reinforcement routes down parts of its southern flank and of the old mines and prospect adits that served as concealment and protection for the enemy. The enemy mounted attacks from the underground at night. His good appreciation of "military height" allowed him to use the hummocky terrain of sloping ridge line spurs to mount the counterattacks that won back terrain gained by Allied forces at high cost during the day. What was eminently clear early on in this struggle was that small forces could not take the terrain piecemeal. The question that we are left with to this day is why this costly sacrifice was allowed to proceed for as long as it did.

Know yourself, know the enemy; and the victory will not be at risk. Know the terrain, the natural conditions; and the victory will be total.

—Sun Tzu, *The Art of War*, circa 300 B.C.

THE LEGACY OF WAR

Environmental impacts

If geology is the fourth dimension of terrain then, surely, vegetation is the fifth. In the general case, and particularly on a peninsula located at middle latitudes, vegetation provides a protective terrain cover. Most often this cover is pervasive on hilly and mountainous terrain. In such situations the vegetation camouflages the rock mass, to the despair of geologists and remote sensing terrain analysts. The geographic position of Korea results in a particularly diverse floral region. Some 4500 kinds of vascular plants were growing in the country in 1946, more than twice as many as in England at roughly the same latitudinal position (Korean Overseas Information Service, 1979). As diversified as this flora is, it has suffered greatly during periods of accelerated human impacts on the land, particularly during the past century. Prior to the late ninetinth century, impacts on the land were related to the pervasive construction of rice paddies in low-lying areas along stream valleys and on terraced slopes, particularly on those of gently rolling granite terrain. Small hydraulic structures and roads were part of the overall agricultural scheme.

Partial domination by Japan, aided by Western powers, commenced in 1885. Timber exploitation, expanded farming, mining exploration, and mineral exploitation were key aspects of Japanese colonial policy. By 1911, Japanese domination was total; vast tracts of land were expropriated and given to Japanese farmers who pushed agricultural production to record yields. In the same year Japanese lumber companies were given permission to fell trees. Timber was needed for the huge gold mines in the northern portion of the peninsula, for the construction of a railroad network, and for export to Japan to support its continued industrial expansion. Vast tracts of forests, previously preserved for generations, were expropriated and clear-cutting of forested land followed.

The extensive erosion of mountainous and hilly terrain that resulted from land overuse and deforestation can scarcely be exaggerated and the effects are with us still today. Vegetation recovery was barely underway in the early years following World War II when an equally devastating environmental disaster impacted the land, the Korean War. Most of the vegetation that survived the ravages of the Japanese empire and any new growth were destroyed right down to the roots during the battles that raged along the ridges, mountain and hill tops, and along the stream valleys. Huge artillery and mortar barrages raked the hills and striped them clean. Allied air power dropped tens of thousands of tons of bombs, rockets, and napalm on the terrain. During the frigid Korean winters both the soldiers of giant armies and large numbers of civilian refugees scavenged the land for firewood. Tales are told of a civilian populace at such risk that roots of felled trees were excavated from the soils and rocks to be used for both warmth and sustenance. This activity alone insured the reinitiation of severe erosion and gullying, but still other impacts exacerbated a dismal situation.

The Korean War in its last two years underwent a change from a war of movement to one of static fortification and siege. Soldiers dug into the terrain of the central Korean Peninsula and moved uncounted millions of tons of soil, saprolite, and rocks, as they continued to fight, blast the hills with artillery and bombs, plant minefields, bury their dead, and construct line after line of trenches, bunkers, dugouts, tunnels, magazines, artillery pads, fighting positions of all sorts, field hospitals, and airfields. What could not be moved with a shovel was blasted or, in the case of the UN forces, ripped and plowed with bulldozers.

The recovery of the Korean countryside since the Korean War has been remarkable. However, in central Korea the logistics and training requirements of large military forces continue to impact the land. Building access routes to the hilltops and military infrastructure along ridgeline roads produced unstable talus slopes in many instances. An armistice halted the Korean War, but did not end it. Military commanders along the DMZ are often forced to cut down saplings and young trees to provide fields of fire and to inhibit infiltration through the DMZ.

The impacts cited above combined with two millennia of organized farming have significantly modified the natural state of the terrain. This is an important factor with respect to analog studies that seek to compare, for example, terrain aspects and rock mass physical properties of weathered granite in a relatively pristine setting with that of a central Korean granite hill mass. Unless the human impact(s) can be adequately assessed and quantified, such analog modeling is inherently flawed.

Geologic mapping

The regional geologic map shown in Figure 2 was synthesized in part from 1:1 000 000 scale maps produced by the KIER (Hyun et al., 1981), and the DPRK Geological Research Institute (GRI) (Paek et al., 1993b). There are several important discrepancies between the KIER and GRI maps, particularly in the DMZ sector and immediately adjacent military zones to the north and south. Most inconsistencies in this regard are the result of the fifty-year division of Korea by politics and war; detailed modern geologic mapping and sampling are generally lacking in this part of Korea. The area is relatively uninvestigated since the mapping that accompanied mineral resource exploration and exploitation by the Japanese during the 1920s and 1930s, and even modern regional

compilations appear to be based on the early Japanese mapping and by extrapolations from areas outside the military zones.

The differences in regional interpretation expressed in the mapping appear to be greatest in the areas proximal to the DMZ. The access problem has improved significantly in the past few years in the ROK, but many areas important to geologists are still inaccessible in and along the DMZ. Further complicating access and scientific investigation are minefields and unexploded ordnance in the shallow soils of hill slopes, fields, and valleys. Off-road movement in the hills in and around the DMZ and adjacent military areas is invariably restricted to narrow patrol trails and pathways. The author's detailed field mapping at Kumhwa, on Kyeungsan, and in adjacent areas to the east and west was used to partially resolve these discrepancies.

The bedrock terrain to the east and south of Kumhwa consists of metasedimentary schist and gneiss assigned to the Paleoproterozoic Mach'ollyong (Macheonryeong) Supergroup on the regional geologic map published by the KIER (Hyun et al., 1981). Rocks of this succession typically yield metamorphic radiometric age dates in the range 1400–2000 Ma and are inferred to unconformably overlie the basement gneiss, schist, and migmatite of the Archean Kyônggi Gneiss Complex (Kim, 1970, 1973; Sang and Hee, 1984; Kim and Na, 1987). The Mach'ollyong Supergroup was originally described in the Kwanmobung Massif of the northernmost DPRK. Parts of the succession in the Kwanmobung region (e.g., Puktaech'on Group) contain significantly more carbonate than stratigraphic equivalents that overlie portions of the Kyônggi Massif in central Korea. Combining this information with petrography and metamorphic facies studies, the metasedimentary rocks unconformably overlying the Kyônggi Complex are assigned to the Ch'unchon Supergroup (Paleoproterozoic) or to the Yonch'on (Meso- and Neoproterozoic) by Na (1978) and Na et al. (1982).

On the other hand, the GRI assigns all of the early Precambrian schist and gneiss in the areas immediately south and east of Kumhwa to the Kyônggi Gneiss Complex (Paek et al., 1993b). Facies of the Ch'unchon Supergroup are present only in the area proximal to the city for which the unit is named on the GRI regional map. The northern extent of the Ch'unchon metamorphic rocks is very difficult (if not impossible) to establish in the field in the areas south of the DMZ in central Korea. Adequate geochronology to assist regional mapping is still lacking in this regard. For this reason, and because the rock mass physical properties of the schist and gneiss of the region are similar, all of the older (basement) metamorphic rocks are included as part of the Kyônggi Gneiss Complex in this chapter.

The most notable mapping discrepancy in the Kumhwa area involves the distribution of the Late Proterozoic Sangwon system metasediments comprised of the Chik'yon, Sadang-u, and Kuh'yon Series. Whereas the GRI mapping assigns a large area to the north and northeast of Kumhwa to these units, the KIER map shows portions of the same area to be underlain by the Great Limestone of Ordovician age. The author's mapping supports the overall interpretation of the GRI geologists in this area. However, on the basis of descriptions in Lee, D.-S. (1987) and Paek et al.

(1993a), it is mainly facies ascribed to the Sadang-u Series that crop out on the southern flanks of Kyeungsan and in immediately adjacent terrain to the south-southeast. The underlying Chik'yon Series, if present at all, is very thin and masked by colluvium on the lowermost portions of the ridge slopes.

All of the granite plutons in the eastern Chorwon region are assigned to the Jurassic Daebo event by the GRI. On the other hand, the KIER map assigns a large area of granite north of the DMZ at Kumhwa to the Cretaceous Bulguksa event, including the large hill mass of Osongsan situated 7.5 km north of Kumhwa. This assignment is suspicious as it is apparently based on the pronounced topographic expression of Osongsan. It seems prudent to regard all the Mesozoic granite in the eastern Chorwon as part of the Daebo orogeny pending further radiometric age dates. The use of topographic expression as a geochronological tool in central Korea is likely to prove misleading based on results to date (Cameron, 1998b).

CONCLUSIONS

Terrain of the eastern Chorwon is controlled by a complex interplay of petrology and structural geology that juxtaposes lithologies of variable rock mass properties to weathering and erosion. The regional unconformity between the Kyônggi Gneiss Basement Complex and younger calcareous sediments of the Sangwon System acted as a conduit for invading magmas, portions of a Daebo granite batholith. Heat from the magma was sufficient to thermally metamorphose the rocks of the Sadang-u Series, which was structurally uplifted and tilted, probably during the same episode. The area was tectonized by elements of the Wonson-Seoul fault system; disruption of the granite rock mass resulted in widespread mylonitization and brecciation within the fault zones. Normal fault displacement is responsible for the preservation of the Kyeungsan and Triangle Hill terrain in the Kumhwa area. Deep weathering controlled by Pleistocene sea-level fluctuation overprints the granite. Human impacts on terrain are also evident. The effects of accelerated erosion, the result of almost a century of deforestation followed by a war with a necessary emphasis on aerial and artillery bombardment, are visible on many hills and mountainsides. The evidence includes extensive talus fans and chaotic colluvial deposits that cover otherwise resistant and stable slopes. Military fortification and construction projects stripped the upper part of the granite weathering profile areas proximal to the DMZ. The absence of a normal soil profile is manifested in thin, sparse, and stunted vegetation growth.

Key elements of military geology in this region include terrain controls on staging areas, attack corridors, and defensive positions; suitability of terrain for underground construction; groundwater supplies and the availability of natural construction materials; and mine and UXO clearing. The latter will prove to be a particularly complicated problem in this sector of the Korean DMZ. The variable magnetite content of the calc-silicates in the lower Sadang-u Series will probably produce an unacceptable level of false magnetic and electromagnetic anomalies. Careful mapping and sampling of the distribution of magnetic calc-silicates, perhaps by high-resolution airborne magnetometry and/or electromagnetics, is a necessary prerequisite to mine detection and clearing in this area.

Given the dominating nature of Osongsan, *Operation Showdown* and the horrific loss of life during the battles for Triangle Hill and Sniper Ridge are difficult to understand. The lessons from the battlefields of the eastern Chorwon are clear and reinforce those learned on similar hills and twisted ridge lines along the front to both the east and west. Terrain controls attrition in battlefields like those of the Korean Peninsula. Difficult terrain must be interpreted accurately before the onset of a military operation so as to judge what can be achieved at reasonable cost. Only then can objectives be defined rationally and then these objectives must be pursued swiftly and decisively (Cameron, 1998a). Reversals must be anticipated and good contingency plans must include breaking off contact when attempting to fight uphill against the superior numbers of a well-prepared enemy holding distinctly advantageous ground. This should have been foremost in the minds of the *Operation Showdown* planners since they were unable, for political reasons, to deploy their forces at the Corps level necessary to achieve victory.

Any assault from Kumhwa without having as its major objective the capture of Osongsan was doomed. The history is clear that meeting such an objective would require a Corps level offensive that coordinated an attack northward from Kumhwa with similar assaults from Chorwon to spread enemy resistance across as wide a front as possible. This point of view was fully appreciated by the commanders but they were prohibited from such action by political considerations. Instead, they sought to achieve modest gains with small forces conducting siege and fortification warfare on the broken and bitter hills in front of Osongsan. Apart from good use by the CCF of defiladed reinforcement routes descending the southern slopes of Osongsan, it was apparent during the first few days of *Showdown* that this was no ordinary operation. The enemy demonstrated that he was well prepared to fight from the underground at night. The CCF made superb use of the terrain, particularly the hummocky approach spurs to Triangle Hill and Sniper Ridge, knowing full-well the implications of "military height" in rough country. The stubborn refusal of UN Command to adapt to the reality of an implacable foe well situated in a difficult mountain stronghold suggests a lack of appreciation for one of the fundamental precepts of warfare in difficult terrain. A War Department Observer, cited in Wilson (1946, p. 49), best stated this fundamental tenet over half a century ago:

The secrets to all battlefields are disclosed in advance by a careful study of the terrain.
—Anonymous U.S. War Department observer, circa 1945

ACKNOWLEDGMENTS

The data and concepts described herein are the result of field investigations funded by the US Army Belvoir Research,

Development, and Engineering Center and by the U.S. Defense Threat Reduction Agency (DTRA) through a series of Broad Agency Grant Contracts issued by U.S. Army Engineer Waterways Experiment Station. This work was performed for the U.S. Eighth Army (J-2) Tunnel Neutralization Team (EUSA-TNT) during the periods 1987–1993, and for the DTRA during 1995. Sincere appreciation is extended to the many individuals in these agencies, too numerous to mention here, who provided long-term support and encouragement during the course of this work. I am also very grateful to the officers and enlisted soldiers of EUSA-TNT (J-2), the ROK Army Tunnel Detection Section (ROKA-TDS-G2), and the ROKA soldiers who man the frontline divisions along a still dangerous frontier. Fieldwork in the DMZ sector would not have been possible without their enthusiastic support, help, and protection. I owe a special debt of gratitude to Lt. Col. Kuk Hwan Kim, 3rd ROKA Division, for providing me with a very special perspective of Triangle Hill and Sniper Ridge. This chapter benefited substantially from very helpful reviews and suggestions by Judy Ehlen, Russ Harmon, an anonymous reviewer, and Bill Leith.

REFERENCES CITED

Appleman, R.E., 1961, The United States Army in the Korean War, south to the Naktong, north to the Yalu (June–November, 1950): Washington, D.C., U.S. Government Printing Office, 813 p.

Bieniawski, Z.T., 1989, Engineering rock mass classifications: New York, John Wiley and Sons, 251 p.

Booth, G.A., 1999, Discontinuity analysis of the central Korean Peninsula [M.S. Thesis]: Hattiesburg, Mississippi, University of Southern Mississippi, 186 p.

Cameron, C.P., 1998a, Dearly bought ridges, steep access valleys, and staging grounds, *in* Underwood, J.R., Jr., and Guth, P.L., eds., Military geology of the eastern DMZ, central Korean Peninsula: Military geology in war and peace: Geological Society of America, Reviews in Engineering Geology, v. 13, p. 83–98.

Cameron, C.P., 1998b, Clandestine Tunnel 4, northern Punchbowl, Korean Demilitarized Zone, *in* Underwood, J.R., Jr., and Guth, P.L., eds., Military geology in war and peace: Geological Society of America, Reviews in Engineering Geology, v. 13, p. 99–110.

Cameron, C.P., Sundeen, D.A., and Booth, G.A., 1995, Intrusive style, thermal metamorphism, and regional structural geology, Kyeungsan (Kumhwa) area, Chorwon-Gun, (Kangwon-Do), Republic of Korea: Geological Society of America Abstracts with Programs, v. 27, n. 6, p. A317.

Deere, D.U., and Deere, D.W., 1989, Rock quality designation (RQD) after twenty years: Vicksburg, Mississippi, U.S. Army Corps of Engineer Waterways Experiment Station, Contract Report, GL-89-1, 67 p.

Hastings, M., 1987, The Korean War: New York, Simon and Schuster, 389 p.

Hermes, W.G., 1966, The United States Army in the Korean War, truce tent and fighting front: Washington, D.C., U.S. Government Printing Office, 571 p.

Hyun, B.K., Um, S.H., and Chun, H.Y., compilers, 1981, Geologic map of Korea: Korea Institute of Energy and Resources (KIER), scale 1:1 000 000, 1 sheet.

Kim, H.S., and Na, K.C., 1987, Chapter 4: Stratigraphy, *in* Lee, D.S., ed., The geology of Korea: Seoul, The Kyohak-Sa Publishing Company, p. 289–344.

Kim, O.K., 1970, Geology and tectonics of the mid-central region of South Korea: Journal of the Korean Institute of Mining Geology, v. 2, p. 73–90.

Kim, O.K., 1973, The stratigraphy and geologic structure of the metamorphic complex in the northwestern area of the Kyônggi massif: Journal of the Korean Institute of Mining Geology, v. 6, p. 201–218.

Korean Overseas Information Service, 1979, A handbook of Korea: Seoul, Samhwa Printing Company, 823 p.

Lee, D.-S., ed., 1987, The geology of Korea: Seoul, The Kyohak-Sa Publishing Company, 514 p.

Lee, S.G., 1987, Weathering and geotechnical characterization of Korean granites [Ph.D. thesis]: London, Imperial College of Science and Technology, University of London, 415 p.

Murphy, W.L., 1985, Geotechnical descriptions of rock and rock masses: Vicksburg, Mississippi, U.S. Army Engineer Waterways Experiment Station, Technical Report GL-85-3, 40 p.

Na, K.C., 1978, Regional metamorphism in the Kyônggi Massif with comparative studies between Yeoncheon and Okcheon metamorphic belts. 1.: Journal of the Geological Society of Korea, v. 15, p. 67–88 (E-K).

Na, K.C., Kim, H.S., and Lee, S.H., 1982, Stratigraphy and metamorphism of the Sosan Group: Journal of the Korean Institute of Mining, v. 15, p. 33–39 (K-E).

Paek, R.J., Kan, H.G., Jon, G.P., Kim, Y.M., and Kim, Y.H., eds., 1993a, The geology of Korea: Pyongyang, Korea, Foreign Languages Books Publishing House, 619 p.

Paek, R.J., Ri, S.R., Kim, S.J., and Im, M.G., eds., 1993b, Geological map of Korea: Pyongyang, Korea, DPRK Geological Research Institute (GRI), Foreign Languages Books Publishing House, scale 1:1 000 000, 1 sheet.

Sang, H.O., and Hee, Y.C., 1984, Geological evolution and tectonic classification of Korea: Seoul, Korean Institute of Energy and Resources Report 86-7, p. 35–90.

Tamaki, K., 1995, Opening tectonics of the Japan Sea, *in* Taylor, B., ed., Backarc basins, tectonics and magmatism: New York, Plenum Press, p. 407–420.

Wilson, J.E., 1946, The fourth dimension of terrain: Fort Leavenworth, Kansas, Command and General Staff College, Military Review, v. 6, p. 49–55.

MANUSCRIPT ACCEPTED BY THE SOCIETY OCTOBER 27, 2000

Geological Society of America
Reviews in Engineering Geology, Volume XIV
2001

Military engineering on the Rock of Gibraltar and its geoenvironmental legacy

Edward P.F. Rose

Department of Geology, Royal Holloway, University of London, Egham, Surrey TW20 0EX, UK

ABSTRACT

The 400-m-high Rock of Gibraltar is a partly overturned klippe of Early Jurassic dolomitic limestone, notched by raised shorelines and flanked by Quaternary scree breccias and windblown sands. It dominates a narrow 5-km-long peninsula jutting south from Spain at the western entrance to the Mediterranean Sea. Fortified from at least 1160 to World War II successively by the Moors, Spanish, and British, and subjected to 15 major sieges between 1309 and the Cold War of 1947 to 1989, Gibraltar is arguably one of the most densely fortified and fought over places in Europe. Stone walls, bastions, and numerous artillery positions built to enhance the natural defenses of the coastal cliffs now provide a tourist attraction, but constrain development of the modern city. Occasional rockfalls and the need for slope-safety measures are continuing concerns, especially in areas of scree breccia quarried to provide fill for the extension of a Royal Navy harbor between 1893 and 1905 and a Royal Air Force airfield largely between 1941 and 1943. Water supply has posed a problem throughout the history of the fortress, leading to innovative development of rainwater catchment areas on natural slopes, dual potable/sanitary water supplies, and projects to enhance these by cloud condensation or groundwater abstraction, before near total commitment to desalination from 1993. Tunnels and underground chambers are major features of the Rock. Mostly excavated in five phases between 1782 and 1968 to provide access, reservoirs, accommodation, or storage, they now total over 50 km in length, generally unlined. Tunnel integrity is dependent on excavation technique and bedrock characteristics.

From the early eighteenth century to recent years, much of the major construction work on Gibraltar was directed and often carried out by Royal Engineers. In 1994, disbandment of 1st (Fortress) Specialist Team RE brought over two centuries of British military engineering on the Rock to an end—and provided a legacy of works and land now largely inherited by civilian bodies responsible to the Gibraltar government.

INTRODUCTION

Gibraltar is a peninsula 5.1 km long, less than 1.6 km wide, and approximately 6 km² in natural land area, that juts south from Spain at the western entrance to the Mediterranean Sea (Figs. 1, 2, and 3). Joined to Spain by a sandy isthmus less than 3 m above present sea level, it is dominated by the Rock: a mass of Lower Jurassic dolomitic limestone whose north face rises precipitously to over 400 m above the isthmus (Fig. 4). The main ridge of the Rock extends southward from the north face for 2.5 km as a sharp, asymmetric crest with peaks more than 400 m high, before descending steeply to two successive southern plateaus. These slope south from 130 to 90 m and 40 to 30 m, respectively, above present sea level, and are fringed by steep cliffs to the sea.

The Rock has a longer record of human occupancy than the American continents. Neanderthals occupied some of its caves from at least 60 000 to about 30 000 years B.P. when they were succeeded by anatomically modern humans with a Late Paleolithic

Rose, E.P.F., 2001, Military engineering on the Rock of Gibraltar and its geoenvironmental legacy, *in* Ehlen, J., and Harmon, R.S., eds., The Environmental Legacy of Military Operations: Boulder, Colorado, Geological Society of America Reviews in Engineering Geology, v. XIV, p. 95–121.

Figure 1. Gibraltar is strategically positioned between the Mediterranean Sea to the east and the Atlantic Ocean to the west.

culture (Rose and Stringer, 1997). Indeed, Neanderthal Man might today be known as Gibraltar Man if the significance of a relatively well-preserved (but probably female) skull obtained from a quarry at the north face by Lieutenant E.H.R. Flint of the Royal Artillery in 1848 had been realized at that time. Its discovery pre-dated that of the type Neanderthal skeleton found in Germany by eight years.

The Rock and Gebel Musa in Morocco, its counterpart 24 km to the south across the Strait of Gibraltar, were known to the classical world of the Greeks and Romans as the twin Pillars of Hercules and for centuries marked the western boundary of Mediterranean civilization (Jackson, 1987). Seized from the Visigoths by an Islamic (Moorish) army under Tariq ibn Ziyad, which conquered southern Spain in A.D. 711, the Rock was named Gebel Tariq (mountain of Tariq) in his honor, a name later corrupted to the modern Gibraltar. The Moors developed a fortified city on its western slope from at least 1160, and later contested possession with the Christian Spaniards. Fall of Gibraltar to the Spanish in 1462 heralded the fall of Granada in 1492 and expulsion of the Moors from western Europe in the year that Columbus discovered America. To the Spanish, the fortress of Gibraltar guarding the narrow strait linking the Mediterranean Sea and its major ports with the Atlantic Ocean became the key to their American empire and its wealth, a view symbolized in the city's coat of arms assigned in 1502—a fortress linked to a key (Fig. 5). The importance of the maritime route via the Pillars of Hercules was soon symbolized on the coinage associated with American wealth: Spanish dollars were minted showing on one side the two pillars enwrapped by a ribbon scroll, a device later depicted in simple form as the more familiar symbol $.

Gibraltar was captured by an Anglo-Dutch force in 1704 during the War of Spanish Succession, and at the close of hostilities, ceded to Britain by the Treaty of Utrecht in 1713. It was developed as a naval base under British rule. By the end of the nineteenth century, the growing British Empire contained a quarter of the world's population. Since Britain was an island, control hinged upon global naval supremacy, and Gibraltar was deemed to be

one of the strategic keys with which the Royal Navy locked up the maritime world. It was the base from which General Dwight D. Eisenhower launched the Allied invasion of French North Africa during World War II, and from which elements of a British task force sailed in 1982 to recapture the Falkland Islands in the southern Atlantic. Besieged 15 times since 1309 and the Cold War of 1947–1989, it has been progressively fortified by the Moors, Spanish, and British until its strength has become legendary. Field Marshal Sir John Chapple considered it to be "probably the most fought over and most densely fortified place in Europe; and probably, therefore, in the world" (in Hughes and Migos, 1995, p. vii). For much of its history, it has been regarded as "the type and ideal of a stronghold" (Generals Lothian Nicholson and Goodenough, quoted by Hughes and Migos, 1995, p. 164).

The strength of the fortress is due to topographical features (influenced by their underlying geology) and their enhancement by military engineering. For over 200 years much of the construction work on the Rock was directed, and often actually carried out, by the Corps of Royal Engineers. It was on Gibraltar in 1772 that Engineer officers formed a company of Soldier Artificers as the first rank-and-file unit to work with the Corps, which until then consisted only of officers. In 1856 that unit was assimilated into the Corps itself, with other units of Sappers and Miners founded by that time. Its descendant unit, 1st (Fortress) Specialist Team Royal Engineers, was disbanded in 1994, effectively bringing military engineering on the Rock to a close. Large parts of the military estate have recently been decommissioned for civilian use (Rose and Hardman, 1994, 1996; Rose, 1998). It is thus timely to review the benefits and also the problems inherited with this legacy of major military engineering works, as new details of the geology of the Rock are also revealed.

GEOLOGICAL STUDIES BY MILITARY PERSONNEL

The Rock of Gibraltar has been subject to geological study for over 250 years (Rose and Rosenbaum, 1992; Rose, 2002). The earliest accounts were by officers stationed for some time as part of the garrison. Thomas James served on Gibraltar from 1749 to 1755 as a junior officer in the Royal Artillery. His massive *History of the Herculean Straits* (James, 1771) contains numerous minor geological observations, and some now very curious inferences. Ninian Imrie served as a captain with the First (or Royal) Regiment of Foot, the "Royal Scots", stationed on Gibraltar from 1784 to 1793, and published a "mineralogical" description of the Rock on his return to Edinburgh (Imrie, 1798). Other early studies were by a succession of authors with military rather than geological training, driven by academic curiosity rather than by practical application (Rose, 2000b). Moreover, it was a detailed military trigonometrical survey between 1861 and 1865 culminating in a 1:2500 scale topographic map by Charles Warren, then a lieutenant in the Royal Engineers, that provided the necessary basis for the first geological survey as such. Conducted by two senior officers of the Geological Survey of the United Kingdom to guide well drilling to enhance water supplies

Figure 2. Aerial view of Gibraltar from the southeast, showing the two southern plateaus in the foreground (Europa Flats at 30–40 m above sea level, Windmill Hill Flats at 90–130 m) with the main ridge behind, and part of the isthmus linking the peninsula to mainland Spain top right. Steep scarps along the eastern side of the main ridge contrast with a gentler dip slope westward to the city and harbor. From Rose and Rosenbaum (1990), courtesy of the Institution of Royal Engineers.

for the town and garrison, it generated the first geological map of the peninsula (Ramsay and Geikie, 1876), a report specifically on water supply (Ramsay, 1877), and a detailed account of Gibraltar geology (Ramsay and Geikie, 1878).

The Ramsay and Geikie map and account stood the test of time remarkably well until World War II, when major tunneling and quarrying works by British and Canadian military engineers proved them to be too simplistic. Consequently, a new geological survey was instituted to guide military tunneling works. As described by Rose and Rosenbaum (1990, 1992), the work was entrusted to A.L. Greig, an Oil Technology graduate of Imperial College (University of London) who had enlisted in the army following outbreak of war and by 1943 was serving with 180 Tunnelling Company Royal Engineers on Gibraltar—first as a driver, later as a draftsman, in the basic rank of sapper. Greig thus became the only noncommissioned geologist ever to be used as such by the British army. He returned to civilian life at the end of the war, but his unpublished report and 1:5280 scale map of the bedrock geology provided the basis for a later, published reinterpretation of the geology of Gibraltar (Bailey, 1952).

Tunneling through the Rock continued after the war, and Lieutenant (later Captain) G.B. Alexander of the Royal Engineers

was posted to the garrison from 1945 to 1948 as a geologist to support the tunneling operations (Rose and Rosenbaum, 1990, 1992; Rose and Cooper, 1997). A graduate of the University of Cambridge, Alexander thus became the only British army officer to be employed full time as a geologist in peacetime since the early nineteenth century. Royal Engineer officers had been tasked as full-time geologists in Ireland between 1826 and 1846 (Rose, 1996, 1999), but otherwise had served full time only in wartime (Rose and Hughes, 1993a; Rose and Rosenbaum, 1993a, 1993b, 1998), in peacetime only as part-time reservists (Rose and Hughes, 1993b, 1993c). Alexander's unusual appointment generated an unpublished 1:2500 scale geological map and a few geotechnical reports, but no published data.

During the Cold War, several reserve army geologists from the Royal Engineers paid brief visits to the Rock from 1967 onward to participate in geotechnical tasks—principally relating to groundwater development, road excavation, slope stability, movement of beach sand, and above all, tunnel stability. These generated the first detailed geological map to be published for Gibraltar (Rosenbaum and Rose, 1991a), by the Royal Engineers School of Military Survey, and stimulated additional university-based studies.

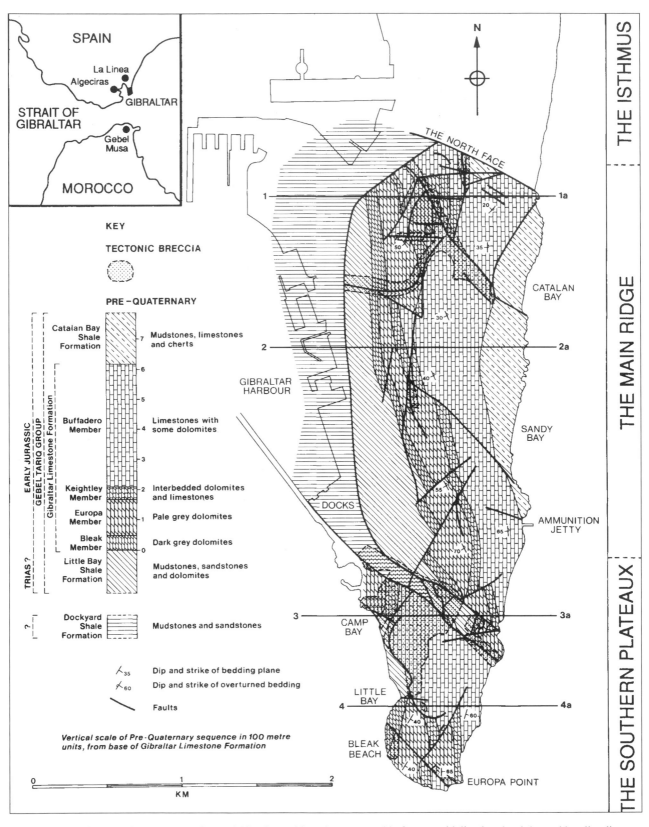

Figure 3. Map of the pre-Quaternary geology of Gibraltar, with major topographic features sidelined to the right, and locality diagram inset top left. For eastings and northings see Figures 15 or 22, and for cross sections along the lines of section shown on the map, see Rose and Rosenbaum (1990, 1991a, 1991b). The modern town of La Linea is named from a line of fortifications constructed by the Spanish in the eighteenth century after British capture of the Rock, to seal the mainland from attack. From Rose and Rosenbaum (1990), courtesy of the Institution of Royal Engineers.

Figure 4. Raising clouds of dust, a Hudson fighter-bomber leaves the dispersal area on the isthmus prior to a reconnaissance flight in August 1942. The sheer north face of the Rock towers to over 400 m in the background, with the Quaternary scree slope at its foot; quarrying provided a major source of fill for the airfield's extension. Courtesy of the Imperial War Museum, London: photo GM1405.

BEDROCK GEOLOGY

According to Ramsay and Geikie (1878), Gibraltar was a mass of Jurassic limestone overlain by shales in the (western) town area, truncated by a normal fault at the north face that downthrew the limestone beneath the isthmus sands, and bisected by a northwest-southeast "Great Main Fault" that separated westward-dipping, uninverted limestone in the main ridge area from eastward-dipping inverted strata in the southern plateaus. A.L. Greig was able to observe "shales" more widely through tunnel and quarry excavations, providing the basis for Bailey's (1952) reinterpretation of the Rock as a klippe of overturned dolomitic limestone, underlain rather than overlain by shales. G.B. Alexander's unpublished map depicted a limestone unit both underlain and overlain by shales, in which only the main ridge sequence is inverted—that in the southern plateaus is not. This last interpretation is maintained by the most recent map (Rosenbaum and Rose, 1991a), by associated research (e.g., Rose and Rosenbaum, 1990, 1991a, 1991b, 1994a, 1994b), and in the most recent detailed account (Rose, 2000a). Three main stratigraphic units are currently distinguished in the exposed bedrock (Fig. 3): the Little Bay Shale, Gibraltar Limestone, and Catalan Bay Shale Formations.

Little Bay Shale Formation

At least 7 m of red and green fissile mudstones with thin beds of fine sandstone and pebble conglomerate, together with thicker beds of dark gray dolomite, crop out at the base of cliffs in Little Bay on the west coast of the southern plateaus. No age-diagnostic fossils have been described from these rocks, but the beds dip steeply eastward beneath uninverted Gibraltar Limestone and so must represent the oldest exposed bedrock. Red and green fissile mudstone with thin chert bands can be traced as sheared exposures at the base of faulted limestone/dolomite cliffs northward into Camp Bay. Further north, vertical "shales" of similar appearance were mapped by Ramsay and Geikie (1876, 1878) along the west coast of the main ridge of the Rock, but have largely been removed or obscured by construction works, so are known now from patchy exposures, boreholes for foundation works, or old records. The Dockyard Shale Formation shown in Figure 3 has been designated (Rose and Rosenbaum, 1990) on the basis of photographs (e.g., Fig. 6) made during construction of the dockyards at the beginning of the twentieth century, but its relationship to the Little Bay Shales is unproven. The engineering implication is that relatively weak bedrock (largely thinly bedded, fractured mudrock) underlies most of the town and harbor area.

Gibraltar Limestone Formation

Most of the Rock is formed by a 400–600-m-thick succession of thickly to massively bedded, well-cemented carbonates, passing gradationally from dark gray bituminous dolomite at the base through pale gray-white dolomite, then a distinctively well-bedded unit of dolomite and limestones, to a very thick, seemingly homogeneous sequence of light or medium gray fine-grained limestones, dolomitic at the base. Rose and Rosenbaum (1990) therefore distinguished and mapped four members within the formation on the basis of gross lithology and weathering characteristics (Fig. 3). Although the Gibraltar Limestone has long been

Figure 5. Coat of arms granted to Gibraltar by the Spanish sovereigns Ferdinand and Isabella in 1502: a red castle upon a white background, chained to a golden key suspended beneath it on a red background, symbolizing the key importance of the fortress as guardian of the strait linking the ports of eastern Spain to the Spanish American empire. (An early copy of the original patent letters making this grant is currently displayed in the Gibraltar Museum.)

described as relatively homogeneous (e.g., by Ramsay and Geikie, 1878; Bailey, 1952), Bosence et al. (2000) have recently demonstrated that this is not true in terms of depositional facies. On the basis of detailed study of carbonate sedimentology, they have distinguished a variety of shallow-water facies stacked as high-frequency (meter scale) cycles, and demonstrated an additional low-frequency cyclicity within the formation as a whole. The lithologies indicate an origin within tropical, peritidal, carbonate platform environments, somewhat similar to present-day conditions bordering the Bahamas. They compare closely with other thick Lower Jurassic carbonate sequences widely developed along the southern continental margin of the Alpine-Mediterranean Tethys region, especially in countries bordering the western Mediterranean. An Early Jurassic (Sinemurian) age for at least part of the Gibraltar Limestone has recently been verified on the basis of rare brachiopods (Owen and Rose, 1997) and strontium isotope ratios from brachiopod shell calcite (Bosence et al., 2000).

The Gibraltar Limestone appears to be homogeneous because of extensive diagenesis. Diagenetic features reported by Qing et al. (1998, 2001) include calcite cements interpreted to have precipitated at an early stage, from seawater in a submarine environment, and an additional cement that filled the remaining pore spaces during burial. Also, two phases of dolomitization can be distinguished: one later than the various marine cements but which is inferred to have occurred penecontemporaneously at or just below the sea floor by interaction with Early Jurassic seawater or evaporated seawater, and another due to precipitation later in pores in the dolomite.

Thick bedding and extensive cementation plus dolomitization give the Gibraltar Limestone its strength as an engineering material.

Catalan Bay Shale Formation

Medium-bedded gray cherty limestones alternating with thinner beds of reddish-gray fissile mudstones are exposed beneath inverted Gibraltar Limestone at four localities on the east coast: near Catalan Bay; the south end of Sandy Bay; some 500 m further south; and at Ammunition Jetty (Fig. 3). They are also exposed at the base of the north face of the Rock. Quarries at Catalan Bay and the north face yielded ammonites to which L.F. Spath (in Bailey, 1952) gave an Early Jurassic age (Domerian, equivalent to the late Pliensbachian), appropriately a stage later than the Sinemurian age ascribed to the Gibraltar Limestone. These strata have recently (Rose, 2000a) been distinguished as the Caleta Member, to distinguish them from those stratigraphically higher in the succession assigned to the North Face Chert Member: thinly bedded argillaceous cherts faulted against the Caleta Member at Catalan Bay quarry, and proved in a borehole at the north face (Rose and Rosenbaum, 1991b). Cherts from a tectonized "shale" outcrop at the base of the north face have yielded a moderately diverse radiolarian assemblage dated by E. Urquhart (in Rose, 2000a) as probably Late Jurassic in age. The Catalan Bay Shales are believed to underlie much of the Rock mass: they have caused significant stability problems in the few tunnels that penetrate them.

The sequence has been subject to thrusting, faulting, and partial overturning, presumably during emplacement of the Betic-Rif nappes, arguably during the Miocene (Rose and Rosenbaum, 1994a; Rose, 2000a). (Gibraltar lies close to the Internal/External Zone structural boundary long recognized in the Betic Cordilleras of southern Spain, recently [Geel and Roep, 1998] interpreted as a suture that separates the former passive southern margin of Iberia from a stack of allochthonous nappe complexes—and therefore two crustal blocks originally several hundred kilometers apart. Gibraltar is also close to the European-African plate boundary.) A thrust plane is inferred to lie beneath the Rock, but has not knowingly been observed during excavation works. A major transcurrent fault has been inferred to lie beneath the Isthmus Sands, rather than the normal fault claimed by Ramsay and Geikie (1878). Within the Rock itself, the pattern of faulting is complex, with three major fault sets trending northwest-southeast, northeast-southwest, and north-south, but vectors of movement are never clear. Joint patterns have been analyzed from discontinuity mapping and scanline surveys in some of the numerous tunnels that penetrate the Rock, but coverage is patchy, and there is as yet no overall analysis.

QUATERNARY GEOLOGY

Features of Quaternary geology have excited interest on Gibraltar from the mid-eighteenth century onward (Rose, 2002). In addition to contemporary and Recent beach sands, the most recent reviews (Rose and Rosenbaum, 1990; Rose and Hardman, 1994, 2000) recognize five units of Quaternary sediments (Fig. 7)

Figure 6. Photograph taken in 1903 during construction of the Gibraltar docks, before lining with concrete and masonry (Scott, 1914), revealing steeply dipping, medium-bedded strata designated the Dockyard Shale Formation by Rose and Rosenbaum (1990). From Rose and Rosenbaum (1990), courtesy of the Institution of Royal Engineers. © British Crown Copyright/MoD. Reproduced with the permission of Her Britannic Majesty's Stationery Office.

which have a surface distribution sufficiently widespread to be shown on a 1:20 000 scale map (Rosenbaum and Rose, 1991a).

Raised shorelines are represented by marine sediments and landforms, and are best developed to the south and east of the Rock. Despite partial destruction by quarrying, landscaping, or overbuilding, significant evidence remains or has been documented at heights of 1–3, 7–9, 15–17, 20–25, 30–40, 50–60, 80–86, 90–130, ~180, and ~210 m and arguably higher above present sea level. Two periods when sea level relative to the Rock remained constant for a significant length of time are represented by the extensive wave-cut platforms, backed by steep cliffs, which form the southern plateaus. Other fossil shorelines and the easterly continuation of the southern plateaus are marked by narrower platforms and associated cliffs. On some of these, the platform is overlain by thin, patchy conglomerates and thicker,

well-cemented quartz- or calc-arenites. Marine erosion through the late Cenozoic, punctuated by periods of local tectonic uplift and global sea-level change, has thus shaped the bedrock, providing platforms attractive to engineering work, and a series of steep cliffs that inhibit military attack.

The Catalan Sands form the surface layers of a slope 1 km long banked against the eastern cliffs to a maximum height of about 200 m. Prior to road widening and construction of a retaining wall in 1997 and 1998, quarrying at the toe of the slope revealed an ~10 m thickness of cross-bedded, weakly cemented, yellow-brown, medium-grained quartz sands. These moderately well-sorted sands with subrounded, highly spherical grains represent beach sands redeposited as eolianites (i.e., windblown sediments). They are currently still visible, although to a lesser extent than formerly, above the completed wall.

The Alameda Sands, known locally as the "red sands," underlie much of the town area on the western side of the Rock. They occur as a narrow strip nearly 2 km long, with preserved height within 50 m of present sea level, and maximum reported thickness of 16 m. They are well-sorted quartz sands, having their mode in the fine sand fraction. Sorting, roundness, and sphericity of the grains indicate deposition as eolianites, but the red color appears to be the product of well-developed pedogenesis—the process of soil formation. Neither the Catalan nor the Alameda Sands are generally suitable for use as fine aggregate, being too well sorted, but both have been quarried as a necessary expedient under "siege" conditions.

The Isthmus Sands, now completely obscured by the airfield and associated buildings plus the city cemetery, are known from records pre-dating construction work to have formed a sandy plain, full of marine shells. Borehole records indicate that the surface layer of fine- to medium-grained marine sands is about 10 m thick, underlain by an extensive marine clay, which is in turn underlain by more variable sediments to a total depth of some 20 m in the west and at least 60 m in the east. The Isthmus Sands are as yet undated, but it is assumed that at least the upper part of the sequence is Holocene, and that deposition of the sands is associated with the well-known rise in global sea level in this epoch. They have long been studied for use as an aquifer.

Scree breccia occurs widely on the flanks of the Rock, most obviously at the base of the north face; in the vicinity of the Catalan Sand slope on the east coast; and to a lesser extent south of the main dockyard area along the west coast. These breccias are largely composed of very poorly sorted, angular fragments of Gibraltar Limestone, which may be up to several meters in diameter. Infrequent terrestrial gastropods indicate that most were deposited under terrestrial conditions, the large size and angularity of the clasts indicating a climate significantly colder or more extreme than that of present-day Gibraltar. The screes have been extensively quarried to provide fill for land reclamation.

The products of karstic solution are a pervasive feature of the Rock, with over 140 principal caves distinguished to date above present sea level, and yet more below it. The largest natural caves have at times served as storerooms for the military (Fig. 8), and some coastal caves as building sites (Fig. 9).

FORTIFICATION

Because of its geographical situation, Gibraltar has assumed a position of importance in world history out of all proportion to its small size. A Moorish army from North Africa crossed the narrow Strait of Gibraltar in A.D. 711 to seize a foothold in western Europe, an area from which Islamic forces were expelled only in 1492. From that date also there was a progressive transfer of power from states that bordered the Mediterranean Sea to those beside the Atlantic Ocean as new, aggressive naval forces equipped with new types of ships emerged. Gibraltar was situated at a cross-route junction, for movement south and north between Africa and Europe, and east and west between the Mediterranean

and Atlantic. Anyone in possession of the Rock could exploit the situation, and if in possession also of a sufficiently strong fleet, deny movement to ships of other nations.

Fortification was begun by the Moors and extended by the Spanish (Hughes and Migos, 1995; Rose, 1998). The British made use of existing fortification with relatively minor alterations until the Great Siege by French and Spanish troops from 1779 to 1783. Thereafter there were major construction works. Initially, defense was concentrated against an attack from the land (Fig. 10): flooding of part of the isthmus to create a major obstacle; scarping and scaling of potential access routes across the base of the north face to make them too difficult to climb; fortification of lowland areas by wall and bastion to deny ready access; and tunneling to provide vantage points for cannon fire. The southern boundary of the town was also fortified, but less extensively (Fig. 11), being deemed less vulnerable to attack. British pride in the impregnability of Gibraltar about this time generated some truly fanciful ideas for its defense (Rose, 1994). Later the perceived threat was greater from the sea, as screw-driven, armored steamships began to ply the Mediterranean in place of wooden sailing vessels, and formidable batteries of coastal artillery were developed (Figs. 12, 13, and 14). During World War II, airpower increasingly replaced sea power. Guns were additionally directed skyward, and the garrison was largely accommodated underground to provide protection from air attack.

The fortifications as they exist at the present day comprise thirteen groups of defensive structures and battery positions (Fig. 15 and Table 1), categorized by Hughes and Migos (1995) according to their role in the protection of the Rock. In many cases, the sites have been progressively modified over centuries of use as a response to developments in weapon technology. Thus high towers for refuge and discharge of light armament, built by the Moors in medieval times at intervals along the town wall, were reduced in height and reconstructed by the Spanish during the sixteenth century to serve as platforms for mounting cannon.

The coastal defenses of Gibraltar had been brought to their near final state of development by 1914, the outbreak of World War I. Fourteen 9.2-inch, eleven 6-inch, and seven 3-inch caliber guns were in place (Figs. 16 and 17). During World War II, the serious threat came from the air, and defenses were built up accordingly, adding twenty-eight 3.7-inch guns, four 3-inch, forty-eight 40-mm Bofors, two pom-poms, and twenty-four searchlight positions by 1942 when fortification reached its peak of development.

Much of this military estate has been decommissioned in recent years, as Ministry of Defence contribution to Gibraltar's Gross Domestic Product has fallen from a peak of 65% to about 5% by the year 2000 (Rose, 1998). The civilian authorities have thus inherited much of an intact fortress in a very short period of

Figure 7. Map of the most widespread Quaternary sediments on Gibraltar. From Rose and Rosenbaum (1990), courtesy of the Institution of Royal Engineers.

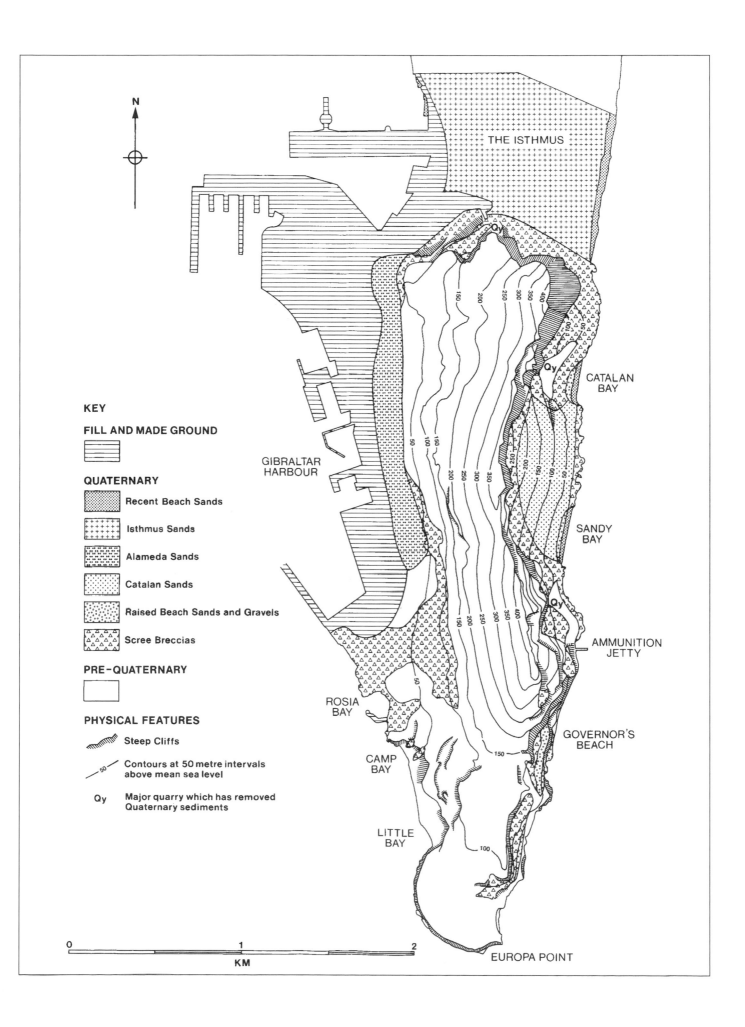

N

KEY

FILL AND MADE GROUND

QUATERNARY

Recent Beach Sands

Isthmus Sands

Alameda Sands

Catalan Sands

Raised Beach Sands and Gravels

Scree Breccias

PRE-QUATERNARY

PHYSICAL FEATURES

Steep Cliffs

50 — Contours at 50 metre intervals above mean sea level

Qy Major quarry which has removed Quaternary sediments

THE ISTHMUS

GIBRALTAR HARBOUR

CATALAN BAY

Qy

Qy

SANDY BAY

AMMUNITION JETTY

ROSIA BAY

GOVERNOR'S BEACH

CAMP BAY

LITTLE BAY

Qy

EUROPA POINT

0   1   2

KM

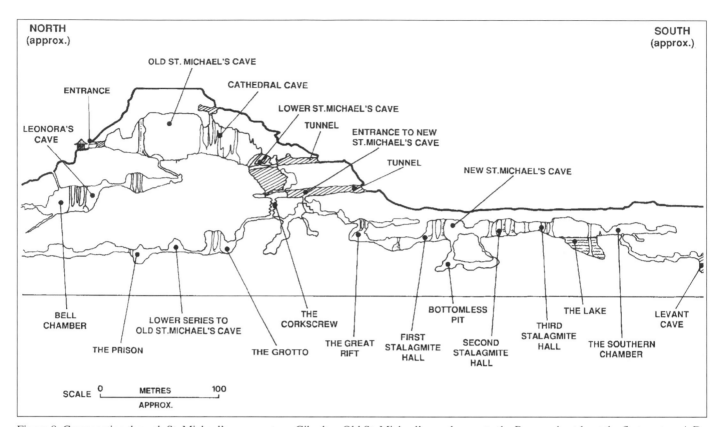

Figure 8. Cross section through St. Michael's cave system, Gibraltar. Old St. Michael's was known to the Romans in at least the first century A.D., but the New St. Michael's system was discovered only during the 1939–1945 World War, during military tunneling to provide improved access for storage. The apparent horizontality of the cave systems, which cut across bedding steeply inclined to the west, indicates that their formation was determined primarily by former groundwater levels. From Rose and Rosenbaum (1990), courtesy of the Institution of Royal Engineers.

time—and have the challenge of what to do with it. The massive walls, bastions, and gun emplacements provide an obvious tourist attraction, but do constrain development of the modern city if they are to be preserved. Some sites are being actively maintained or restored, notably under the auspices of the Gibraltar Heritage Trust, but the very large number of military sites presents a problem for the local population—30 000 people in total but of whom only about 20 000 are Gibraltarian nationals rather than expatriates. A proposal is currently being formulated that Gibraltar should be designated as a world heritage site, and receive international funding for conservation work. Meanwhile, the urgent necessity is to adapt former military structures to appropriate civilian use.

QUARRYING AND LAND RECLAMATION

The walls and bastions of the fortress were largely constructed of stone quarried locally. Quarries developed in the Gibraltar Limestone provided the main source of building stone—James (1771) described several in operation during the eighteenth century, and Ramsay and Geikie (1878) referred to quarrying at the north face of the Rock. Additionally, well

cemented Quaternary sandstone was quarried above a 55 m raised beach near the southeast coast of the Rock to provide a lining for gun embrasures (Rose, 1998). Quarrying has now ceased, as cheaper and more versatile building materials are imported, and disused quarry sites have been variously adapted, often for bulk storage of materials or urban waste.

Extension of the harbor at the end of the nineteenth century required considerable quantities of rock fill (Fig. 18). A northern breakwater (the Old Mole) had been constructed in 1309 and a southern breakwater (the New Mole) between 1620 and 1660—extended to about 400 m in length in 1851. However, between 1893 and 1905 massive new harbor works involved further extension of the southern breakwater by about 900 m; construction of a 900 m detached breakwater between those existing to the north and south; development of a large northern mole with coaling jetties; development of an extended naval yard with three large graving docks, a small graving dock, wharf walls, slipways for destroyers, and associated buildings; and dredging of the harbor (Scott, 1914). The breakwaters were largely constructed as a rubble-mound base supporting a vertical-wall superstructure of concrete block work finished above high-water level with limestone ashlar masonry and mass concrete. During the first phase of this work, substantial quantities of rock were required for extension of the South Mole. Rubble (from Quaternary scree breccia) and dressed limestone were obtained chiefly from quarries a short distance to the south, notably in Camp Bay. To provide access, tunnels were driven under Parson's Lodge Battery and in Camp Bay itself. Ultimately the stone was transported by a meter-gauge railway especially constructed for the purpose. When disused, the railway tunnels subsequently provided road access to the area. This enabled Camp Bay and the adjacent Little Bay to be developed in recent years as popular bathing areas, but the quarried faces have been subject to instability, particularly during periods of above-average winter rainfall. In 1989 a serious rock fall necessitated stabilization measures along a 500 m length of cliff (Anonymous, 1992). Rappelling techniques were used for work on a major rock stabilization project then thought to be on a scale larger than anything attempted before in this field. Stabilization was effected by grouting of the limestone, colluvium, and breccia exposed in natural cliff and old quarry faces. It was also achieved by inserting rock anchors using specially designed cliff face drilling rigs, four down-the-hole-hammer (DTH) rigs, and a specially made rotary percussion drifter rig. Drilling conditions were very difficult: the solution voids that riddled the Gibraltar Limestone caused three DTH drill bits to break, an "unheard of" occurrence, which meant that both holes and hammers had to be abandoned. The original contract was for 120 permanent anchorages, of 4 to 15 m length. Additionally, boulders of up to four metric tons weight were removed by crowbar or by winches and hydraulic jacks, and larger boulders were retained in place by a combination of steel cable strapping and rock bolts, plus steel mesh where required. Other areas thought to be unstable, such as breccia faces and gullies, were consolidated using rock bolts and shotcrete, reinforced with mesh. In the worst zone, where the original failure occurred, a grid pattern of rock bolts was used, large jammed boulders were identified and stabilized using anchorages, and the whole area encapsulated in shotcrete. However, as reported in *The Sunday Times* of 24 February 1997, additional rockfalls occurred along the cliff line above Camp Bay, again following heavy winter rainfall (Fig. 19). The winter of 1996/1997 was the wettest ever recorded in Gibraltar, and the December 1996 rainfall total of 652 mm was the highest December total in 150 years. More heavy rains followed in January, as reported in *The Gibraltar Chronicle*, prior to the major rockfall, which occurred on January 16. A survey to assess the scope for further stabilization measures was rapidly put in hand, and major stabilization works were effected through 1999 (Anonymous, 1999, 2000).

The later phases of harbor extension needed more fill than the Camp Bay quarries alone could provide and so rubble for the detached breakwater and the northern mole was obtained from other sites—quarries immediately west of Catalan Bay village and along the north face of the Rock. Roughly dressed limestone required for the dockyard buildings was also obtained from Catalan Bay and other quarries along the east coast. All these quarries began by exploiting the Quaternary scree brec-

Figure 9. View north along the east coast of Gibraltar, across Governor's Beach (cf. Fig. 7). Cave systems in the Gibraltar Limestone eroded or breached by former (Quaternary) shorelines can be seen at about 1–3 and 80 m above present sea level. The latter includes Monkey's Cave, which is large enough to contain a hospital built for the convalescence of servicemen injured during World War II. From Rose and Rosenbaum (1991b), courtesy of the Gibraltar Heritage Trust.

cias (Fig. 20) before tackling the intact and stronger Gibraltar Limestone beneath. Access to the south end of Sandy Bay was provided by a new tunnel driven from the dockyard area eastward through the Rock. Railway communication was established from the dockyard through the tunnel and then round via Catalan Bay and the base of the north face to the town and dockyard, completing the circle. The bulk of the limestone ashlar, for quay walls, docks, and buildings, was obtained ready-dressed from Spain, being brought by railway to the town of Algeciras and then transported by boat across the Bay of Gibraltar to the works. Granite used to floor the docks and to construct copings and landing steps was mostly imported from England (Cornwall), but some came from Norway and a little from Italy. Sand used for concrete came from Quaternary sand

Figure 10. View of the northern limit of the city of Gibraltar, looking northeast, as shown on a model of the Rock, now in the Royal Engineers Museum, Chatham, constructed in 1781 by command of the Master-General of the Ordnance. Scale of model 1 inch:100 feet (1:1200). Fortifications are shown as in 1779. Marshy ground on the isthmus was excavated in 1735 to form the "Inundation," with access to the town limited to a narrow causeway. Fortifications across the "Landport" area and at the "Moorish Castle" area perched higher up the Rock bar land access across the low ground on the western flank of the Rock. The natural steepness of the north face has been enhanced by military quarrying as the face declines in elevation to the west (left of photo), and is fortified by the King's, Queen's and Prince's Lines. The Line Wall beginning as a sea wall with projecting bastions extends south from the Old Mole breakwater. From Rose (2000b), courtesy of The Geological Society, London.

Figure 11. View of the southern limit of the town, looking east, from the same model as illustrated in Figure 10, showing the Line Wall continuing to fortifications at the South Front (South Bastion, and Flat Bastion further uphill); the Moorish Wall extending from the town to a lookout tower on the crest of the main ridge; and the Charles V (Spanish) Wall zig-zagging across the upper Rock to the south (right) of the Moorish Wall. From Rose (2000b), courtesy of The Geological Society, London.

Figure 12. The Saluting Battery (one of the West Side batteries, see Table 1) prior to the 1890s when it was re-sited as a consequence of dockyard extension. Twenty-one embrasures cut the parapet of the defensive wall in front of guns typical for the Rock early in the nineteenth century. (Gibraltar guns were smooth-bore muzzle loading until rifled muzzle loading [RML] guns were progressively introduced in the 1860s, in turn replaced by fewer breech loading guns after 1888. By 1867 there were some 32 RMLs installed, but still 566 smooth-bore guns and 51 iron Carronades.) From a lithograph by Captain J.M. Carter, circa 1830–1840, courtesy of the Garrison Library Trust, Gibraltar.

slopes on the east side of the Rock, for it had a grading suitable for use in concrete with careful mix design (Rose, 1998); limestone crushed to provide aggregate came from two quarries also on the east side.

From early 1942 until mid-1943 construction of the airfield (Fig. 4) brought a new demand for fill. The old quarry west of Catalan Bay was reopened and worked both southward and northward, and a new quarry, adjacent to the airfield, was developed in the Quaternary scree slope at the base of the north face. This quarry was calculated to have a potential volume of 1 338 000 m³ (Haycraft, 1946a). Initially, it was worked by diamond drilling to insert gelignite for blasting. However, due to the lithologically variable and fractured nature of the cemented scree, the drills tended to jam and the boreholes to collapse when the bit was withdrawn. Consequently, progress was slow. Moreover, it proved difficult to judge the correct weight of charge for use in the anisotropic rock. Either the force of the explosion was dissipated through the fractures in the breccia, or the spoil was blasted all over the isthmus (Haycraft, 1946a). A Canadian officer solved these problems by adapting the pumps supplied to operate static flamethrowers to propel seawater at high speed to extract the material. Two pumps were installed, one at either end of the scree. A jet of water was directed so as to develop a vertical rock face from below, and the two ends of the scree worked on alternate days so as to alternate "hydraulicing" with spoil removal. In time, it was shown that volume of water, rather than head of pressure, controlled the process.

The airfield was extended into the Bay of Gibraltar beginning in 1941 by using spoil from tunnel excavation together with considerably larger amounts of quarried scree breccia (Haycraft, 1946a). Large rock fragments were deposited to form the sides of the extension, accumulating at their natural angle of rest. Smaller material was used to infill the extension core, and tunnel spoil with a water-bound finish was used to pave the runway surface. By 3 April 1942 the runway had been extended to a length of 1050 m 27 days ahead of schedule, "one of the great constructional achievements of the war" (Ramsey, 1978, p. 14). This allowed aircraft to take off with enough fuel to fly directly to Egypt, bypassing the beleaguered island of Malta. An extension to almost 1417 m was completed by November 1942, providing a base for the air cover necessary to support Operation Torch, the Allied invasion of French North Africa commanded from the Rock by General Dwight D. Eisenhower. Six hundred aircraft were packed into the Gibraltar airfield, and used to give cover to Allied landings (Dear, 1995). By July 1943 the full planned extension, to 1645 m, was complete, with a width of 137 m raised to a height of 3.05 m above high water level. By that time 1.15×10^6 m³ of fill had been placed in position—creating an airfield that supported a formidable force of Dakotas, Hudsons, Halifaxes, Hurricanes, and Spitfires assembled for the invasion of southern France in July 1944 (Fig. 21) (Ramsey, 1978). After the war, an additional 183 m of fill was added to the airfield length.

Postwar, the size of the Royal Navy has decreased in proportion to its global operational role, and the Naval presence at Gibraltar has been reduced in scale accordingly. The docks and dockyard have now been largely converted to civilian use. Part of the now over-large harbor has been infilled by sea-dredged sand to reclaim land for housing and office development (Fig. 18). The airfield too has largely passed from Royal Air Force to civilian control. Its construction as a wartime necessity on "neutral" ground whose sovereignty has been disputed by Spain provides a

Figure 13. Parson's Lodge Battery (one of the West Side batteries), north of Camp Bay on the southwest coast of Gibraltar, viewed from the south. First fortified in the eighteenth century, abandoned in the 1950s, and visually one of the most impressive batteries on Gibraltar, this is one of the sites recently restored under the auspices of the Gibraltar Heritage Trust. It was armed in 1884 with three 10-inch, 18-ton rifled muzzle loading guns, mounted in stone-built casemates with laminated iron embrasures. The entrance to a short road (formerly railway) tunnel north to the harbor area can be seen to the lower right of the photograph. From Rose (1998), courtesy of The Geological Society, London.

Figure 14. The 100-ton gun at Napier of Magdala Battery is a 17.72-inch rifled muzzle loading gun, replacing one mounted at this site in 1883. The heaviest coastal defense gun in British service, with an effective range of about 5 km, but a slow rate of fire (1 round per 4 minutes); it was obsolete by 1906.

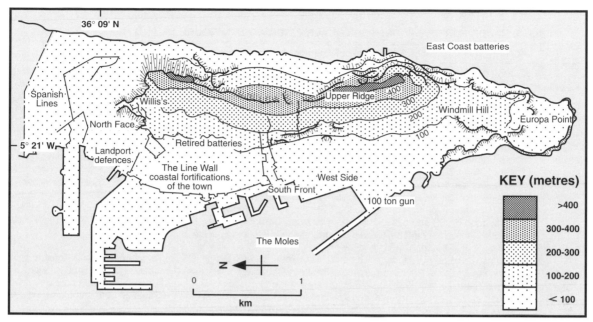

Figure 15. Topographic map of Gibraltar, contoured at 100 m intervals and with major cliffs hachured, showing the main areas of fortification listed in Table 1. The former siege positions shown as the Spanish Lines are now entirely concealed by the airport tarmac. After Hughes and Migos (1995).

legacy of political conflict of continuing current concern. It is probably unique as a joint military/international airfield whose runway is crossed by a major highway (Fig. 21). The only road between Spain and Gibraltar crosses the airfield, so air and surface traffic alternate in their use of the isthmus.

UNDERGROUND EXCAVATION

The well-documented tunnels and underground chambers constructed by the military are a major feature of Gibraltar and now total over 50 km in length (Figs. 22 and 23) (Wilson, 1945; Haycraft, 1946b; Cotton, 1948; Lauder, 1963; Ramsey, 1978). Most date from five periods (Rosenbaum and Rose, 1991b, 1992a, 1992b, 1994) defined in Table 2. Gibraltar tunnels thus provide an excellent example of underground excavation technology over a 200-year time span.

Stable tunnels have all been cut through the Gibraltar Limestone. During construction of the early tunnels (Upper Galleries of Fig. 22), the rock was fragmented by gunpowder charges and then removed by crowbar and sledgehammer. Some records indicate that the rock was also fragmented by fire setting (building fires against the face of the rock and then quenching the heated rock with cold water), use of quicklime (tamped into boreholes and then slaked with water to cause an expansion that cracked the surrounding rock), and wooden wedges (hammered into cracks and soaked with water to cause expansion). These methods were very slow (about 200 m per year for a tunnel of some 2 to 3 m cross section), but they caused minimal damage to the unexcavated rock, and this has been repaid by the long-term stability of the smooth walls so created.

By World War II, tunneling techniques had become much quicker. Blasting with high explosives and excavation by British and Canadian military engineers equipped with mechanized plant allowed a peak rate of advance to be achieved in 1942 of some 60 m of tunnel of 2 to 3 m cross section in a week. Communications tunnels were cut to about 2.5 m diameter, but main tunnels to 4 m, and the largest excavation (REME Chambers, Figs. 22 and 24) had a span of 16 m, a height of 10 m to crown of arch, and a length of 120 m. Tunnels were excavated in several stages using the newly developed blast-hole diamond drilling technique. Either the tunnel was undercut and the back then brought down by diamond drill blasting, or a central portion of the tunnel was excavated to the full height and the sides then diamond drill blasted. Drill holes were spaced 2.1 to 2.4 m apart and the distance from the final surface to a free face varied between 2.1 and 4.6 m, requiring an average of 0.56 kg of gelignite per meter length of drill hole. In hindsight, it seems that spacing between drill holes and the distance to a free face was too great for the advantages of smooth blasting to have been gained, and an excessive amount of explosive charge may have been used (Rosenbaum et al., 1994).

Tunneling after the 1939–1945 war benefited from the lessons learned and, with the advantage of excavating under less urgent, peacetime conditions, new tunnels were advanced using smaller charges in each round. These were fired electrically in a full-face pattern of drill holes, the centre of the face being fired first in order to create a void into which the rock from the tunnel's periphery could then fall (Lauder, 1963). Unfortunately, this tended to fracture the previously intact limestone around the tunnel profile, resulting in a rather jagged line to the tunnel walls.

TABLE 1. MAJOR FORTIFICATIONS PER LOCALITY INDICATED IN FIGURE 15, AND THEIR PURPOSES

Location	Major type of fortification and time of construction	Purpose
North Face	The King's, Queen's and Prince's Lines—walls and rock-cut trenches partly Moorish in origin but enhanced by the Spanish and later (largely during the 18th century) by the British; the Upper, Middle, and Lower Galleries—tunnel systems pierced behind the north face of the Rock between 1782 and 1799; casemated batteries (Bombproof, Forbes', Hanover, Orillon, and Tower Batteries)—largely developed in the 18th and 19th centuries but with some 20th century enhancement.	To bar land attack from the central isthmus into the town area; to provide cannon ports from which to bombard enemy siege positions on the isthmus; and to provide defensive fire-power to counter an attack via the isthmus.
Landport defenses	The inundation—an area flooded in 1735 (but infilled after World War II); the Moorish Castle—a fortress developed between the 12th and 15th centuries; plus walls and bastions (Hesse's, North) developed from the 18th to 20th centuries on earlier Moorish and Spanish sites.	To constrain access to a single causeway leading to a gated/tunneled city entrance; to bar other access from the isthmus to the town.
The Line Wall	Walls (Chatham Counterguard, Line Wall Curtain, Prince Albert's Front, Wellington Front) and bastions (King's, Montagu, Orange) largely British 18th century in construction but on the site of earlier (Spanish, probably also Moorish) walls and towers.	To counter bombardment from ships in the Bay of Gibraltar, and to withstand an amphibious landing.
Willis's	Batteries (Catalan, Farringdon's, Governor's Lookout, Green's Lodge, Princess Amelia's, Princess Caroline's, Princess Charlotte's, Princess Royal, Queen's, and Willis's) sited on an area named in honor of a British artillery officer active during the capture of Gibraltar in 1704—an area of rising ground progressively armed from the 18th century, partly with 5.25-inch guns after World War II.	To command the isthmus to the north and Bay of Gibraltar in the west; the 5.25-inch guns had a dual defensive role, against both ships and aircraft.
South Front	Classic wall and bastion fortifications, the walls both Moorish and Spanish (Charles V), the bastions (Flat, South) Spanish in origin but enhanced by the British: defended since the 18th century by the Genoese and Prince Ferdinand's Batteries and Healey's Mortar (a fougasse—cut in the solid rock).	To protect the town from attack from the south—a purpose which became superfluous as long-range artillery was developed.
The Moles	Two breakwaters, Spanish in origin but greatly altered by the British at the end of the 19th century, were built out into the Bay of Gibraltar on the Atlantic side of the Rock; a detached mole (with lighthouse at each end) was finally constructed between them.	To shelter the fleet, and to provide facilities for loading and unloading heavy cargos, protected by guns.
The 100-ton guns	One 17.72-inch Rifled Muzzle Loading gun was mounted in each of two batteries (Napier, Victoria) from 1883. The heaviest coast defense guns in British use, they were obsolete by 1906.	To protect Gibraltar from similarly armed and heavily armored enemy battleships.
Retired batteries	The Calpe, Devil's Gap, Jones', Civil Hospital, Raglan, Gardiner's, and Queen Victoria's Batteries were sited inland after a recommendation of 1841 that siting uphill would decrease vulnerability to attack, improve concealment, and increase range of firepower.	To protect the town from bombardment from ships in the Bay of Gibraltar to the west.
Windmill Hill	Buffadero, Edward VII, Genista, Jews' Cemetery, Levant, South, West, and Windmill Hill Batteries were developed in fixed positions from the 19th century; additionally, the plateau provided an ideal area over which to disperse mobile gun sites. A retrenched barracks provided garrison accommodation.	To provide counter-bombardment against ships approaching from either the Atlantic or the Mediterranean, and close defense against an amphibious attack from the south.
West Side	Alexandra, Cumberland, Devil's Bowling Green, Buena Vista, Engineer, Lewis's, Rooke, Rosia, Hayne's Cave, Parson's Lodge, Lady Augusta's, Prince of Wales, Prince George's, Prince William's, St. George's, Scud Hill, Tovey, and the Saluting Batteries were variously developed from the 18th to 20th centuries. South Barracks (built 1730s) and Buena Vista Barracks (1840s) housed troops.	To counter bombardment from ships in the Bay of Gibraltar to the west, and to prevent amphibious assault on low-lying and therefore vulnerable west coast areas south of the town.
Europa Point	Both Moors and Spaniards sited some fortifications at Europa, but these were considerably developed by the British. Natural cliffs were enhanced as an obstacle by scarping, construction of perimeter walls, siting of batteries (Elliott's, Europa Advance, Europa, Europa Pass, Half Way, Harding's, Hutment, Lady Louisa's, Lighthouse, Woodford's), and a defensible barracks.	To protect from amphibious attack—unlikely because of the rocky coastline, fast currents, and lack of a beach. The barracks housed and protected a small garrison from sudden attack.
Upper Ridge	Martin's, Middle Hill, Rock (or Royal), Signal Hill, Spyglass and the Upper Batteries were all mounted high on the Rock. Breakneck, Lord Airey's, O'Hara's and Spur Batteries were constructed 1899/1902 for 9.2-inch breech loading guns—the linchpin of defenses up to and including World War II.	To engage ships approaching from either the Atlantic or the Mediterranean, and to cover the North African coast and the Spanish mainland.
East Coast batteries	There were only a few batteries (e.g. White Rock, an anti-aircraft gun position manned from 1941 to 1944) or other defenses on the Mediterranean coastline, mainly because the Rock rose steeply on the eastern side, thereby barring access to and sheltering the town.	To provide the limited defense deemed necessary from unlikely amphibious attack from the east, or from aerial attack.

Figure 16. Breakneck Battery (one of the Upper Ridge batteries; see Table 1) in January 1942, with a 9.2-inch MkX on an MkV mounting. Courtesy of the Imperial War Museum, London: photo GM278.

Figure 17. View north along the crest of the main ridge from O'Hara's Battery at the present day, with south-facing 9.2-inch gun at Lord Airey's Battery in the foreground at a height of 418 m. Gibraltar Limestone here dips at a high angle to the west. The main east coast water catchments are clearly visible to the right of the photograph (cf. Figs. 18, 23, and 27). From Rose (1998), courtesy of The Geological Society, London.

Current thinking would prefer the early firing of a ring of holes along the desired profile, thereby creating a continuous fracture that would subsequently limit further rock breakage arising from firing the main bulk of the explosives.

Military tunneling ceased on Gibraltar by April 1968 and therefore throughout the British army. The final Tunnelling Troop was disbanded, and all remaining Royal Engineer tunnelers left Gibraltar on posting to other units. The responsibility for maintenance of the tunnel network then fell largely upon the Gibraltarian Ministry of Works and the British Ministry of Public Building and Works, and their successor organizations. Early excavation methods created relatively small tunnels, which after 200 years are still stable, in contrast to the spalling of highly fractured rock fragmented by the use of high explosive during the more recent phases of tunnel excavation. Tunnel integrity has been monitored by a program of scanline surveys; loose blocks developed by stress relief have been removed by periodic scaling (Fig. 25); and, where necessary, support has been provided by rock bolts, weld mesh, props, arches, or occasional tunnel linings.

POTABLE AND SANITARY WATER SUPPLIES

The supply of adequate potable water on Gibraltar has been a long-standing problem, one that generated the first geological survey of the Rock by A.C. Ramsay and J. Geikie, in 1876 (Ramsay, 1877; Ramsay and Geikie, 1878; Rose, 2002). Separate water supplies were developed for the army and navy, to complement those developed for the town. The town supply has the most impressive storage system—thirteen reservoirs excavated within the Rock (Fig. 23), the final twelve between 1898 and 1961 (Rose and Rosenbaum, 1991b; Rosenbaum and Rose, 1991b). Water has sometimes been imported by tanker (Rose, 1998), and a pilot scheme indicated some potential for generating water by cloud condensation on metallic meshes (Hurst, 1959), but the primary sources have been rainwater, groundwater, and seawater (Gonzales, 1966; Doody, 1981; Wright et al., 1994).

Rainwater

The climate of Gibraltar is mild Mediterranean, warm dry summers alternating with cool wet winters. Monthly rainfall averages are highest in December and lowest in July (Wright et al., 1994, Table 1). Daily rainfall records are available for one or more stations on Gibraltar since 1790. Analysis of these data indicates that frequency distribution of annual values is normal with a mean of 838 mm, a standard deviation of 262 mm, and a range from 381 to 1956 mm (Wright et al., 1994). Secular plots of raw and smoothed data of departures from the mean (Fig. 26) show no long-term trend to wetter or drier conditions, but do show some obvious periodicities.

The Moors derived water supplies for their developing town from roof catchment of rainwater, wells in the Quaternary sands that fringe the Rock, and storage by cistern of local surface run-

off. Roof catchments and an aqueduct constructed by the Spanish to convey runoff from an area south of the town continued to provide the main means of public supply after the town and fortress were ceded to Britain in 1713 (Rose, 1998), but from 1863 onward increased efforts were made to collect rainwater from surface catchments. Small areas were constructed on natural slopes of the Gibraltar Limestone exposed on the Upper Rock (Fig. 18) by clearing surface vegetation and sealing fissures with a cement or mortar grout. The most spectacular were constructed on the east side of Gibraltar, on the Catalan Sand slope (Fig. 27), by smoothing the surface of the slope and then covering it with corrugated iron sheets fastened to a timber framework (Gonzales, 1966; Rosenbaum and Rose, 1991b). Rain falling on this catchment area flowed down into a channel constructed at its foot, and thence via a tunnel into reservoirs within the Rock. An area of 40 000 m^2 was surfaced in 1903, increased by 56 000 m^2 between 1911 and 1914, and an additional 40 000 m^2 between 1958 and 1961. Government catchments eventually occupied an area of 243 000 m^2, but their percentage contribution to total potable water consumed on the Rock fell from 12% in 1976 to 1% by 1992 (Wright et al., 1994). Use of the Catalan catchments was discontinued in 1993 because of high maintenance costs. The toe of the Catalan Sand slope was quarried between 1969 and 1982 (Fig. 28), and there is concern that if the deteriorating corrugated iron covering is removed, water entering the sands beneath may generate slope failure. Current plans to stabilize the surface of the slope include the use of plastic matting and sowing of locally collected seed (Rose, 1998) as well as proven techniques of soil reinforcement. A major retaining wall has recently been constructed along the base of the slope as part of a road-widening scheme.

Groundwater

During the Moorish, Spanish, and early British occupation of the Rock, some (largely brackish) water was obtained from shallow wells as well as from surface runoff. There were no major springs, except perhaps associated with the major (Orillon) fault zone near the northwestern corner of the Rock (Wright et al., 1994, Fig. 5).

An aquifer within the Gibraltar Limestone bedrock has been identified only recently (Wright et al., 1994): a thin lens of fresh water overlying seawater occurs within the Limestone close to sea level. Recharge rates have been calculated by soil moisture and chloride balance to be of the order of 400 000 m^3 per year, significant in relation to the present demand for

Figure 18. Map showing marine areas reclaimed by emplacement of rock fill; main quarry areas; and lined rainwater catchment areas. The full extent of the southern breakwater and the position of the detached breakwater that lies between it and the end of the northern breakwater are not indicated on this and comparable map figures herein but are visible in the photograph reproduced in Figure 2. From Rose and Rosenbaum (1990), courtesy of the Institution of Royal Engineers.

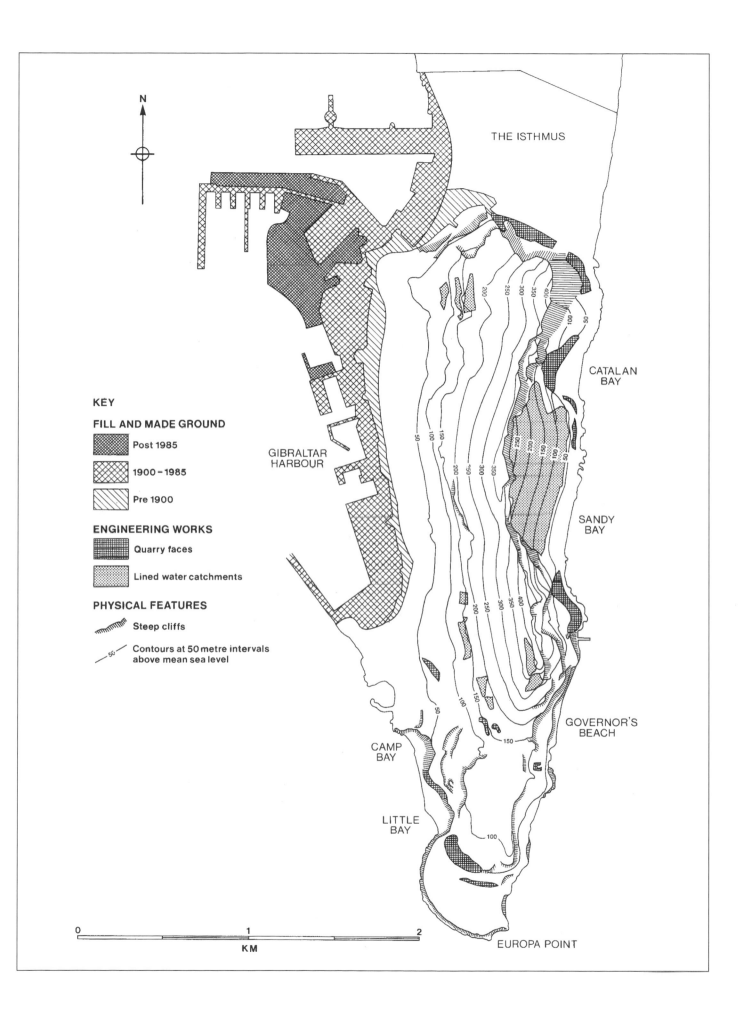

N

THE ISTHMUS

CATALAN
BAY

SANDY
BAY

GIBRALTAR
HARBOUR

KEY

FILL AND MADE GROUND

Post 1985

1900 – 1985

Pre 1900

ENGINEERING WORKS

Quarry faces

Lined water catchments

PHYSICAL FEATURES

Steep cliffs

50 Contours at 50 metre intervals
above mean sea level

GOVERNOR'S
BEACH

CAMP
BAY

LITTLE
BAY

0   1   2

KM

EUROPA POINT

Figure 19. View north in Camp Bay in September 1997 showing major rockfall earlier in the year adjacent to beach resort facilities. Parson's Lodge Battery (Fig. 13) can be seen to the top left.

Figure 20. Quaternary scree breccia exposed in a disused quarry north of Catalan Bay, viewed from the south (cf. Figs. 3 and 18). The large size and sharp angularity of the Gibraltar Limestone clasts have been used to infer formation by freeze-thaw action under a more extreme climate than presently exists on Gibraltar. From Rose and Rosenbaum (1990), courtesy of the Institution of Royal Engineers.

potable water of some 1×10^6 m^3 per year. Exploration drilling focused on locating fracture zones. Vertical boreholes were tested for pumping yield and generally demonstrated a rapid decline in water quality, even where drawdown was very small. The greatest potential for sustained discharge was found to occur in shallowly inclined boreholes. Discharge quality was clearly sensitive to a range of factors, including immediate rainfall events, tidal fluctuations, permeability of the aquifer, borehole design, and anthropogenic effects. However, exploration also revealed oil contamination of the groundwater within the Rock, most significantly near the naval dockyards to the southwest and less so beneath the north face, one of the factors influencing the decision not to develop the aquifer at present.

An upper unconfined aquifer of fresh water and a lower confined aquifer of brackish water are known from the Quaternary sands of the isthmus. Some 9% of Gibraltar water is supplied from 19 shallow wells developed in the upper aquifer, whose water is high in chloride content and has a high degree of hardness, but is useful for blending with water produced by desalination. Construction of the Royal Air Force airfield has largely sealed the surface of the isthmus with tarmac, inhibiting rainwater recharge, but unpublished studies have investigated the possibility of storage and/or artificial recharge utilizing surface runoff from the airfield.

Seawater

Since 1953, but particularly since 1966, desalination of seawater has been developed as the main source of potable water on Gibraltar. It contributed some 49% of the total public water supply in 1976, which had increased to about 90% by 1992—although on running costs alone, water derived from desalination is about three times as expensive as water derived from wells.

To reduce demand for potable water, there is a separate sanitary water supply (Fig. 29). Seawater is pumped, stored, and distributed to all households for flushing toilets, fire fighting, street cleaning, and any purpose where the use of potable water is not essential. Water is pumped from the sea at two sources, because the system of reservoir storage and supply is divided into two districts, one for the north and town, the other for the south (Rose, 2000 b). Nearly 4×10^6 m^3 are pumped annually, about four times the consumption of potable water.

THE GEOENVIRONMENTAL LEGACY

Gibraltar has been progressively fortified by military engineering works for over 800 years, successively by the Moors, Spanish, and British. From the early eighteenth century until recent years much of the major construction work was directed and often carried out by Royal Engineers, but in 1994 disbandment of 1st (Fortress) Specialist Team Royal Engineers brought over two centuries of British military engineering on the Rock to an end—and provided a legacy of works and land now largely

Figure 21. Part of the Gibraltar airfield, viewed aerially from the west on 18 July 1944, showing the frontier fence bordering Spain to the north (left) and a large force of aircraft (predominantly Dakotas for troop transport) parked adjacent to the airstrip in preparation for the imminent Allied invasion of southern France. The only road from Spain to Gibraltar is seen in the foreground: it extends south (right) across the airstrip to the city. Courtesy of the Imperial War Museum, London: photo MH24024.

inherited by civilian bodies responsible to the Gibraltar Government. That legacy includes:

Geological database

Published geological observations and interpretations were generated from 1771 to the 1860s by a succession of military personnel; in 1876, the first geological survey was carried out to improve water supply to the town and naval/military garrison; in 1943, geological mapping to facilitate tunnel construction was carried out by the only noncommissioned British military geologist ever to serve as such; between 1945 and 1948, more detailed mapping and geotechnical studies were carried out by the only British military geologist to serve full time as such in peacetime since the early nineteenth century; between 1967 and 1990, and to lesser extent subsequently, part-time British reserve army geologists carried out a series of geotechnical studies, primarily relating to slope and tunnel stability; and in 1991, the Royal Engineers School of Military Survey published the only detailed geological map sheet available for the peninsula—the only geological map as such published by the British army in peacetime during the twentieth century.

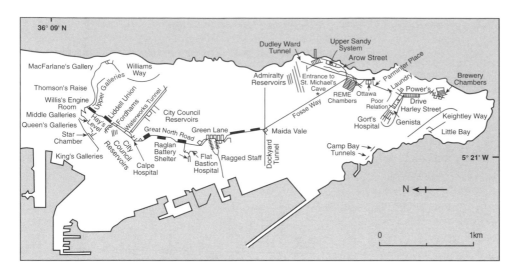

Figure 22. Plan of the main tunnels on Gibraltar. A northern system was built first, largely developed behind the north face of the Rock, which overlooks the isthmus extending northward into Spain. A southern system was developed later, in the then-main military base area on the southeast side of the Rock, facing the Mediterranean Sea. These two systems were later joined by a north-south access tunnel, the Great North Road, and its continuation as the Fosse Way, completed in 1944. (Other tunnels cannot conveniently be illustrated on this scale, but cf. Figure 23.) From Rose (1998), courtesy of The Geological Society, London.

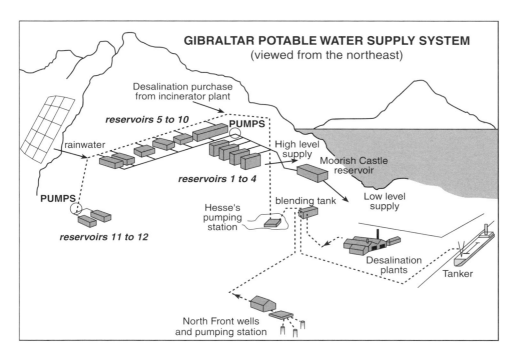

Figure 23. Cross section diagram of collection, storage, and supply of domestic potable water, showing main underground reservoirs and associated tunnel systems. Major reservoirs are about 60 m long, 15 m high, and 6 m wide, each with a capacity of about 4500 m^3. From Rose (1998), courtesy of The Geological Society, London, based on a diagram provided by Lyonnaise des Eaux (Gibraltar) Ltd., courtesy of M. Perez.

TABLE 2. PERIODS AND PURPOSES OF MAJOR TUNNELING ON GIBRALTAR

Period	Purpose
1782–1799	When Gibraltar was besieged by Spanish and French forces entrenched across the isthmus at the Spanish lines (Fig. 15), the British garrison tunneled behind the north face of the Rock to achieve vantage points from which cannon fire could be brought to bear on enemy batteries, so producing the Upper Galleries of Figure 22.
1880–1915	After a long gap in which there had been no tunneling, the Army, the Admiralty, and the City Council all began underground excavation to provide ammunition magazines, communications tunnels, or water reservoirs. The army extended the Genista Cave to form the Beefsteak Magazine in 1895 and Admiralty contractors drove the Dockyard Tunnel east through the Rock to provide access to quarries in Sandy Bay in 1898/1899 (Fig. 22). Construction of the modern water supply for the city commenced with excavation of four reservoirs within the western Rock (Figs. 22 and 23).
1933–1938	Construction of reservoirs for water storage (reservoirs 6 to 9 and the first part of 10 as shown in Fig. 23, leading off Waterworks Tunnel shown in Fig. 22), and more particularly the construction of air raid shelters and underground hospitals, caused much tunneling activity.
1939–1945	A greatly increased garrison during World War Two required new accommodation space, and space for reserves of food, equipment, and ammunition. The northern system indicated in Figure 22 was developed first, followed by the main military base area on the southeastern side of the Rock, where it was hidden and protected from Spain. The two areas were soon joined by a north-south access tunnel.
1956–1968	The existing tunnels were linked together in a more efficient manner, and additional storage chambers, reservoirs (11 and 12 of Fig. 23) and access routes (e.g., Dudley Ward Tunnel and Keightley Way of Fig. 22) were hewn out of the Rock.

Figure 24. The early stages of construction of the REME (Royal Electrical and Mechanical Engineers) workshop chamber during World War II. With a span of 16 m, height to crown of arch of 10 m, and length of 120 m, this unlined chamber was the largest excavated within the Gibraltar Limestone. Courtesy of the Imperial War Museum, London: photo RG128.

Figure 25. Scaling to remove the loose rock that in time develops by stress relief in the tunnels and chambers of Gibraltar, which are mostly unlined. The most extensive parts of the system were excavated during World War II, when communication tunnels were cut initially to 2 × 2 m, later to 2.6 × 2.6 m cross section. Chambers were cut to accommodate huts of standard 7.3 and 11 m span, for speed and economy. Initially chambers were cut with flat roofs, but later those with span exceeding 3.7 m were driven with arched roofs to minimize the incidence of rock falls. Main tunnels were increased to 3.7 × 3.7 m cross section to accommodate vehicle traffic, later extended to 4.6 × 4.2 m for through traffic routes. From Rosenbaum and Rose, 1991b, © British Crown copyright 1991/MoD. Reproduced with the permission of Her Britannic Majesty's Stationery Office.

Historically significant fortifications

Fortifications as they currently exist on Gibraltar have been repeatedly upgraded and adapted since at least the twelfth century, but still include elements dating from the period of Moorish occupation (notably the Tower of Homage: part of a largely fourteenth century castle), and later that of the Spanish (notably the Charles V Wall to the south of the city). British fortifications developed over 13 main areas, each with a specific role in the defense of the Rock, now provide a wealth of sites of historical interest that constrain development of the modern city but merit consideration for increased development as tourist attractions.

Large harbor

The harbor, greatly extended at the end of the nineteenth century to support a large British fleet, was partly infilled at its northern end in 1989 as pressure for civilian building land came to outweigh demand for port facilities. Infill was by sand dredged from just off the southeast shore, transported by suction dredge for hydraulic placement behind rock fill bunds. Progress was slowed, however, by the need to deal with unexploded ordnance dumped earlier in the source area.

Operational airfield

The Royal Air Force airfield, constructed by the military largely as a very necessary wartime expedient, has mostly been transferred to civilian use. The airport tarmac covers much of the surface of the Isthmus Sands, limiting recharge to the unconfined aquifer which exists within the Sands, but providing some potential for artificial recharge.

Extensive tunnel system

Tunnels and underground chambers are a major feature of the Rock, mostly constructed in five phases between 1782 and 1968, predominantly during World War II. Total length is now about 50 km. A program of scanline surveys has monitored tunnel integrity in recent years, followed by scaling of loose blocks (Fig. 25) or emplacement of support structures where necessary to facilitate regular pedestrian or vehicular use. Some tunnels now provide civilian road access, tourist sites, or storage areas;

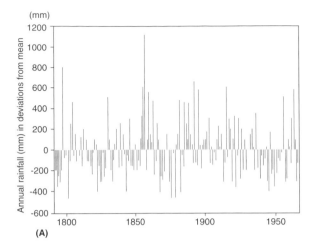

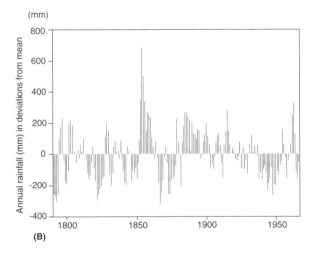

Figure 26. Annual rainfall from the late eighteenth to mid-twentieth centuries, expressed as deviation from the mean: (A) raw, (B) filtered. From Wright et al. (1994), courtesy of The Geological Society, London.

others have yet to be assigned a significant civilian role on decommissioning from military use.

Quarried slopes

Lack of major winter frosts ensures that most natural and cut slopes on Gibraltar are relatively stable, but high groundwater pressure following seasonally heavy rainfall leads to some instability, and pressure to utilize land beneath cliff or former quarry faces for new building construction or car parking has heightened local concern for slope stabilization measures (Fig. 30).

Dual water-supply system

At their peak strength on the Rock, the armed forces utilized potable water supplies separate from those of the civilian population. Both stored water mostly in underground reservoirs (sup-

plemented by surface-built tanks for the armed forces), and for much of the twentieth century used rainwater collected from surface catchments to supplement other sources, but eventually came to adopt desalination as the primary source of potable water. Demand for potable water on Gibraltar is currently reduced by about 80% by provision of a separate supply of salt water for sanitary use. A fresh water lens within the Rock might be developed as a groundwater source in the future, but is subject to some contamination from suspected fuel leakage.

Areas of natural habitat

Restricted access to much of the Rock on the grounds of military security has preserved substantial areas from urbanization. The Upper Rock Nature Reserve was created from land decommissioned from military use and made accessible to the public in 1991. It contains about 1 220 000 m^2 of land, about 60% of which is still in a fairly natural state on Gibraltar. Militarily restricted access has also preserved some sites of significant archaeological interest, notably the Late Pleistocene sequences in the Governor's Beach area (Rose and Stringer, 1997). About 30% of the former military estate has been decommissioned in recent years, generating potential for both development and also conservation (Rose and Hardman, 1994, 1996; Rose et al., 1997).

CONCLUSIONS

As a consequence of long-term military occupation and engineering on Gibraltar, the present civilian community has inherited its understanding of the geology of the Rock; numerous fortifications with the potential for development as sites of tourist interest; a large harbor and an operational airfield; and a significant area of land still in a natural state—all of value as the former fortress is now increasingly developed as a center for finance and tourism.

But the geoenvironmental legacy includes problems. The massive fortifications constrain development of the modern city, for there is a need to balance increasing urbanization with appropriate conservation. Engineering works relating to the natural slopes and cliffs have affected their long-term stability, necessitating a variety of stabilization measures. Excavation through the Rock has produced a network of largely unlined tunnels and chambers, now partly redundant, whose roof integrity requires monitoring and some maintenance for continued safe use. If groundwater is to be developed, either by skimming from a fresh water lens within the Rock or by artificial recharge of unconsolidated sands beneath the airfield tarmac, contamination by fuel leakage must be eliminated. Geotechnical studies on the famous Rock are not yet at an end.

ACKNOWLEDGMENTS

Information used in this chapter has been derived from work begun on Gibraltar in 1973 and still continuing. It provides

Figure 27. The main east coast water catchments above Sandy Bay viewed from the south prior to decommissioning in 1993. Sheets of corrugated iron fastened to wooden battens cover the smoothed upper surface of a 200 m high Quaternary scree breccia/Catalan Sand slope. Hotel developments at the toe of the slope indicate scale (cf. Figs. 7, 17, and 18). From Rose and Rosenbaum (1990), courtesy of the Institution of Royal Engineers.

Figure 28. Disused quarry in the Quaternary Catalan Sands, at the toe of the main east coast water catchment slope, viewed from the north in 1989. Failure of part of the weakly cemented eolianites blocked the road in 1996. Stabilization measures were introduced as part of a road-widening scheme in 1997–1998, including the construction of a major retaining wall. From Rose and Rosenbaum (1990), courtesy of the Institution of Royal Engineers.

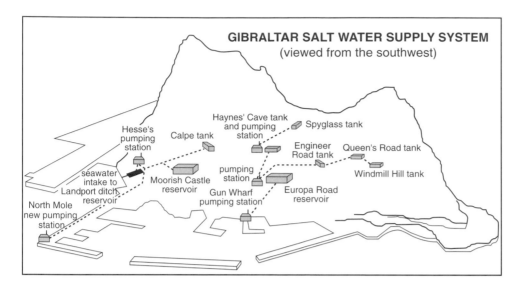

Figure 29. Gibraltar's salt-water supply system, for sanitary use. From Rose (2000b), courtesy of The Geological Society, London, based on a diagram provided by Lyonnaise des Eaux (Gibraltar) Ltd., courtesy of M. Perez.

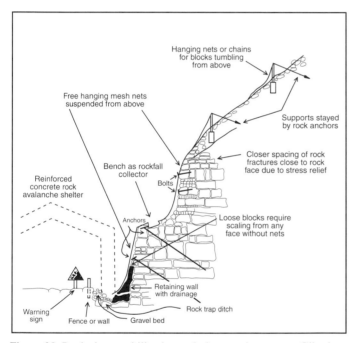

Figure 30. Rock slope stabilization techniques to be seen on Gibraltar. From Rose and Rosenbaum (1991b), courtesy of the Gibraltar Heritage Trust; after Fookes and Sweeney (1976).

a synthesis and review, amplified by new data, of work published by the author solely or jointly in a variety of books and journals since 1989. Grateful thanks are due as acknowledged in figure captions for permission to reuse illustrations, and to K. D'Souza, N. Wilson, and J. Pickard of Royal Holloway, respectively, for printing of photographs, artwork, and word processing the manuscript. The original manuscript has benefited from constructive comment by Michael S. Rosenbaum and Marie C. Johnson.

REFERENCES CITED

Anonymous, 1992, Abseil anchoring saves Gibraltar cliff face: Ground Engineering, v. 25, March, p. 10–11.

Anonymous, 1999, Sweat on the Rock: Ground Engineering, v. 32, August, p. 12–13.

Anonymous, 2000, Taking to the slopes: Ground Engineering, v. 33, February, p. 19 and 27.

Bailey, E.B., 1952, Notes on Gibraltar and the Northern Rif: Geological Society [London] Quarterly Journal, v. 108, p. 157–175.

Bosence, D.W.J., Wood, J.L., Rose, E.P.F., and Qing, H., 2000, Low- and high-frequency sea-level changes control peritidal carbonate cycles, facies and dolomitization in the Rock of Gibraltar (Early Jurassic, Iberian Peninsula): Geological Society [London] Journal, v. 157, p. 61–74.

Cotton, J.C., 1948, The tunnels of Gibraltar, in Anonymous, The civil engineer in war, Volume 3: London, Institution of Civil Engineers, p. 229–248.

Dear, I.C.B., ed., 1995, The Oxford companion to the Second World War: Oxford, Oxford University Press, 1343 p.

Doody, M.C., 1981, Gibraltar's water supply: Institution of Water Engineers and Scientists Journal, v. 35, p. 151–154.

Fookes, P.G., and Sweeney, M., 1976, Stabilisation and control of local rock falls and degrading rock slopes: Quarterly Journal of Engineering Geology, v. 9, p. 27–35.

Geel, T., and Roep, T.B., 1998, Oligocene to middle Miocene basin development in the eastern Betic Cordilleras, SE Spain (Vélez Rubio Corridor—España): Reflections of West Mediterranean plate-tectonic reorganizations: Basin Research, v. 10, p. 325–343.

Gonzales, F.J., 1966, The water supply in Gibraltar: Aqua: International Water Supply Association Quarterly Bulletin, v. 2, p. 58–67.

Haycraft, T.W.R., 1946a, The Gibraltar runway: Royal Engineers Journal, v. 60, p. 225–230.

Haycraft, T.W.R., 1946b, The Gibraltar tunnels: Royal Engineers Journal, v. 60, p. 310–320.

Hughes, Q., and Migos, A., 1995, Strong as the Rock of Gibraltar: Gibraltar, Exchange Publications, 416 p.

Hurst, G.W., 1959, Collection of water from cloud at Gibraltar: Institution of Water Engineers Journal, v. 13, p. 341–352.

Imrie, N., 1798, A short mineralogical description of the mountain of Gibraltar: Royal Society of Edinburgh Transactions, v. 4, p. 191–202.

Jackson, W.G.F., 1987, The Rock of the Gibraltarians: Cranbury, New Jersey, Associated University Presses, 379 p.

James, T., 1771, History of the Herculean Straits, commonly called the Straits of Gibraltar: London, Rivington, v. 1, 389 p.; v. 2, 416 p.

Lauder, J.G., 1963, Tunnelling in Gibraltar: Royal Engineers Journal, v. 77, p. 339–369.

Owen, E.F., and Rose, E.P.F., 1997, Early Jurassic brachiopods from the Rock of Gibraltar, and their Tethyan significance: Palaeontology, v. 40, p. 497–513.

Qing, H., Bosence, D.W.J., and Rose, E.P.F., 2001, Dolomitization by pene-saline seawater in Early Jurassic peritidal platform carbonates, Gibraltar, western Mediterranean: Sedimentology, v. 48, p. 153–163.

Qing, H., Rose, E.P.F., and Bosence, D.W.J., 1998, Petrography and O-C-Sr iso-tope systematics of dolomites in the Lower Jurassic Gibraltar Limestone Formation, Gibraltar, *in* Cañaveras, J.C., et al., eds., International Sedi-mentological Conference Abstracts, 15th: Alicante, Spain, p. 643–644.

Ramsay, A.C., 1877, Report on the question of the supply of fresh water to the town and garrison of Gibraltar: British Geological Survey, printed report, 10 p.

Ramsay, A.C., and Geikie, J., 1876, Geological map of Gibraltar: British Geo-logical Survey, hand colored, scale 1:2500, 4 sheets.

Ramsay, A.C., and Geikie, J., 1878, On the geology of Gibraltar: Geological Society [London] Quarterly Journal, v. 34, p. 505–541.

Ramsey, W.G., ed., 1978, After the battle no. 21: Gibraltar: London, Battle of Britain Prints International, 54 p.

Rose, E.P.F., 1994, A curious plan of defence for Gibraltar: Royal Engineers Journal, v. 108, p. 100–101.

Rose, E.P.F., 1996, Geology and the army in nineteenth century Britain: A sci-entific and educational symbiosis?: Geologists' Association Proceedings, v. 107, p. 129–141.

Rose, E.P.F., 1998, Environmental geology of Gibraltar: Living with limited resources, *in* Bennett, M.R., and Doyle, P., eds., Issues in environmental geology: A British perspective: Geological Society [London], p. 81–121.

Rose, E.P.F., 1999, The military background of John W. Pringle, in 1826 found-ing superintendent of the Geological Survey of Ireland: Irish Journal of Earth Sciences, v. 17, p. 61–70.

Rose, E.P.F., 2000a, The pre-Quaternary geological evolution of Gibraltar, *in* Finlayson, J.C., et al., eds., Gibraltar during the Quaternary: The south-ernmost part of Europe in the last two million years: Gibraltar, Gibraltar Government Heritage Publications, p. 1–29.

Rose, E.P.F., 2000b, Geology and the fortress of Gibraltar, *in* Rose, E.P.F., and Nathanail, C.P., eds., Geology and warfare: Examples of the influence of ter-rain and of geologists on military operations: Geological Society [London], p. 236–275.

Rose, E.P.F., 2002, Founders of Gibraltarian geology: Gibraltar, Gibraltar Gov-ernment Heritage Publications (in press).

Rose, E.P.F., and Cooper, J.A., 1997, G.B. Alexander's studies on the Jurassic of Gibraltar and the Carboniferous of England: The end of a mystery?: Geo-logical Curator, v. 6, p. 247–254.

Rose, E.P.F., and Hardman, E.C., 1994, The caves, tunnels and rocks of Gibraltar: Sanctuary: The Ministry of Defence Conservation Magazine, v. 23, p. 16–17.

Rose, E.P.F., and Hardman, E.C., 1996, Conservation and the geology of Gibral-tar: Almoraima, Revista de Estudios Campogibraltareños, v. 15, p. 35–51.

Rose, E.P.F., and Hardman, E.C., 2000, The Quaternary geology of Gibraltar, *in* Finlayson, J.C., et al., eds., Gibraltar during the Quaternary: The south-ernmost part of Europe in the last two million years: Gibraltar, Gibraltar Government Heritage Publications, p. 39–84.

Rose, E.P.F., Hardman, E.C., and Cooper, J.H., 1997, Cave studies on Gibraltar: Sanctuary: The Ministry of Defence Conservation Magazine, v. 26, p. 30–31.

Rose, E.P.F., and Hughes, N.F., 1993a, Sapper Geology. 1. Lessons learnt from world war: Royal Engineers Journal, v. 107, p. 27–33.

Rose, E.P.F., and Hughes, N.F., 1993b, Sapper Geology. 2. Geologist pools in the reserve army: Royal Engineers Journal, v. 107, p. 173–181.

Rose, E.P.F., and Hughes, N.F., 1993c, Sapper Geology. 3. Engineer Specialist Pool geologists: Royal Engineers Journal, v. 107, p. 306–316.

Rose, E.P.F., and Rosenbaum, M.S., 1990, Royal Engineer geologists and the geology of Gibraltar: Gibraltar, Gibraltar Museum, 55 p. (Reprinted from the Royal Engineers Journal, v. 103 [for 1989], p. 142–151, 248–259; v. 104 [for 1990], p. 61–76, 128–148).

Rose, E.P.F., and Rosenbaum, M.S., 1991a, The Rock of Gibraltar: Geology Today, v. 7, p. 95–101.

Rose, E.P.F., and Rosenbaum, M.S., 1991b, A field guide to the geology of Gibraltar: Gibraltar, Gibraltar Museum, 192 p.

Rose, E.P.F., and Rosenbaum, M.S., 1992, Geology of Gibraltar: School of Mil-itary Survey Miscellaneous Map 45 (published 1991) and its historical background: Royal Engineers Journal, v. 106, p. 168–173.

Rose, E.P.F., and Rosenbaum, M.S., 1993a, British military geologists: The for-mative years to the end of the First World War: Geologists' Association Proceedings, v. 104, p. 41–49.

Rose, E.P.F., and Rosenbaum, M.S., 1993b, British military geologists: Through the Second World War to the end of the Cold War: Geologists' Association Proceedings, v. 104, p. 95–108.

Rose, E.P.F., and Rosenbaum, M.S., 1994a, The Rock of Gibraltar and its Neo-gene tectonics: Paleontologia i Evolució, v. 24–25, p. 411–421.

Rose, E.P.F., and Rosenbaum, M.S., 1994b, The pre-Quaternary geological evo-lution of Gibraltar, *in* Rodríguez Vidal, J., et al., eds., Gibraltar during the Quaternary: Seville, Asociación Española para el Estudio del Cuaternario Monografías, v. 2, p. 6–11.

Rose, E.P.F., and Rosenbaum, M.S., 1998, British military geologists through war and peace in the 19th and 20th centuries, *in* Underwood, J.R., Jr., and Guth, P.L., eds., Military geology in war and peace: Geological Society of America, Reviews in Engineering Geology, v. 13, p. 29–39.

Rose, E.P.F., and Stringer, C.B., 1997, Gibraltar woman and Neanderthal Man: Geology Today, v. 13, p. 179–184.

Rosenbaum, M.S., and Rose, E.P.F., 1991a, Geology of Gibraltar: Hermitage, School of Military Survey Miscellaneous Map 45, scales 1:10 000 and 1:20 000, 1 sheet (2 sides).

Rosenbaum, M.S., and Rose, E.P.F., 1991b, The tunnels of Gibraltar: Gibraltar, Gibraltar Museum, 32 p.

Rosenbaum, M.S., and Rose, E.P.F., 1992a, Geology and military tunnels: Geology Today, v. 8, p. 92–98.

Rosenbaum, M.S., and Rose, E.P.F., 1992b, Subterranean Gibraltar: The tunnels and caves of the Rock: Bulletin Subterranea Britannica, v. 28, p. 3–12.

Rosenbaum, M.S., and Rose, E.P.F., 1994, The influence of geology on urban renewal, *in* Oliveira, R., et al., eds., International Congress of the Interna-tional Association of Engineering Geology Proceedings, 7th, Lisbon, Vol-ume 3: Rotterdam, A.A. Balkema, p. 2283–2291.

Rosenbaum, M.S., Rose, E.P.F., and Wilkinson-Buchanan, F.W., 1994, The influence of excavation technique on the integrity of unlined tunnel walls in Gibraltar, *in* Oliveira, R., et al., eds., International Congress of the International Association of Engineering Geology Proceedings, 7th, Lis-bon, Volume 6: Rotterdam, A.A. Balkema, p. 4137–4144.

Scott, A., 1914, The new harbour works and dockyard at Gibraltar: Institution of Civil Engineers Minutes of Proceedings, v. 197, p. 1–78.

Wilson, W.H., 1945, Tunnelling in Gibraltar during the 1939–1945 War: Insti-tute of Mining and Metallurgy Transactions, v. 55, p. 193–269.

Wright, E.P., Rose, E.P.F., and Perez, M., 1994, Hydrogeological studies on the Rock of Gibraltar: Quarterly Journal of Engineering Geology, v. 27, p. S15–S29.

Manuscript Accepted by the Society October 27, 2000

Geological Society of America
Reviews in Engineering Geology, Volume XIV
2001

Fifty-four years of ephemeral channel response to two years of intense World War II military activity, Camp Iron Mountain, Mojave Desert, California

Kyle K. Nichols
Paul R. Bierman
Department of Geology, University of Vermont, Burlington, Vermont 05405, USA

ABSTRACT

During World War II, U.S. Army personnel lived, trained, and executed mock battles on low gradient piedmonts (~2°) in the Mojave Desert. For example, Camp Iron Mountain (established in 1942 by General George S. Patton, Jr., and used until 1944) housed up to 20 000 Army personnel at any specific time. The camp is located on the large alluvial piedmont that extends from the Iron Mountains and is drained by shallow ephemeral channels.

At this camp, we made 18 detailed topographic maps in order to compare drainage networks of six undisturbed control plots and 12 plots disturbed by army activities. There are significant differences between the morphometery of small-scale, ephemeral drainage networks on control plots, on plots bisected by stone-walled walkways, and on plots down gradient of former army roads. Control plot channels are wider (2.05 ± 1.48 m) and deeper (8.8 ± 4.5 cm) than channels in walkway plots (width: 1.19 ± 0.71 m, depth: 7.4 ± 4.1 cm) and in road plots (width: 1.18 ± 0.61 m, depth: 7.2 ± 6.7 cm).

The military's modification of the landscape affected subsequent channel originations and orientations. Channel heads were found in 76% of the compacted and smoothed walkways. In walkway plots, 80% of walkways caused the orientation of channels to deviate from the steepest piedmont gradient by more than 20°. After more than 50 years, road berms still act as local drainage divides. Down gradient of each intact road berm, there is a wide (20–40 m) zone in which no channels exist. Where channels have developed below intact road berms, they are smaller than channels in undisturbed control plots. Down gradient of breached road berms, wide, braided channels are common. Fifty-four years after camp abandonment, the channel network at Camp Iron Mountain has yet to recover, primarily because rock alignments and road berms continue to influence drainage patterns and local gradients.

INTRODUCTION

A significant amount of military training is done in arid regions where rates of surface processes are slow and surface

kknichol@zoo.uvm.edu

change is often episodic and thus difficult to observe and quantify. The U.S. military, as a steward of large tracts of land, is required by Army Regulation AR 200-2 to monitor the environmental effects of training exercises in arid regions (Prose, 1985). In order to place in perspective the effect of military maneuvers on the desert environment, one must understand

Nichols, K.K., and Bierman, P.R., 2001, Fifty-four years of ephemeral channel response to two years of intense World War II military activity, Camp Iron Mountain, Mojave Desert, California, *in* Ehlen, J., and Harmon, R.S., eds., The Environmental Legacy of Military Operations: Boulder, Colorado, Geological Society of America Reviews in Engineering Geology, v. XIV, p. 123–136.

rates of geomorphic processes and the rate at which natural systems recover from disturbance. Because many desert processes are so slow, results of short-term monitoring are often inconclusive (Abrahams et al., 1984). A longer-term perspective may be gained by studying areas where military activity occurred over a known and discrete time frame. Such data may allow identification and implementation of training protocols that minimize environmental impact.

From 1942 to 1944, the U.S. Army established twelve temporary base camps and living quarters in the Desert Training Center (Fig. 1A). Camp Iron Mountain (~ 6 km^2) was built on a low-gradient piedmont surface extending > 10 km from the Iron Mountains to Danby Lake playa in the Mojave Desert (Fig. 1B). At this camp, the Army constructed an extensive (4 km by 1.5 km) grid of roads (Fig. 1C). During road construction, berms (30–40 cm high) were built on both sides of each road. Troops outlined walkways, tents, and roads with angular granitic clasts ranging in size from 10 to 20 cm (Fig. 2). After two years of continuous use, the Army dismantled the camps in May 1944 (Henley, 1989). Today, the only evidence of occupation is the presence of road berms, rock alignments, rock designs, and other artifacts, in various states of deterioration.

The Iron Mountains are Cretaceous granite (Miller et al., 1981). The piedmont meets the mountain front at a sharp angle and is dominated by granular granitic alluvium (grus); median grain size is 2 mm. The piedmont slopes uniformly ~2° to the east where Camp Iron Mountain is located (Fig. 1B). Shallow, 10-cm deep ephemeral channels form gentle channel-terrace topography and dissect the surface.

The Iron Mountain piedmont receives an average of 7.9 cm of precipitation a year (National Oceanic and Atmospheric Administration, 1982). Late summer thunderstorms and midwinter cyclonic events produce the majority of precipitation. Most precipitation infiltrates the grus. Runoff occurs only during rare, high-intensity rainfall events. Iverson et al. (1981) determined that runoff events in the western Mojave Desert probably occur about once per decade in undisturbed areas and more frequently in disturbed areas. As overland flow moves down the piedmont, some of the flow infiltrates the unsaturated grus (Bull, 1991; Ritter, 1978).

In areas where no channels exist, sheetwash is the dominant overland flow mechanism (Horton, 1945). Sheetwash continues until flow depth is great enough that: (1) a critical basal shear stress is reached and channel incision begins (Horton, 1945; Montgomery and Dietrich, 1994), or (2) raindrops cannot obliterate incipient channels as they begin to concentrate flow (Dunne, 1980). Small channels then form and transport sediment until the sediment load becomes greater than the transport capacity. When deposition occurs, caused by flow loss (infiltration) or a decrease in local gradient, many of the small channels diffuse into the planar surface. Such discontinuous channel morphologies dominate inside Camp Iron Mountain.

Historic photographs document that constant foot, vehicle, and tank traffic destroyed most, if not all, of the small channels

during the occupation of Camp Iron Mountain (Fig. 2). Thus, we can reasonably assume a surface absent of channels inside the camp when our experiment began in May 1944. We assume that road berms and rock alignments were intact at the time of evacuation. Because the area is remote and the nearest populated town is more than 55 km away (Desert Center, California, population 120), post-army activity is limited to natural processes (overland flow and bioturbation) and occasional off-road vehicle (ORV) use. Around 1980, a fence was constructed around Camp Iron Mountain that stopped all ORV traffic (Bureau of Land Management, 1986).

Camp Iron Mountain provides a unique opportunity to investigate the redevelopment of an ephemeral channel network after two years of intense military training. We collected data 54 years after camp abandonment, in May 1998. In this chapter, we use our observations and data, in conjunction with previous research illustrating that human influence increases soil density (Prose, 1985; Webb et al., 1986), soil compaction, and soil surface smoothness (Iverson, 1980; Iverson et al., 1981), to develop a process model of channel response to military activity on low-gradient arid landscapes.

METHODS

In order to determine whether environmental impacts persisted half a century after the U.S. Army abandoned Camp Iron Mountain, we compared ephemeral channel depths, widths, areas, orientations, and drainage densities in three types of experimental plots (60 m by 60 m square areas). *Control plots* are representative of undisturbed conditions and are outside Camp Iron Mountain. *Walkway plots* contain rock alignments and are representative of disturbed conditions inside the camp. *Road plots* contain road berms at the up-gradient boundary and are also representative of disturbed conditions inside the camp. By comparing data gathered from these different types of plots, we determine the degree to which past military activities still affect the desert surface, in particular, the geometry of ephemeral channels that drain the Iron Mountain piedmont.

Survey methods

We outlined plot boundaries by using a Pentax PCS-2 total station to delineate 60 m orthogonal sides on all plots except Control Plot 3, where we used a tape and compass survey. We used flags to outline all channels within plot boundaries. Each plot was surveyed using a Trimble 4400 real time kinematic differential Global Positioning System (GPS), precise to within several centimeters horizontally and ~1 cm vertically. We surveyed topography using a five-meter grid spacing and surveyed each channel by making a series of cross sections, with the exception of Control Plot 3 and Road Plot 1, where cross sections were not measured. Each cross section consisted of two bank-top points, two bank-bottom points, and any points of significant topographical change within the channel. In places

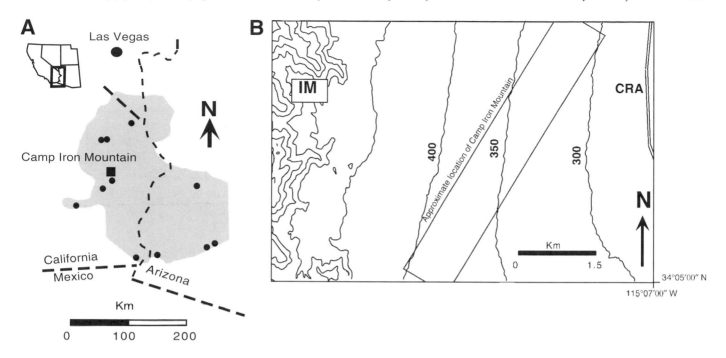

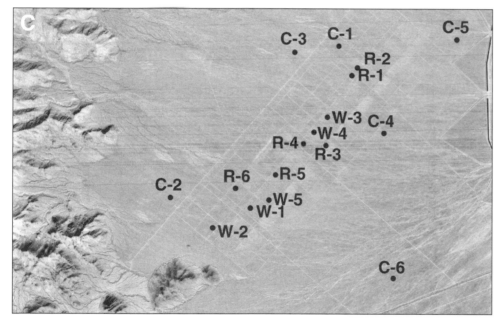

Figure 1. A: Location of the Desert Training Center (shaded in gray) in the southwestern United States. Circles are temporary base camps, Camp Iron Mountain shown by solid square. B: Topography of the Iron Mountain piedmont and the Iron Mountains. IM—Iron Mountains, CRA—Colorado River Aqueduct. Contour interval is 50 m. Map based on the Granite Pass, California 7.5′ U.S.G.S. quadrangle, 1985. C: Aerial photograph of Camp Iron Mountain area and location of all plots at approximately same scale as 1B. Roads are orthogonal. C—Control plots, W—Walkway plots, and R—Road plots (U.S. Geological Survey aerial photograph NAPP 6822-240 10/2/95).

where channel banks could not be defined, the channel margins were labeled as wash banks. In walkway plots, we also surveyed all rock alignments. For each plot, an average of 454 topographic data points was collected.

After surveying each plot, we contoured the data at ten-centimeter intervals. Before removing the channel boundary flags, we field-checked maps of each plot to verify the accuracy of channel locations. We made observations of characteristics, inside and outside each plot, that influence channel morphology. We made a photographic record of each plot, and noted photograph locations and orientations on each map.

Plot locations

We randomized the selection of all plot locations within characteristic areas. Control plots were located outside Camp Iron Mountain. Walkway plots were inside the camp and contained visible rock alignments and no roads. We chose walkway plot locations by walking inside the camp until we could see rock alignments extending approximately 80 m in all directions. To minimize bias, we walked 20 additional steps, in the same direction, before setting up the plot boundaries. All road plots contained a road berm that formed the up-gradient boundary. Road

Figure 2. Photograph of Camp Iron Mountain after a sandstorm. Rock alignments are visible in front of tents. After camp abandonment, rock alignments were left intact. Foot and vehicle traffic has obliterated ephemeral channel network. National Archives photo #111-SC-145201.

plots did not contain roads or rock alignments, except for one plot that contained a 10-m rock alignment. We chose the road plots by walking along a road until we could not see rock alignments for at least 60 m.

Data reduction

We used cross section data to calculate channel depths, widths, and channel cross-sectional areas. Channel depths are defined as bank-bottom elevations subtracted from bank-top elevations. We used the GPS northing (N) and easting (E) coordinates and the following equation to define the channel widths:

$$W = [(E_L - E_R)^2 + (N_L - N_R)^2]^{1/2} \qquad (1)$$

where W is the width, E_L is left bank easting coordinate, E_R is right bank easting coordinate, N_L is left bank northing coordinate, and N_R is right bank northing coordinate. Cross-sectional areas are defined as the channel width multiplied by the average channel depth.

We used our high-resolution topographic maps to determine channel surface areas, drainage densities, and channel orientations. We digitized each map to calculate the total area of each plot occupied by channels. Drainage densities for plots are defined as the sum of channel lengths divided by the plot area (Dunne and Leopold, 1978). The drainage densities for channels inside old walkways (inside the walkway plots) are defined as the sum of channel lengths inside old walkways divided by the old

walkway area. Since most channels in the plots are linear, we determined channel orientation by measuring each representative channel orientation with respect to north. For channels with curvature, we measured the average direction of flow determined by connecting the upstream end of the channel to the downstream end of the channel.

RESULTS

Visual observations made at Camp Iron Mountain imply that human influences on the surface morphology persist 54 years after the camps were abandoned. Detailed topographic mapping shows differences in channel characteristics between control and experimental plots. The data support visual observations that ephemeral channel networks have not recovered to background conditions more than a half-century after Army abandonment.

Depth, width, and cross-sectional area data

On average, control plot channels are significantly deeper (99.9% confidence level) than walkway ($t = 6.27$, $df = 1396$, $P < 0.001$) and road ($t = 7.63$, $df = 1397$, $P < 0.001$) plot channels, and have an average depth of 8.9 ± 4.5 cm ($n = 756$), where t is the statistic, df is the degrees of freedom, P is the probability value, and n is the sample population. Average channel depths in walkway and road plots are 7.4 ± 4.1 cm ($n = 647$) and 7.2 ± 6.7 cm ($n = 653$), respectively (Table 1). Channel depths in walkway and road plots are not statistically different ($t = 0.65$, $df = 1272$, $P > 0.52$). Data for all plots are right skewed (Fig. 3).

Channels in control plots are significantly wider (99.9% confidence level) than channels in walkway ($t = 9.29$, $df = 428$, $P < 0.001$) and road ($t = 8.53$, $df = 531$, $P < 0.001$) plots. Control plot channel widths average 2.05 ± 1.48 m ($n = 319$). Average channel widths for walkway and road plots are 1.19 ± 0.71 m ($n = 418$) and 1.18 ± 0.61 m ($n = 224$), respectively (Table 2). Widths of channels in walkway and road plots are not statistically different ($t = 0.58$, $df = 372$, $P > 0.56$). Control plot channels have a greater range in widths compared to widths in disturbed plots. Data are skewed to the right for all plots (Fig. 3).

Control plot channels have, on average, statistically larger cross-sectional areas than walkway ($t = 8.01$, $df = 409$, $P < 0.001$) and road ($t = 11.04$, $df = 385$, $P < 0.001$) plot channels (Table 3). The average cross-sectional area for control plot channels is 0.157 ± 0.039 m^2 ($n = 288$). The average cross-sectional areas for walkway and road plot channels are 0.077 ± 0.031 m^2 ($n = 331$) and 0.086 ± 0.060 m^2 ($n = 198$), respectively. Road plot channels have statistically larger cross-sectional areas than walkway plot channels ($t = 5.01$, $df = 449$, $P < 0.001$).

Channel area and drainage density

Control plot channel areas are statistically larger than walkway channel areas at the 90% confidence level ($t = 2.07$, $df = 9$, $P < 0.1$), and road channel areas at the 70% confidence level ($t = 1.26$, $df = 9$, $P < 0.3$). Channels in control plots cover an average of 733 ± 297 m^2, 20% of the average control plot area. Walkway plot channels cover an average of 432 ± 199 m^2, 12% of the average walkway plot area. The average road plot channel area is 490 ± 367 m^2, 14% of the average road plot area (Table 4). Walkway and road plot channel areas are not statistically different ($t = -0.34$, $df = 9$, $P > 0.5$).

Control plot drainage densities are not statistically different than walkway plot drainage densities ($t = 0.68$, $df = 9$, $P > 0.5$). The average drainage density for control plots is 0.096 ± 0.036 m/m^2, while walkway plots have an average drainage density of 0.084 ± 0.027 m/m^2. Road plots have an average drainage density of 0.067 ± 0.023 m/m^2 (Table 5). Road plot drainage densities are statistically smaller than control plot drainage densities at the 80% confidence level ($t = 1.71$, $df = 9$, $P < 0.2$) and walkway plot drainage densities at the 70% confidence level ($t = 1.19$, $df = 10$, $P < 0.3$).

Channel orientations

Channels are usually oriented down the Iron Mountain piedmont's steepest gradient, $103 \pm 16°$ based on a plot-by-plot analysis of our topographic maps. Walkway plot channel orientations are bimodal (Fig. 4). In fact, more channels in walkway plots have the same orientation as walkways (126°) than have the orientation of the average steepest gradient (103°). Control plot channels exhibit the largest range of orientations ($101 \pm 20°$), but

TABLE 1. CHANNEL DEPTHS FOR CONTROL, WALKWAY, AND ROAD PLOTS

Plot	Control (cm)	Walkway (cm)	Road (cm)
1	10.7 ± 5.4 (126)	6.5 ± 2.8 (100)	9.0 ± 4.0 (222)
2	7.4 ± 2.5 (59)	8.4 ± 4.1 (125)	6.1 ± 2.9 (127)
3	9.9 ± 5.0 (178)	5.5 ± 2.5 (80)	5.8 ± 2.5 (77)
4	7.9 ± 3.9 (155)	7.1 ± 4.4 (120)	7.6 ± 2.9 (69)
5	8.2 ± 4.1 (142)	6.1 ± 3.0 (61)	5.1 ± 2.4 (86)
6	8.1 ± 4.1 (96)	8.8 ± 4.8 (161)	7.7 ± 3.5 (72)
Average of all channels	8.9 ± 4.5 (756)	7.4 ± 4.1 (647)	7.2 ± 6.7 (653)

Note: Average and standard deviations are determined using *n* values in parenthesis. Paired depths for channel cross sections are assumed to be independent observations because left and right banks are poorly correlated ($r^2 = 0.05$).

control plots are more widely distributed across the piedmont surface than walkway and road plots (Fig. 1C). Road plot channels have the smallest range of orientations ($103 \pm 11°$), following the steepest piedmont gradient and consistent with the smooth surface topography below the intact road berms.

DISCUSSION

Camp Iron Mountain has been recovering from a discrete environmental impact for the past 54 years. Our data for ephemeral channels show that recovery is far from complete. There remain measurable and distinct differences between channel characteristics in control and experimental plots. The differences are primarily due to the presence of rock alignments, road berms, and the smoothing and compaction of the surface. By diverting shallow overland flow and changing surface roughness, human activity has altered surface water flow patterns within the camp as indicated by measurements made in the experimental plots. Our data support the conclusions of Iverson (1980) that ORV use, or in this study, military activity, reduces infiltration and changes the roughness of desert surfaces.

Control plots

Control plots are representative of undisturbed conditions on the Iron Mountain piedmont. Control plots are located both upslope and downslope of Camp Iron Mountain. The average channel depths, channel widths, channel areas, channel orientations, and drainage densities are similar for all control plots (Tables 1, 2, 3, 4, and 5).

On average, control plot channels are almost a meter wider and are more continuous than walkway and road plot channels, thus providing for greater channel areas and drainage densities (Tables 4 and 5). Control plot channels are on average 1.5 cm deeper than average walkway and road plot channels (Table 1). Average channel orientations deviate little ($101 \pm 20°$) even though control plot six is located at the convergence of the Iron Mountain and Granite Mountain piedmonts. The internal consistency of the

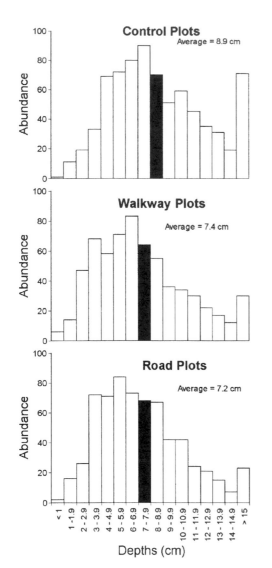

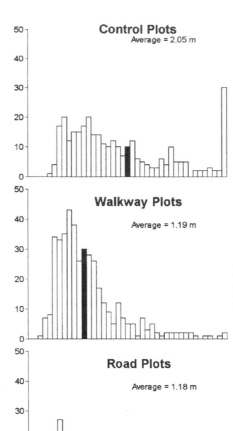

Figure 3. Distribution of channel depths and widths for control, walkway, and road plots. The black bar represents mean value.

TABLE 2. CHANNEL WIDTHS FOR CONTROL, WALKWAY, AND ROAD PLOTS

Plot	Control (m)	Walkway	Road
1	2.42 ± 1.37 (75)	1.02 ± 0.63 (78)	N.D.*
2	2.02 ± 2.02 (34)	1.10 ± 0.45 (65)	1.15 ± 0.50 (50)
3	N.D.*	1.34 ± 0.97 (58)	0.88 ± 0.57 (41)
4	2.10 ± 1.27 (75)	1.43 ± 0.83 (57)	1.36 ± 0.52 (35)
5	1.94 ± 1.58 (69)	1.09 ± 0.50 (76)	0.63 ± 0.27 (59)
6	1.63 ± 1.31 (55)	1.40 ± 0.69 (84)	2.23 ± 1.44 (38)
Average of all channels	2.05 ± 1.48 (308)	1.19 ± 0.71 (418)	1.18 ± 0.61 (223)

Note: Average and standard deviations are determined using *n* values in parenthesis.
   *N.D. = not determined

control plot data, despite the distance between plots (up to 3 km), supports the observation that the Iron Mountain piedmont is a homogeneous planar surface experiencing similar ephemeral channel processes along its entire length and width (Fig. 5).

Walkway plots

Channel characteristics in walkway plots are influenced strongly by the combination of rock alignments and the compaction and smoothing of roughness elements caused by two years of foot traffic on the walkways. Up gradient of some walkway areas, there are discontinuous rock alignments that disperse overland flow and impede channel incision. Where channels have incised, rock alignments influence the orientation of flow. Eighty percent of all walkway rock alignments act as a barricade to flow and cause channel orientations to deviate at least 20° from the steepest gradient (Fig. 4). Small channels that form in, or just up

TABLE 3. CHANNEL CROSS-SECTIONAL AREAS FOR CONTROL, WALKWAY, AND ROAD PLOTS

Plot	Control (m²)	Walkway (m²)	Road (m²)
1	0.219 ± 0.143 (64)	0.046 ± 0.031 (55)	N.D.*
2	0.119 ± 0.105 (30)	0.095 ± 0.058 (65)	0.061 ± 0.047 (48)
3	N.D.*	0.052 ± 0.046 (39)	0.040 ± 0.025 (31)
4	0.040 ± 0.025 (31)	0.101 ± 0.098 (56)	0.106 ± 0.062 (35)
5	0.106 ± 0.062 (35)	0.046 ± 0.040 (40)	0.029 ± 0.022 (59)
6	0.115 ± 0.122 (52)	0.127 ± 0.089 (78)	0.193 ± 0.146 (35)
Average of all channels	0.157 ± 0.039 (288)	0.077 ± 0.031 (331)	0.086 ± 0.060 (198)

Note: Average and standard deviations are determined using *n* values in parenthesis.
*N.D. = not determined

gradient of walkways, have orientations along the walkway (Fig. 6), until either the walkway ends, the flow has enough power to breach the rock alignment, or sediment load exceeds the transport capacity and the channels diffuse into the surface. Larger channels usually have flow directions controlled by overall topography, regardless of the presence of rock alignments (Fig. 7).

Interestingly, walkway plot channel areas are approximately half that of the control plot channel areas, while drainage densities are similar. Channel areas differ and drainage densities are similar because the more numerous, smaller, and discontinuous walkway channels (Fig. 7) have approximately the same total channel length as the less frequent, wider, and more continuous control plot channels (Fig. 5).

Compacting the soil and smoothing surface roughness elements aid in the incision of new channels (Iverson, 1980). Compaction decreases infiltration capacities (Hillel, 1980) and allows runoff at lower precipitation intensities and durations. Smooth surfaces generate greater flow velocities than rough surfaces, increasing basal shear stresses and promoting channel incision. Prose (1985) found that soils at Camp Iron Mountain were compacted enough after only one pass of a medium-sized tank to promote rill and gully formation within the tank tracks. The walkways experienced two years of foot traffic, which was effective in smoothing roughness elements and compacting the soil. Over 76% of walkways have channels that start within them, due presumably to decreased infiltration capacities and the smooth surface. Many of these channels dissipate further down gradient, but some channels extend beyond the plot boundaries.

Road plots

Most literature on the impact of roads on drainage networks centers on logging roads in mountainous regions. Logging roads cause increased erosion rates and landslide initiation (Montgomery, 1994), more peaked hydrographs (Wemple et al., 1996), and changes in channel morphology. We, however, are investigating the effects of temporary roads, established on a low-gradient surface in an arid environment. Our data do not suggest increased erosion rates, landslide initiation, or more peaked hydrographs, but do reveal changes in channel morphologies.

Channel characteristics of road plots are strongly influenced by the presence of paired road berms up gradient. Road berms act

TABLE 4. CHANNEL AREAS FOR CONTROL, WALKWAY, AND ROAD PLOTS

Plot	Control (m²)	Walkway (m²)	Road (m²)
1	1064	287	1160
2	477	302	630
3	603	361	314
4	1100	547	258
5	765	307	152
6	394	787	427
Average	733 ± 297	432 ± 199	490 ± 367

Note: Average and standard deviation are determined using plot values.

TABLE 5. DRAINAGE DENSITIES FOR CONTROL, WALKWAY, AND ROAD PLOTS

Plot	Control (m/m²)	Walkway (m/m²)	Road (m/m²)
1	0.123	0.071	0.100
2	0.052	0.068	0.091
3	0.068	0.056	0.052
4	0.138	0.097	0.049
5	0.124	0.078	0.045
6	0.073	0.132	0.061
Average	0.096 ± 0.036	0.084 ± 0.027	0.066 ± 0.023

Note: Average and standard deviation are determined using the plot values.

as local drainage divides, channeling and diverting overland flow. The paired berms around each road collect surface runoff and concentrate flow until either a crossroad of steeper gradient is encountered, or there is enough water to breach the berm and flow unconfined down the steepest gradient (Fig. 8). Intact road berms divert water away from some road plots. Down gradient of the intact road berms there is usually a zone (20 to 40 m) where shallow sheetflow must dominate and channels are absent (Fig. 9). Down gradient of a berm breach, the flow disperses and forms a braided channel (Fig. 10). The presence of wide, braided channels accounts for the larger average and standard deviation in cross-sectional area and channel area for road plots in comparison to the walkway plots (Tables 3 and 4). However, the relatively few channels in road plots (compared to walkway plots) account for a lower drainage density (Fig. 11).

Channel orientations in road plots are less variable than channel orientations in walkway and control plots (Fig. 4). The

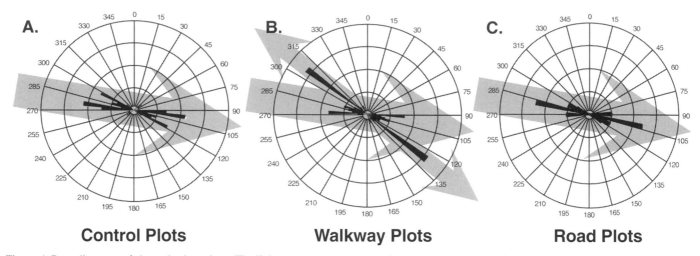

Figure 4. Rose diagrams of channel orientations. The light gray arrow represents the average orientation of the steepest topographic gradient for all plots. Each successive larger circle represents five channels with the same orientation. A: Control plots B: Walkway plots (smaller, double barbed arrow represents walkway orientation) C: Road plots.

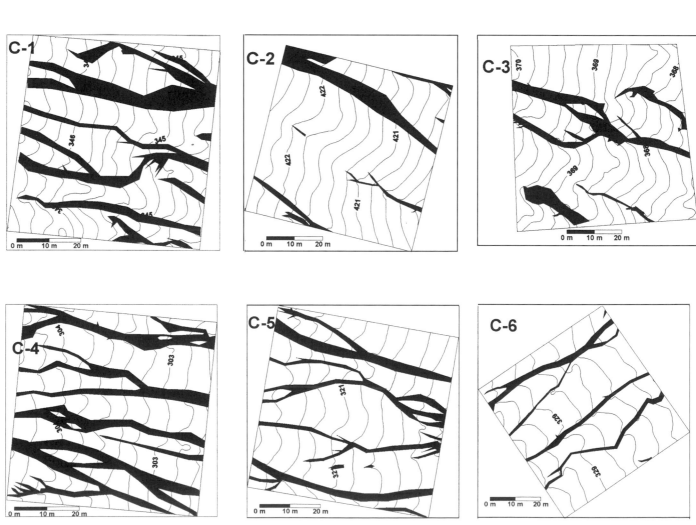

Figure 5. Maps of all control plots. Scale bar and direction are in C-6. Contour interval = 0.2 m. Elevations in maps are precise to ± 1 cm, but real elevations are ± 30 m, due to systematic GPS inaccuracy.

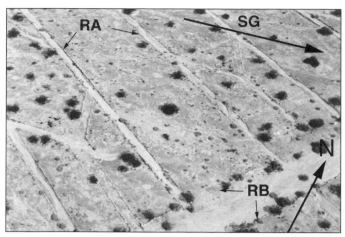

Figure 6. Low-level oblique aerial photograph of channels breaching walkway rock alignments at Camp Iron Mountain (from H. Wilshire). Arrows from RA point to rock alignments; RB point to road berms, and SG point down steepest gradient. Walkways are ~1.5 m wide.

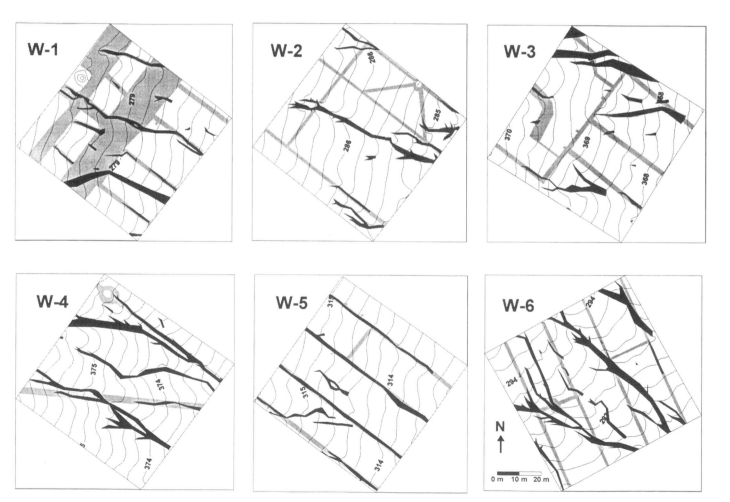

Figure 7. Maps of all walkway plots. Scale bar is in W-6. Contour interval = 0.2 m. Walkways are gray and channels are black. Elevations in maps are precise to ± 1 cm, but real elevations are ± 30 m, due to systematic GPS inaccuracy.

Figure 8. Low-level oblique aerial photograph of Camp Iron Mountain showing road berms channeling flow. Crossroads that are oriented down steeper gradients become wide washes. Roads are ~7 m wide. SG—Steepest gradient (from H. Wilshire).

road plot channels have a uniform surface with few flow obstructions. Most channels in road plots develop within the plots (Fig. 11), their orientation controlled directly by the steepest local gradient. The uniform surface, the closer spatial distribution of road plots when compared to the control plots, and the fact that most channels in road plots are developed within the plot account for the low variance in road plot channel orientations.

Process model

In order to generalize our results in a qualitative model, we must understand the surface processes affecting the Iron Mountain piedmont. Such a qualitative model must not only be consistent with our understanding of desert surface processes, but must also explain our observations at the camp and the observations of others (Iverson, 1980; Iverson et al., 1981; Prose, 1985; Webb et al., 1986). By understanding the dominant physical processes occurring on desert surfaces, we can suggest ways to minimize the impact of military training in arid regions.

Iverson (1980) concluded that ORV use in the western Mojave Desert compacted and smoothed microtopography, which led to hydraulic responses that increased soil erosion in disturbed areas. At Camp Iron Mountain, tanks, vehicles, and troops compacted and smoothed the soil (Prose, 1985). The compacted soil has fewer and smaller pores and thus lower infiltration rates. Reduced infiltration increases the volume and frequency of overland flow (Iverson et al., 1981). Troops and vehicles smoothed microtopography, which normally acts to disperse flow energy and cause localized sediment deposition. Iverson (1980) found a 13-fold decrease in surface roughness after just a few passes of an ORV. As a result of soil compaction and surface smoothing, overland flow volumes increase, along with the

potential for channel incision, especially on heavily impacted areas such as walkways.

Walkways, the most compacted and smoothed features we mapped, have the highest frequency of channel heads (Santos, 1999). As argued above, this observation is consistent with soil compaction and surface smoothing. Iverson (1980) noted a strong positive correlation between runoff power and sediment yield (r^2 = 0.78) for desert surfaces. Increased sediment yield at Camp Iron Mountain is expressed by channel formation. The abundance of channel heads on walkways suggests that runoff power must be higher on walkways than elsewhere. Compacting and smoothing walkway surfaces decreased infiltration, increased local discharge, and thus increased runoff power.

Control plot channels are mostly continuous through the plots, have larger widths and depths, and thus larger channel cross-sectional areas than channels in disturbed plots. For alluvial rivers, larger channel cross-sectional areas correspond to larger drainage areas (Dunne and Leopold, 1978). However, the piedmont experiences overland flow and does not have clearly defined drainage divides, except for road berms. Unlike their larger cousins, individual widths and depths of piedmont channels do not change significantly or predictably as a function of distance from channel head (Fig. 12). Linear models of such relationships have low slopes, and channel widths and depths are poorly correlated with distance from the channel head. Thus, channel widths and depths change little as a function of channel length, and the size of the local drainage area does not control the size of the channels on the piedmont. Rather, the channels appear to attain a "steady state" size at which incoming overland flow and precipitation balance infiltration losses.

Low drainage densities of road plots are a direct result of intact road berms. Road berms collect runoff and divert water to intersections with roads that are sub-parallel to slope, thereby limiting overland flow in areas down gradient of intact berms. In these flow-deprived areas, sheetwash dominates for 20 to 40 m down gradient of the road berm, where there are few or no channels. This zone, absent of channels, lowers the drainage densities for road plots compared to control and walkway plots. At the location where basal shear stress reaches a critical threshold, or rainsplash is unable to obliterate incipient channels (usually 20 to 40 meters from the road berm), channel initiation occurs and channel heads are abundant.

Rock alignments act as barricades to flow. Rock alignments, which outline walkways, are usually orientated 20° from the steepest average gradient of the Iron Mountain piedmont. When small flows encounter the large rock clasts (or when channels form inside walkway boundaries), the water is forced along the alignments until the rock alignment ends, the flow acquires enough power to breach the rock alignment, there is a gap in the alignment, or the channel diffuses into the surface. The most common channel orientation in walkway plots is along the rock alignments, and some channels flow inside walkways for the entire length of the plot.

Figure 9. Photograph of the smooth surface below an intact road berm on map C-4. This area, devoid of channels, is dominated by sheetwash. Bush in center of photograph is ~2 m high.

Figure 10. Photograph of a wide, braided channel down gradient of a breached berm in R-1. Bush in front left is ~80 cm high.

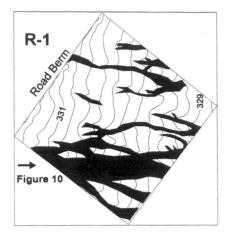
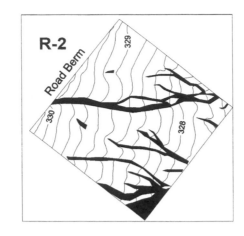
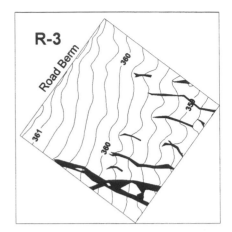
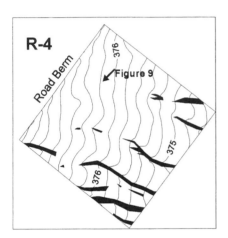
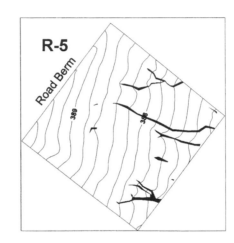
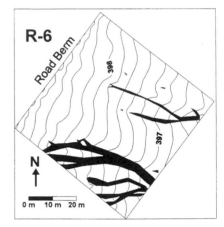

Figure 11. Maps of all road plots. Scale bar and direction are in R-6. Contour interval = 0.2 meters. Road berms form the up-gradient boundary. Area where channel heads are absent is 20 m–40 m wide. Location of Figure 9 photograph is noted in R-4. Location of Figure 10 photograph is noted in R-1. Elevations in maps are precise to ± 1 cm, but real elevations are ± 30 m, due to systematic GPS inaccuracy.

The length of time that the drainage network will continue to be affected by past Army activities is difficult to determine. Webb et al. (1986) suggested that soil densities might take more than a century to recover to natural values after disturbance. Iverson (1980), Iverson et al. (1981), and Prose (1985) conclude that soil lost by erosion in desert environments is probably unrecoverable on human time scales. We observed that more than half of the road berms and rock alignments are still intact more than 50 years after camp abandonment. Since soil compaction is probably only halfway to recovery and rock alignments and road berms will be present for at least the next 50 years, drainage networks should be affected for at least that long and possibly longer.

Persisting army effects might have been significantly reduced by simple remediation at the time of camp abandonment. Because the topography was smooth within camp boundaries and the roads were already compacted (Prose, 1985), grading the road berms at abandonment would have eliminated local drainage divides without further disturbing the surface. Also, removal of the rock alignments would have eliminated the stone-walled flow

boundaries. Neither of these techniques, however, addresses compaction or smoothing of roughness elements, which are more difficult to remediate. Nevertheless, the removal of road berms and rock alignments in 1944 would have greatly reduced many of the lingering hydraulic differences demonstrated by our data.

CONCLUSIONS

Camp Iron Mountain is located on a uniform, low gradient, piedmont surface where sediment is transported primarily in shallow, discontinuous, ephemeral streams. After two intense years of military activity and 54 subsequent years of recovery, channels in affected areas still have not returned to natural geometries due to: (1) the persisting network of road berms and rock alignments, and (2) soil compaction and smoothing. Road berms concentrate runoff and cause zones where channels are absent below intact road berms. Where berms are breached, wide, braided channels dominate. Discontinuous rock alignments disperse flow and inhibit channel formation. Continuous rock alignments influence

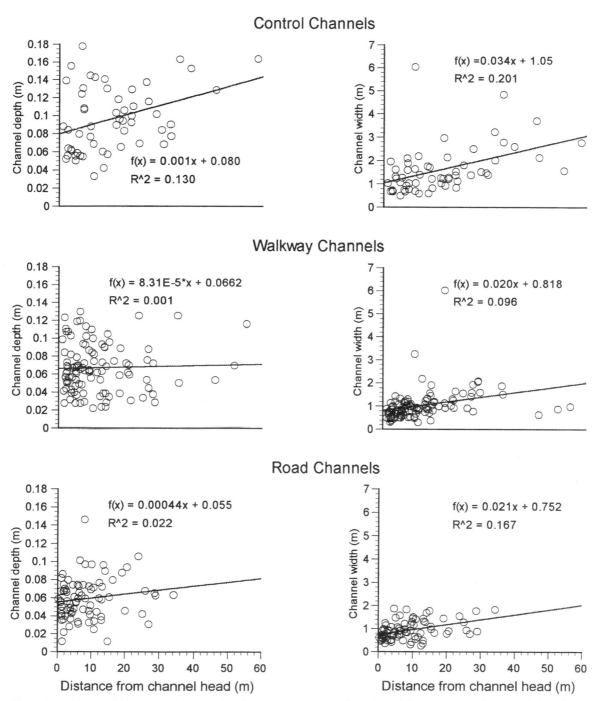

Figure 12. Channel widths and depths as a function of distance from channel head. Low slopes of linear models and poor correlation imply that channels widen slightly but do not appear to deepen significantly down piedmont.

the orientation and increase the frequency of small channels, but not large channels. Compacted and smoothed walkway surfaces change channel morphologies. Destroying road berms and rock alignments when temporary camps are abandoned will likely minimize the long-term impact of army maneuvers.

ACKNOWLEDGMENTS

We thank D. Santos and C. Massey for field assistance, H. Wilshire for the low-level oblique aerial photographs, D. Howell for statistical assistance, and D. Montgomery, S. Gran, A. Noren, K. Jennings, D. Santos, and an anonymous reviewer whose edits improved an earlier version of this chapter. U.S. Army Research Office grants DAAG559710180 and DAAH04-96-1-0036 funded this research.

REFERENCES CITED

Abrahams, A.D., Parsons, A.J., Cooke, R.U., and Reeves, R.W., 1984, Stone movement on hillslopes in the Mojave Desert, California: A 16-year record: Earth Surface Processes and Landforms, v. 9, p. 365–370.

Bull, W.B., 1991, Geomorphic responses to climate change: New York, Oxford University Press, 326 p.

Bureau of Land Management, 1986, Desert Training Center, California-Arizona: Maneuver area interpretive plan: Riverside, California, Bureau of Land Management, California District, 84 p.

Dunne, T., 1980, Formation and controls of channel networks: Progress in Physical Geography, v. 4, p. 211–239.

Dunne, T., and Leopold, L.B., 1978, Water in environmental planning: San Francisco, W.H. Freeman and Company, 818 p.

Henley, D.C., 1989, "The land that God forgot...": The saga of Gen. George Patton's Desert Training Center: Western American History Series, 54 p.

Hillel, D., 1980, Fundamentals of soil physics: New York, Academic Press, 486 p.

Horton, R., 1945, Erosional development of streams and their drainage basins: Hydrophysical approach to quantitative morphology: Geological Society of America Bulletin, v. 57, p. 275–370.

Iverson, R.M., 1980, Processes of accelerated pluvial erosion on desert hillslopes modified by vehicular traffic: Earth Surface Processes and Landforms, v. 5, p. 369–388.

Iverson, R.M., Hinckley, B.S., Webb, R.M., and Hallet, B., 1981, Physical effects of vehicular disturbances on arid landscapes: Nature, v. 212, p. 915–917.

Miller, D.H., Howard, K.A., and Anderson, J.L., 1981, Mylonitic gneiss related to emplacement of a Cretaceous batholith: U.S. Geological Survey Open-File Report 81-0503, p. 73–75.

Montgomery, D.R., 1994, Road surface drainage, channel initiation, and slope instability: Water Resources Research, v. 30, p. 1925–1932.

Montgomery, D.R., and Dietrich, W.E., 1994, Landscape dissection and drainage area-slope thresholds, *in* Krikby, M.J., ed., Process models and theoretical geomorphology: New York, John Wiley & Sons Ltd., p. 221–246.

National Oceanic and Atmospheric Administration, 1982, Monthly normals of temperature, precipitation, and heating and cooling degree days 1951–1980, California: Asheville, North Carolina, National Oceanic and Atmospheric Administration, v. 53, 36 p.

Prose, D.V., 1985, Persisting effects of armored military maneuvers on some soils of the Mojave Desert: Environmental Geology Water Science, v. 7, p. 163–170.

Ritter, D.F., 1978, Process geomorphology: Dubuque, Iowa, W.C. Brown, 603 p.

Santos, D.L., 1999, The effects of two years of intense military activity on the source areas, source-basin lengths and initiation of channels in Camp Iron Mountain of the U.S. Army's former Desert Training Center, Mojave Desert, California [Senior thesis]: Burlington, University of Vermont, 80 p.

Webb, R.H., Steiger, J.W., and Wilshire, H.G., 1986, Recovery of compacted soils in Mojave Desert ghost towns: Soil Science Society of America Journal, v. 50, p. 1341–1344.

Wemple, B.C., Jones, J.A., and Grant, G.E., 1996, Channel network extension by logging roads in two basins, western Cascades, Oregon: Water Resources Bulletin, v. 32, p. 1195–1207.

MANUSCRIPT ACCEPTED BY THE SOCIETY OCTOBER 27, 2000

Geological Society of America
Reviews in Engineering Geology, Volume XIV
2001

Wetlands and erosion studies in support of military training, Camp Shelby Training Site, Mississippi, USA

David M. Patrick
Suzanne A. Boyd
Department of Geology, University of Southern Mississippi, Hattiesburg, MS 39406-5044, USA

ABSTRACT

Interdisciplinary geologic studies at Camp Shelby Training Site, located in southern Mississippi, have supported military training requirements as well as natural resources conservation on this 134 000-acre National Guard facility by delineating *Go* and *No Go* areas for tank maneuver corridors, and by identifying causes of erosion. No Go areas include intermittent and perennial streams, wetlands, slopes in excess of ten percent, and critical habitats. *Go* and *No Go* areas were identified and delineated in the field, with the *No Go* areas clearly marked on the ground by painting the trees if the corridor was wooded or with fence posts if the corridor had been cleared. When it was necessary for a maneuver corridor to cross a stream or wetland, crossing sites were identified, and permits were obtained from the Corps of Engineers. A two-category hydrogeomorphic classification of wetlands was developed that consisted of bottomland and upland wetlands. Bottomland wetlands are further classified as riparian if adjacent to stream channels, or backswamp if they occur in stream valleys distal from the channel. Upland wetlands were classified as either side slope when they occur on valley walls or upland flat if they occurred on the upper portions of slopes. The wetlands classification scheme was found to conform to the lithostratigraphy of the training site; for example, bottomland wetlands are associated with the fine-grained sediments of the Hattiesburg Formation (Miocene) whereas the upland wetlands were associated with perched water tables in the coarse-grained Upland Complex (Pliocene-Pleistocene). These relationships, in turn, contributed to the development of an updated and enhanced geologic map of the training site. The outcrop patterns of the Hattiesburg and Upland Complex were found to correlate with the locations of critical habitats, including those of the gopher tortoise, red cockaded woodpecker, and the Louisiana quillwort. Evaluations of upland and channel erosion in the impact area did not reveal adverse conditions from range firing. Localized erosion was, however, commonly associated with unsurfaced roads. Most channels appeared relatively stable; however, certain ones exhibited knickpoints that were slowly migrating upstream and are the subject of ongoing study.

INTRODUCTION

The training of combat units, particularly ground and air units, has become increasingly complex due to: (1) the military's need for larger training areas, (2) increased statutory environmental restrictions, and (3) pressures from civilian communities. Today, many years after the end of the Cold War, it is ironic that larger training areas are deemed necessary; however, with the passage of each decade, vehicle and aircraft speed, range, and mobility have drastically increased; weapons systems have increased range and lethality, and communication and intelligence systems are providing real-time information over an extended battlefield (Siehl, 1991). The result of these technological advances is that the maneuver space controlled by an armored division in World War II can now be controlled by a battalion.

E-mails: david.patrick@usm.edu; saboyd@boydlaw.com

Patrick, D.M., and Boyd, S.A., 2001, Wetlands and erosion studies in support of military training, Camp Shelby Training Site, Mississippi, USA, *in* Ehlen, J., and Harmon, R.S., eds., The Environmental Legacy of Military Operations: Boulder, Colorado, Geological Society of America Reviews in Engineering Geology, v. XIV, p. 137–149.

During the last twenty to thirty years in the United States, there has been a substantial increase in environmental legislation and laws affecting nearly all aspects of society and the activities on public as well as private lands. Military training is no exception and, therefore, military trainers face a variety of environmental issues, including wetlands, erosion, and water and air quality; habitats, particularly those of threatened and endangered (T and E) species; and cultural sites, to name a few (Patrick et al., 1994). Violations of these laws may result in fines and imprisonment.

During the period that these statutory environmental requirements have been increasing, community pressures at military installations have also increased. Population growth in the vicinity of installations has resulted in space and resource competition between the nearby civilian community and the military installation. Likewise, the environmental awareness of the civilian community has increased and the citizenry are more vocal in their concerns over such issues as water and air quality and noise pollution. Also, some military installations may be considered multiple-use in that some areas of the installation have recreational uses, while other areas may be utilized, under lease, for such activities as grazing, timber production, hunting, and recreation. Thus, the previously mentioned competition may occur within the installation as well as beyond its boundaries.

This chapter presents the results of geological investigations performed as a part of wetlands delineation and erosion studies at the Camp Shelby Training Site, operated by the Mississippi Army National Guard. In many ways, Camp Shelby is typical of U.S. Army installations in the United States because of its large size, the numbers and types of military units trained, the types of environmental issues, and the fact that it is a multiple-use installation. As a National Guard Training Site, however, Camp Shelby is different in that it does not have the large numbers of permanently garrisoned troops, that characterize most active Army installations. It is also somewhat atypical among military installations in the southeastern U.S. because of the low population density around its perimeter.

MILITARY TRAINING AND THE ENVIRONMENT

Stewardship

As the custodian of over 25 million acres (over 10 million hectares) of land, much of which has become a refuge for numerous threatened and endangered (T and E) species, the Department of Defense (DoD) has a significant interest in the effective management of its properties. To this end, the DoD leadership has mandated strict compliance with all local and federal environmental statutes and laws. Furthermore, the DoD has taken the lead in moving beyond compliance by establishing programs that fund management and research activities in order to enhance conservation. These programs provide funding, instruction and guidance, and centers of expertise where environmental managers may seek consultation. Partnerships have also been formed, and working

relationships developed, with numerous institutions as well as local and national environmental organizations. At Camp Shelby, for example, partnerships are in effect with the Mississippi Department of Wildlife, Fisheries and Parks; the Nature Conservancy; Mississippi State University; and the University of Southern Mississippi. These partnerships broaden the level of input on conservation and environmental issues, increase the level of importance of these issues, and strengthen the level of support for management decisions. Effective land stewardship is a high-priority issue at military installations, and commanders take pride in demonstrating their enhancement efforts, which are becoming increasingly visible to, and appreciated by, the public.

Location

Camp Shelby, originally activated in 1917, is located in portions of Forrest and Perry counties, Mississippi, approximately 25 km south of Hattiesburg, and approximately 100 km north of the Gulf Coast (Fig. 1). During World War II, the training site comprised over 146 000 hectares plus an additional 162 000 hectares of leased land, and the troop population undergoing training was 100 000. Currently, the training site occupies approximately 134 000 acres and some 100 000 troops are trained there each year. The training site consists of gently rolling, partially wooded terrain on the south and east side of the Leaf River and north of Black Creek. The principal drainage basins are shown in Figure 2. Black Creek drains most of the training site, and this stream corridor is important because it is a wild and scenic area in the DeSoto National Forest. Most of the public land on which Camp Shelby is located is federal land, of which approximately 88% is a part of the DeSoto National Forest managed by the U.S. Forest Service. The remaining 12% consists of Department of Defense and State of Mississippi lands.

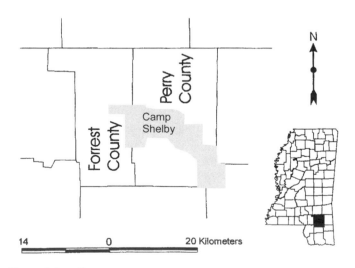

Figure 1. Location map.

Military training

Camp Shelby hosts a wide range of Active and Reserve Component training activities of the Army, Navy, and Air Force, including artillery firing, air-to-ground bombing and strafing, demolitions, and company-sized tracked vehicle maneuvers within the Combined Arms Area (CAA), as well as small arms firing and dismounted infantry maneuvers (Fig. 3). The training site also hosts a number of other State of Mississippi and Department of Defense functions. Abrams (M1) tanks, Bradley (M2) Fighting Vehicles, and helicopter gunnery were enhanced by the construction of a state-of-the-art G.V. "Sonny" Montgomery Range (a multipurpose range complex-heavy) which was under construction in 2001. Training at Camp Shelby is conducted under all applicable federal and state environmental regulations, specifically those covering wetlands, as well some additional local "ground rules." The use of National Forest lands for tracked vehicle (tank or fighting vehicle) maneuver training is conducted under the authority of a special use permit (SUP) issued by the U.S. Forest Service (U.S. Department of the Army et al., 1994). The SUP prohibits tracked-vehicle training on slopes in excess of 10% and on or through areas within 100 ft (30.48 m) of perennial or intermittent streams and wetlands. These stipulations are in place because of concerns about erosion on steeper slopes degrading water quality of the streams. The SUP also specifically addresses wetlands even though wetland protection is required by other federal statutes, namely the Clean Water Act of 1972. The SUP also precludes training activities on cultural sites and in sensitive habitats. Figure 4 illustrates how slopes, streams, and wetlands are protected by designating off-limits, or *No Go* areas, to restrict tracked-vehicle training to upland areas.

Wetlands

The term "wetland," as used in this chapter, refers to a special habitat, defined by the U.S. Army Corps of Engineers (USACE), that is characterized by hydrophytic vegetation, hydric soils, and shallow ground water conditions (Environmental Laboratory, 1987). Geological and botanical studies, described later in this chapter, have also shown that there is great wetland diversity in terms of flora, hydrology, location, and geomorphic setting. Wetlands received attention in the SUP because of their extensive occurrence on Camp Shelby. A recent estimate by the USACE Waterways Experiment Station (Minkin et al., 1998) indicates that there are in excess of 6000 hectares of wetlands on the training site (Fig. 5). Although tank training is restricted to

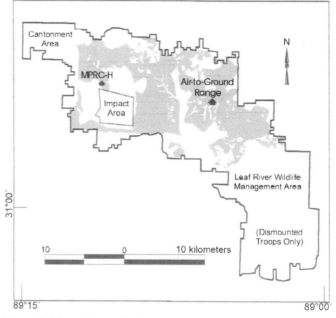

Figure 3. Map of Camp Shelby showing the impact area, air-to-ground range, and Combined Arms Area (CAA). The G.V. "Sonny" Montgomery Range will be located near the northwest corner of the impact area.

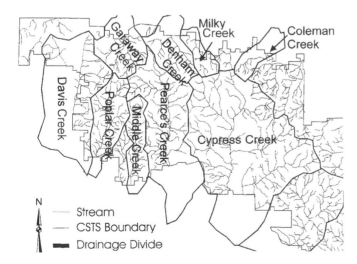

Figure 2. Northwestern part of Camp Shelby showing the Leaf River to the north and Black Creek to the south. The major drainage basins, most of which drain south, are also shown.

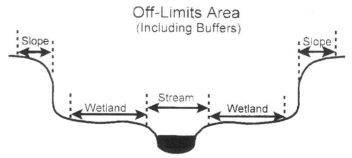

Figure 4. Generalized valley cross section showing mechanized vehicle off-limits, or *No Go* area, and the protection of perennial and intermittent streams, wetlands, and slopes.

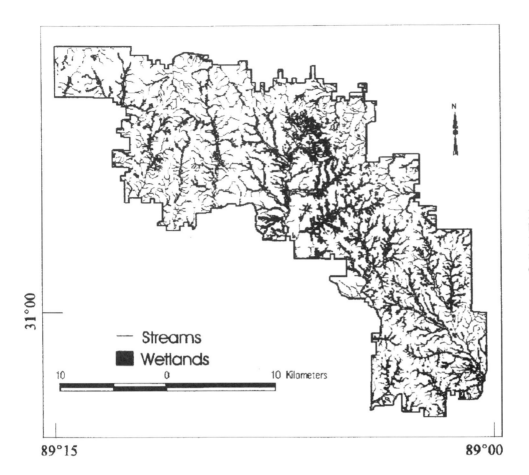

Figure 5. Camp Shelby wetland distribution (shown in black). Note the isolated wetlands not associated with stream channels (modified after Minkin et al., 1998).

TABLE 1. STRATIGRAPHY AND LITHOLOGY OF CAMP SHELBY

Geologic Age	Formation	Lithology
Quaternary	Terrace and undifferentiated alluvium	Fine and coarse clastics
Pliocene-Pleistocene	Upland Complex (Citronelle Formation)	Sand and gravel
Miocene	Hattiesburg Formation	Silt and clay

upland areas because of training doctrine, as well as by requirements of the SUP, wetlands extend upstream along headwaters or first-order streams in many areas, and some wetlands also occur on upland flats. Thus, in some areas, tank maneuver corridors must cross wetlands. Wetland crossings are hardened structures positioned at locations that would minimize loss of wetlands and that conform to training doctrine and minimize loss of training realism. When the locations have been identified, the crossing sites are permitted by the USACE under Nationwide Permit rules under Section 404 of the Clean Water Act (U.S. Dept. of the Army et al., 1994).

Geologic setting

Geologic maps for southern Mississippi are nonexistent, limited in coverage, small scale, or out-of-date (Foster and McCutcheon, 1941; Brown, 1944; Patrick, 1990; May et al., 1995). The lack of detailed mapping is due to a number of reasons, namely the lack of fossils for correlation in these nonmarine, continental sediments; poor exposures due to extensive and relatively deep weathering; locally dense vegetative cover; and veneers of Holocene or Quaternary alluvium. Generally, the oldest Coastal Plain sediments exposed at Camp Shelby consist of the Miocene Hattiesburg Formation and the overlying Pliocene-Pleistocene Upland Complex or Citronelle Formation (Bicker, 1969; Dockery, 1981; Autin et al., 1991) as indicated in Table 1. The Hattiesburg Formation is fine-grained and, where studied in detail, consists of sub-equal portions of silt and clay, the latter comprising predominant smectite and lesser amounts of illite and kaolinite (Adamczak, 1986). The Upland Complex, by contrast, is coarse-grained and mainly sandy. It contains occasional gravels or gravelly sands along with fine-grained interbeds that are similar in composition to the Hattiesburg Formation, with the exception that the clay fraction lacks smectite (Bowen, 1981; Meylan and Li, 1995).

During the initial identification and delineation of wetlands and the subsequent digging of numerous shallow (<0.5 m) test pits to establish soil and hydrology parameters, evidence was found that suggested a relationship existed between the presence or nature of the wetlands and the near-surface geology. Thus, geologic mapping was initiated in the north-central part of the training site.

An interesting aspect of the general geology of Camp Shelby is the Cypress Creek salt dome, located in the northeastern part of the installation at a depth of approximately 305 m. Both Cypress Creek and the larger Richton salt dome, located 20 km northeast of Camp Shelby, were studied by the Department of Energy in the early 1980s under the Nuclear Waste Isolation Program. Surface geologic mapping was also conducted over both domes (Law Engineering Testing Co., 1982). Figure 6 is a very generalized, not-to-scale, north-south cross section showing topographic and stratigraphic relationships and the position of the dome in the headwaters of Cypress Creek (see Fig. 2).

Erosion, compaction, and soils

The identification, prevention, and mitigation of upland soil erosion are important issues associated with mechanized training, particularly that of tanks, and especially in humid regions underlain by unlithified sediments. Images of highly eroded, gullied, or rutted areas and sediment accumulations convey impressions of poor environmental management regardless of the origins or processes involved. However, the primary concern of land managers at Camp Shelby is prevention of sedimentation in streams and the resultant deterioration of water quality. Tank maneuver areas may be particularly susceptible to erosion; however, non-maneuver bivouac and staging areas, as well as roads leading to maneuver areas, are impacted. Erosion can be minimized by locating maneuver corridors on flatter terrain, as previously described; rotating

use of training areas on a periodic basis; improving and maintaining drainage structures and sediment traps; and periodic grading and seeding. Restricting tank maneuvers to upland and stratigraphically higher areas results in this training activity being conducted on sediments of the Upland Complex. It may seem, on the basis of the sandy nature of the Upland Complex, that erosion is a particular problem; however, the deep subtropical weathering and the resulting plinthite soils actually result in less erosion. Also, these plinthite soils retain moisture, helping to maintain vegetation and further decreasing erosional susceptibility.

The presence of tanks and other heavy-tracked vehicles on upland areas may, however, contribute more to compaction of the surface materials than erosion. The compaction may locally decrease erosional susceptibility and, at the same time, decrease infiltration which, in turn, may increase runoff and peak discharges into nearby streams. Thus, the effects of tank maneuvers may include increased channel erosion.

Military training on multiple-use installations is not the only cause of erosion. Most regions having some relief and unpaved roads, regardless of land use, will exhibit some degree of erosion caused by the road system (see Isaacson et al., this volume). For example, the road surface itself will become eroded and thereby deliver sediment to nearby streams because the road surface concentrates runoff and delivers higher discharges to drainage ditches, streams, and side slopes; culverts placed under the roads may concentrate water and sediment discharge into streams and side slopes (Albertson et al., 1995). Data from wetland test pits at Camp Shelby frequently reveal thin sand layers of a few centimeters thickness overlying the hydric soil, with the sand usually thickest near roadways. This sandy veneer, however, apparently has not adversely affected the wetlands. Timber harvesting, particularly clear cutting, may also produce erosion if not conducted properly. Recreational vehicle or four-wheeler activities are another cause

NORTH   SOUTH

Figure 6. Generalized, not-to-scale north-south, cross section showing topographic and stratigraphic relationships. Approximate difference in elevation between top of cuesta and Black Creek is 200 ft.

Upland Formation

Hattiesburg Formation

of erosion, rutting, gullying, and sedimentation. Thus, the attribution of a specific erosional event to a particular cause may not be straightforward or even possible at a multiple-use installation.

WETLAND GEOLOGY, GEOMORPHOLOGY, AND HYDROLOGY

Wetland identification and delineation

The identification of a wetland is based upon specific criteria for the vegetation, soils, and hydrology of a site (Kusler, 1987; Miller, 1991; Mish and Gosselink, 1993; National Research Council, 1995). These criteria are described in the USACE Wetland Delineation Manual (Environmental Laboratory, 1987). In general, the criteria for all three components, vegetation, soils, and hydrology, must be present for an area to be classified as a wetland.

Hydrophytic vegetation is that which is adapted to saturated conditions. Hydrophytic vegetation has been identified and listed for U.S. states or counties by the U.S. Fish and Wildlife Service. Specific hydrophytic vegetation types must be physically identified in the field. Hydric soils are identified and listed by the Natural Resources Conservation Service on a county basis and usually described in soil surveys (U.S. Department of Agriculture, 1979). Because hydric soils often exist as inclusions in broadly based soil associations, the determination of the presence of hydric soils cannot be based upon a soil survey alone. Rather, the hydric soil must be physically identified in the field on the basis of its composition and low Munsell chroma (Munsell Soil Color Charts, 1994). Hydric soils exhibit characteristics of redoximorphic conditions due to prolonged saturation (e.g., organic matter, mottling, etc.). The hydrology criteria require that the area must be inundated or have groundwater levels within 1.5 ft (0.46 m) of the surface for 80% of the growing season. Lacking measurable ground or surface water levels, evidence for periodic surface inundation will satisfy the hydrology criteria (Environmental Laboratory, 1987).

In the recent past, a common misconception of wetlands as "swamps" by the public and military commanders and trainers has led to incredulity since, in some areas, a jurisdictional (i.e., USACE-approved) wetland may be rarely inundated, distant from a stream, and not possess the popular mental picture of a "swamp." Even so, such an area will exhibit characteristic hydrophytic vegetation, hydric soils, and groundwater conditions that are characteristic of a jurisdictional wetland. Currently, at Camp Shelby and other military installations, unit commanders and trainers are periodically briefed on wetland and other environmental issues, and nontechnical publications such as Dame (1993) have been distributed to units throughout the army and its Reserve components.

Most of the jurisdictional wetland delineation at Camp Shelby has been for the purpose of obtaining USACE approval for small wetland crossing sites along maneuver corridors in the CAA under Nationwide Permit rules. For a Nationwide Permit to be issued, the USACE requires a brief description of the project

(wetland crossing); design plans; wetland data sheets describing the vegetation, soils, and hydrology; and a map (usually topographic) of the project showing the delineated wetlands. However, due to the expected loss of larger areas of wetlands in the planned G.V. "Sonny" Montgomery Range, located northwest of the impact area (Fig. 3), an Individual Permit must be obtained. For the Individual Permit, a jurisdictional delineation must be made and all applicable National Environmental Protection Act (NEPA) requirements must be met. Also, the Individual Permit requires significant additional information on the nature, type, and condition of the wetlands to be lost as a result of the planned activity in order to determine the amount and type of wetlands that must be set aside and mitigated in direct compensation. Also, Individual Permits generally require that the set-aside wetlands be several times the acreage of the wetlands lost through construction or other activity. The wetlands in the broad headwaters of Cypress Creek were proposed for the mitigation area of the G.V. "Sonny" Montgomery Range.

Geologic constraints on wetland occurrence

From a geological perspective, the occurrence of a wetland is determined by the geological conditions of a particular site, which pertain to the presence or absence of water. This conclusion results from the definition of a wetland since both hydrophytic vegetation and hydric soils occur because of the presence of water. The water is present because of the nature of the underlying parent material (from which the hydric soils are derived) and the geomorphic setting of the site. The geomorphic setting, in turn, is in part controlled by the parent material and climatic conditions.

At Camp Shelby, the occurrence of many wetland surfaces is associated with streams and stream valleys, an obvious geomorphic association. Other wetlands, however, are not associated with stream systems, occur at higher elevations, and appear to result from perched water tables. Early in the study, it was suspected that these wetland surfaces, which were not associated with stream systems, must owe their presence to the lithology of the materials underlying these surfaces. The more that was learned about the wetland surfaces, the more was learned about the surface geology and vice versa. Thus, the development of a geologic map of Camp Shelby was a result of wetland studies.

Geologic and lithologic controls

The fine-grained and relatively impermeable nature of the Hattiesburg Formation makes it an excellent candidate for supporting wetland surfaces by perching water tables, whether it occurs in and along stream valleys or at higher elevations. With a few exceptions, wetland surfaces do not occur on the stratigraphically higher and coarser-grained Upland Complex because it is sufficiently well drained. Exceptions occur in those locations where the Upland Complex is highly weathered, usually at or along the upper parts of slopes. Here, the soils produced upon the

Upland Complex are reddish brown, relatively hard, and indurated. The induration is produced by a combination of leaching, oxidation of iron in the sediments, and the formation of the sesquioxide-rich plinthite, which is the principal component of tropical laterites. The presence of plinthite tends to restrict drainage locally and perch water tables, thereby providing suitable conditions for the development of a wetland surface.

Geologic mapping

Figure 7 presents the geologic map for the north-central portion of Camp Shelby. The southeastern part of the installation was not mapped because tracked vehicle maneuver is not permitted, and the wetlands in this area have not been studied in detail. The outcrop pattern of the Hattiesburg Formation and Upland Complex conform to the topography, with the Hattiesburg Formation occupying valleys and the Upland Complex occupying the hilltops and higher elevations. The outcrop pattern of the Hattiesburg Formation, veneered with alluvium, is extensive along the valley of Cypress Creek in the northeastern part of the training site; the pattern is particularly wide in the extreme, upstream part of the valley. Therefore, it is not surprising that the largest contiguous wetlands on Camp Shelby occur in the Cypress Creek area. Generally, most of the wetlands at Camp Shelby are associated with streams and, therefore, occur in stream valleys cut into the Hattiesburg Formation. The relationship between the Hattiesburg Formation and riparian wetlands is shown in Figure 8.

The approximate subcrop location of Cypress Creek dome is also shown on the geologic map (Fig. 7). Note the coincidence of the subcrop pattern of the dome and the widening of the outcrop pattern of the Hattiesburg Formation. Cross sections of Cypress Creek dome indicate that sediments of the Hattiesburg Formation have been pierced and upturned by emplacement of the dome. The data suggest, but do not conclusively demonstrate, that the widening of the Hattiesburg Formation outcrop may be due to possible collapse over the dome.

Wetland geomorphology and hydrology

In terms of landscape position and geomorphic surface, wetlands at Camp Shelby may be classified as either bottomland, occurring in stream valleys, or upland, occurring above the stream valleys, as generalized in Figure 9 and tabulated in Table 2. Bottomland wetlands are either riverine, fringing streams, or back swamp depending upon whether or not the location is beyond the natural levee and near the valley wall. These wetlands generally occur within the outcrop pattern of the Hattiesburg Formation. These riverine wetlands may be further classified depending upon stream order (low order or higher order). The riverine wetlands were classified as either low order (first or second order) or high order (greater than second order). A first-order stream is one that has no tributaries; a second-order stream has two first-order tributaries, etc. A typical low-order riverine wetland is shown in Figure 10. For this study, those wetland surfaces that occur at elevations above the floodplains and stream terraces are defined as upland wetlands. This term is meaningful from a geomorphic standpoint; however, the meaning of the term "upland" to most wetland biologists and regulatory agencies indicates a nonwetland area because "upland" plants are classified as nonhydrophytic. In any event, the upland wetlands may be subdivided into two types, side slope or flat. The side-slope wetlands (Fig. 11) occur on valley walls or hillslopes, and the flat wetlands occur on relatively flat areas at higher elevations on or near hilltops. These wetlands occur in areas mapped as Upland Complex (Fig. 7).

Brinson (1993) developed a wetland classification system or model that incorporated hydrology and geomorphology; this system is termed HGM. The names of geomorphic surfaces used in this model are not, however, ones commonly used by geomorphologists. The HGM has not been officially accepted by regulatory agencies; however, it is being regionally tested by the USACE, Environmental Protection Agency, National Resource Conservation Service, and state agencies. Table 2 illustrates the geomorphic relationships between the classification system presented in this chapter and the HGM system of Brinson (1993). As indicated in Table 2, landscape position is not a part of the HGM; therefore, the term "upland" is excluded.

At Camp Shelby, both the HGM and the classification system presented in this chapter have been used to classify wetlands in both the G.V. "Sonny" Montgomery range and the Cypress Creek mitigation areas. Both classification systems were a part of the wetlands mitigation plan and permit application. Table 3 illustrates this classification system and the incorporation of the hydrologic controls of Brinson (1993).

The geomorphic/hydrologic classification of wetland hydrology is based upon water source (Brinson, 1993). Sources include direct precipitation, stream flow, groundwater flow, or a combination of these sources. Low-order riparian wetlands receive water from stream flow and groundwater. A groundwater source for first-order streams occurs in some locations near the contact between the Upland Complex and the Hattiesburg Formation. Stream flow is the source of water to the high-order riparian wetlands. The source of water in both types of upland wetlands is perched groundwater. Groundwater may be perched at the contact between the Hattiesburg Formation and the overlying Upland Complex, above fine-grained interbeds within the Upland Complex, and above plinthite soil horizons in the Upland Complex.

Wetland soils

As indicated in column 3 of Table 3, the types of soil present on a wetland surface reflect the hydrogeomorphic setting. Organic-rich mucks indicative of highly reduced conditions due to nearly constant saturation or inundation are one of the key indicators of hydric soils. These soils are easily identified by the color, texture, presence of highly decayed organic matter, and their characteristic "rotten egg" odor, indicating the presence of hydrogen sulfide. At Camp Shelby, these soils usually occur in wetlands along first-order streams and in uplands upon side

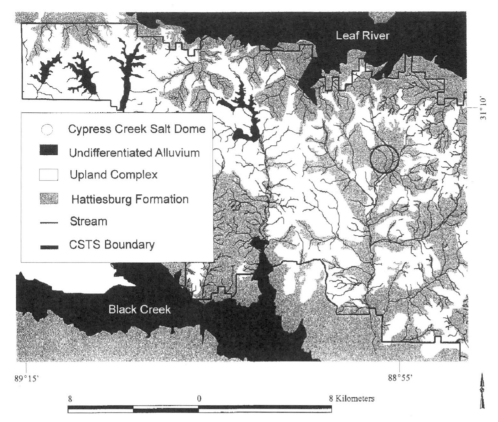

Figure 7. Geologic map.

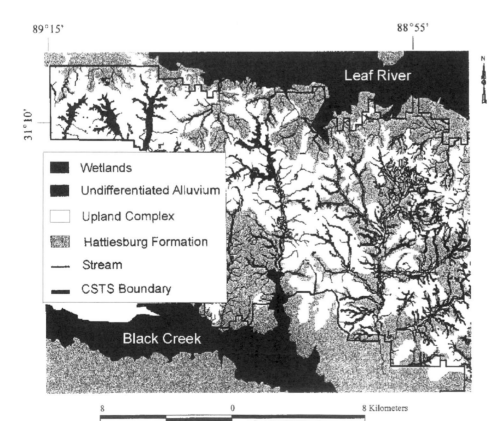

Figure 8. Geology and wetland distribution.

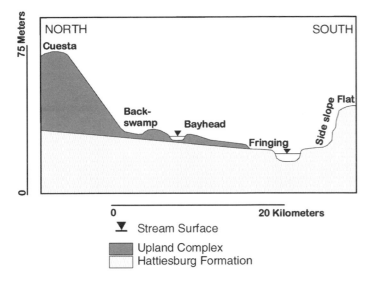

Figure 9. Conceptual cross section showing wetland types.

TABLE 2. COMPARISON OF WETLAND CLASSIFICATION SYSTEM PRESENTED IN THIS PAPER AND HGM

Landscape position (this paper)	Wetland classification by geomorphic surface (this paper)	HGM
Bottomland	Riverine (low order)	Riverine
	Riverine (high order)	Riverine
	Backswamp	Depression
Upland	Side slope (>5% slope)	Slope
	Upland flat (<5% slope)	Mineral soil flat

slopes; they have been formed by nearly year-round saturation by groundwater seepage. Thin, organic-rich soils also occur on upland flats; their thin nature is probably due to seasonal groundwater level variations. The thin mucks on the upland flats overlie mottled, leached, fine-grained soils. Mottling is a redoximorphic feature that indicates variation in saturation of the soils. Thus, wetland soils found on high-order riparian and back swamp surfaces are characterized by mottled silt loams, indicating seasonal wetting and drying (Broderson, 1994).

Wetland vegetation

Although this chapter does not address wetland vegetation in any detail, it was apparent that this type of vegetation is dependent upon water source and, therefore, very general relationships between vegetation and water source are shown in column 4 of Table 3. Representative vegetation shown in the table is based upon both dominance and ease of field identification. Also, the species listed in the table are very common and tend to occur as characteristic floral assemblages. Important information concerning degree of saturation within each wetland class can be roughly determined by identifying the dominant vegetation assemblage and correlating that data with the underlying soil type (Reed, 1988).

EROSION STUDIES

Impact area sediment sampling

One of the earliest systematic and quantitative erosion studies at Camp Shelby was that initiated in 1991 and managed by the U.S. Army Research and Development Center Construction Engineering Research Laboratory (CERL). The study was intended to provide data for the development of a management plan for the impact area. Five sediment and water samplers (Isco, Inc.) were sited on Davis, Poplar, Middle, and Pearce's creeks, which drain the impact area (Figs. 2 and 3). The samplers were programmed to collect water and its contained sediment at selected intervals upon activation by either precipitation or rise of stream stage. The samplers also measured stream discharge. After a precipitation event, discharge data were downloaded, water and sediment samples were collected, grain-size analyses of the sediment conducted, and discharge and sediment data were sent to CERL for further analysis using Universal Soil Loss models that the laboratory had developed. Approximately three years of data were collected and analyzed, and the results of these studies indicated that erosion on the impact area was rather modest and was quantitatively similar to that produced by agricultural activities in this area (Sharif and Engel, 1995).

Impact area overflights and imagery studies

During the end of the water and sediment sampling project, a qualitative study of erosion in the impact area was initiated using photographic documentation collected during helicopter overflights and from historical U.S. Department of Agriculture panchromatic aerial imagery (Patrick et al., 1982; Smith and Patrick, 1991). The overflight photos, taken approximately 214 m above land surface, showed current conditions,

Figure 10. Typical riverine wetland on Denham Creek.

Figure 11. Typical slope wetland.

and the historic imagery showed the changes that had occurred since the 1960s. It was previously known that over the last half century, the impact area had been converted from primarily forestland to primarily grassland. The conversion was caused by inadvertent burns from range firing. The modern photos showed numerous craters, 2–3 m in diameter, and scarring in the main target areas. However, the first-order tributaries, for the most part, were lined with vegetation and showed little evidence of erosion. The comparison with the historical imagery showed clearly the decrease in forest area; however, again, the first-order stream channels were observed to have maintained their vegetation over the years. Furthermore, there appeared to be a wider margin of riparian vegetation along the streams. Since these streams are similar to others on Camp Shelby, it was presumed that these vegetated areas would be classified as wetlands and, therefore, a historical increase in wetland areas has occurred in the impact area over the last five decades. These data suggested that the increase occurred for two reasons. First, the removal of the pine forest cover and conversion to grass raised the groundwater levels, a common occurrence when

pines are removed; second, the cratering resulted in increased infiltration to the water table. Although the craters exhibited scarring, the scarring occurred on the inner part of the crater, indicating sediments eroded in the crater remained there and were not transported beyond the crater and into the stream system. Thus, the disturbances experienced by the impact area may produce positive results in terms of wetland generation.

Gullying and channel erosion

It might be expected that the conversion of forestland to grassland, as described above, and similar conversions in areas in which the CAA is being expanded, would lead to increased runoff rates and peak stream discharges, and, in turn, enhanced gullying and/or channel erosion. Gullying, as used in this chapter, refers to the erosion of rills lying upon side slopes of upland areas or first-order stream tributaries. Gullying, however, does not appear to be prevalent on Camp Shelby. Some gullying occurs locally due to drainage from roads or through culverts. Ground observations downstream (south) of the impact area do indicate localized bank erosion on streams draining this area. In this downstream area, the streams have incised into the Hattiesburg Formation, forming small knickpoints. Figure 12 illustrates a knickpoint on Cypress Creek; here the channel has incised into the Hattiesburg Formation and has retreated upstream approximately 5 m over the last two years. Whether this and other knickpoints have been eroding over the last few decades, or during the present cycle of erosion and deposition, is not known. It is possible that peak discharges have increased somewhat over the last few decades and have produced this incision, but not to a level so large that gullying was initiated. In any event, knickpoints such as that on Cypress Creek represented some of the best outcrops on Camp Shelby and thereby provided detailed stratigraphic information for the wetland studies and geologic mapping.

DISCUSSION

Interdisciplinary studies

The investigations previously described were highly interdisciplinary and required coordination and interaction with a number of natural resource professionals, including botanists, wildlife biologists, soil scientists, foresters, and engineers, as well as military personnel. Not only was the nature of the work interdisciplinary, but the product of the work, such as reports and maps, had to be prepared with these natural resource professionals and military personnel in mind. Thus, the reports had to meet the needs of a rather wide constituency. Regarding interdisciplinary training, the actual wetland delineation work was conducted by geology undergraduate and graduate students with backgrounds in biology, who had also completed one or two university-level botany courses as well as wetland delineation courses conducted by the USACE.

TABLE 3. WETLAND HYDROLOGY, SOILS, AND REPRESENTATIVE VEGETATION IN TERMS OF GEOMORPHIC SURFACE*

Geomorphic surface	Hydrologic source	Soils	Representative vegetation
Riverine (low order)	Stream flow Groundwater	Histic (muck)	Red Titi, Red Maple, Sweetbay Magnolia, Wax Myrtle, Cinnamon Chain Fern, Royal Fern
Riverine (high order)	Stream flow	Mottled silt loam	Golden Club, Reeds, Alder, Wax Myrtle, Red Titi
Backswamp	Precipitation Stream flow	Mottled silt loam	Pitcher Plants, Gallberry, Sparkleberry
Side slope	Groundwater	Histic (muck)	Stinkbay, Florida Anise, Sweetbay Magnolia, River Birch, Beech, Big-leaf Magnolia
Upland flat	Groundwater	Thin histics over mottled silt loam	Pitcher Plants, Pipeworts, Sundews, Black Gum, Clethra

* Modified after Brinson, 1993

Geologic mapping

Most geological practitioners would agree that the solution to most geologic and related problems in a region may be better understood through a geologic map and, if no maps exist, one should be prepared before such studies are initiated. This was particularly true at Camp Shelby where, early in the project, wildlife biologists studying habitats of T and E flora and fauna expressed interest in up-to-date geologic maps. This interest was generated by their attempts to better understand the physical environments and distribution of these plants and animals and the notion that knowledge of site geology would enhance this understanding. Table 4, Figure 13, and the following paragraphs show and describe the relationships, as they are currently understood, between T and E plants and animals, sensitive habitats, and the stratigraphic units upon which the habitats lie.

The gopher tortoise (*Gopherus polyphemus*) digs and occupies burrows in the moderately well-drained, coarse clastics of the Upland Complex. The ease of burrowing in these sandy materials is apparent; however, not any sand will suffice. In order for the burrows to remain open and stable with adequate roof support, there must be some cementation in the sands, such as plinthite, which is unique to the Upland Complex. The Upland Complex provides the habitat for red cockaded woodpeckers (*Picoides borealis*) because these birds build their nests mainly in pine forests, which occur on this unit. Generally, softwoods such as pine prefer moderately well-drained soils, whereas hardwoods will tolerate poorer drainage. Thus, the vegetative associations are pines on the Upland Complex, and hardwoods such as the southern mesophytic hardwood forests on the Hattiesburg Formation. The Camp Shelby dusky burrowing crayfish (*Fallicambarus gordoni*) habitat is restricted to wetland environments and presently only occurs in the headwaters of Cypress Creek which, in turn, is underlain by the Hattiesburg Formation. The Louisiana quillwort (*Isoetes louisianensis*) habitat is riparian and occurs adjacent to stream channels that experience overbank scouring. It is speculated that such scouring is enhanced at or near the Hattiesburg Formation-Upland Complex contact because of increased channel slope.

Figure 12. Knickpoint on Cypress Creek.

Understanding military training and operations

Because of the increased sophistication of modern weapons systems, individual and unit training in the operation of these systems has likewise become increasingly complex. For the best results in addressing environmental and resource management issues at military installations, individuals charged with addressing these issues must have (or develop) some fundamental insight into the requirements and doctrine of the military trainers. Of course, this is a two-way street and the trainers need to understand the fundamentals of the common environmental issues. In our wetland and erosion studies, it was necessary to understand some basics of tank maneuver doctrine in order to help develop maneuver corridors that conformed to relative elevation of the corridors with respect to each other, line of sight, and slope while, at the same time, avoiding wetlands, streams, and other environmental hazards.

CONCLUSIONS

Natural resource investigations at military installations can be significantly advanced by the inclusion of geologic principles,

**TABLE 4. RELATIONSHIPS BETWEEN HABITATS
AND COMMUNITIES AND STRATIGRAPHY**

Important habitats or communities	Formation
Gopher tortoise	Upland Complex
Red cockaded woodpecker	Upland Complex
Southern mesophytic hardwood forests	Hattiesburg Formation
Camp Shelby dusky burrowing crayfish	Hattiesburg Formation
Louisiana quillwort	Upland Complex–Hattiesburg Formation Contact

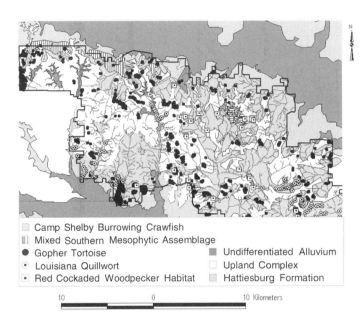

Camp Shelby Burrowing Crawfish
Mixed Southern Mesophytic Assemblage
Gopher Tortoise
Louisiana Quillwort
Red Cockaded Woodpecker Habitat

Undifferentiated Alluvium
Upland Complex
Hattiesburg Formation

10   0   10 Kilometers

Figure 13. Geologic map showing the relationships between lithostratigraphy and habitat

methods, and data. An inclusion of geology contributes to the understanding of the natural and historic framework and baseline surficial conditions of the installation. Geologic studies of wetland surfaces are not commonplace; however, such studies are important in understanding the specific location of these surfaces as well as their hydrology. The geologic and geomorphic terminology, as applied to wetland surfaces in this chapter, is not entirely consistent with the terminology used by most wetland biologists and regulators; some translation, therefore, is necessary. Since erosion is a natural process that can be accelerated by human activities, including military training, geologic insight into this process contributes toward placing existing erosion processes in proper perspective.

Investigations of any kind at military installations must support the mission of the installation and be integrated with that mission, as well as with the work of other natural resource scientists and engineers. Mission support may be obvious and direct, such as identifying areas on the landscape suitable for ongoing training missions, for example, or indirect and less obvious by

providing background or baseline scientific data that may be used in the future for new missions.

In this age of environmental regulation and litigation, the scientific data must be sound and defensible. Furthermore, the data must be presented in a manner that is meaningful to a rather wide range of constituents, including military personnel and other natural resource scientists and engineers, and possibly the general public.

ACKNOWLEDGMENTS

The studies described in this chapter were funded by the U.S. National Guard Bureau and Mississippi Army National Guard (MSARNG) under the auspices of the Integrated Training Area Management (ITAM) program. Col. R. Lee, Lt. Col. R. Piazza, and Capt. R. Lemire at Headquarters MSARNG, are acknowledged for their support and encouragement during the course of the studies. At Camp Shelby, Col. I. Pylant, Training Site Commander; Lt. Col. E. Shows, C. King, D. Allen, and C. Roberts, respectively, are acknowledged for providing us with military training perspectives, environmental insight, and geographic information systems products for these studies.

We have benefited from the insight of R. Bowen and M. Meylan, Department of Geology, University of Southern Mississippi (USM), regarding the local and regional geology of southern Mississippi. S. Rosso, Department of Biological Sciences, USM, contributed to our botanical studies, and we acknowledge his contributions. We also acknowledge the studies and information provided by J. Moore and S. Leonard, The Nature Conservancy; and D. Epperson, Mississippi Department of Wildlife, Fisheries and Parks (Natural Heritage Program), all at Camp Shelby. M. Hanley, J. Goff, A. Roberts, B. Humber, B. Lee, and K. Wollschlager were USM student members of our field crew without whom the work could not have been conducted.

The views expressed in this chapter are exclusively those of the authors and have not been endorsed by the DoD, U.S. National Guard Bureau, or the MSARNG. The use of brand names is included for informational purposes only and is not an endorsement of products.

REFERENCES CITED

Adamczak, D.L., 1986, The petrology of the Hattiesburg lutite (Miocene), northern Forrest County, Mississippi [M.S. thesis]: Hattiesburg, University of Southern Mississippi, 56 p.

Albertson, P.E., Bush, A.J., III, Webster, S.L., Titre, J., Patrick, D.M., and Brown, J.W., 1995, Road management plan and workshop, Eglin Air Force Base: Vicksburg, Mississippi, U.S. Army Engineer Waterways Experiment Station, Miscellaneous Paper GL-95-13, 122 p., 9 appendices.

Autin, W.J., Burns, S.F., Miller, B.J., Saucier, R.T., and Snead, J.I., 1991, Quaternary geology of the Lower Mississippi Valley, in Morrison, R.B., ed., Quaternary nonglacial geology: Boulder, Colorado, Geological Society of America, Geology of North America, v. K-2, p. 547–582.

Bicker, A.R., Jr., 1969, Geologic map of Mississippi: Jackson, Mississippi Geological Survey, scale 1:50 000, 1 sheet.

Bowen, R., 1981, Stratigraphy and economic geology of the Eastabuchie Quadrangle, Forrest and Jones Counties, Mississippi: Oxford, Mississippi Minerals Resources Institute, Report of Investigation No. 79-10, 17 p.

Brinson, M.M., 1993, A hydrogeomorphic classification of wetlands: Vicksburg, Mississippi, U.S. Army Engineer Waterways Experiment Station, Wetlands Research Program, Technical Report WRP-DE-4, 101 p.

Broderson, W.D., 1994, From the surface down: An introduction to soil surveys for agronomic use: Lincoln, Nebraska, U.S. Department of Agriculture, Soil Conservation Service, 26 p.

Brown, G.F., 1944, Geology and ground-water resources of the Camp Shelby area: Jackson, Mississippi State Geological Survey, Bulletin 58, 72 p.

Dame, Kerrin J., 1993, Commanders guide to environmental management: Aberdeen Proving Ground, Maryland, U.S. Army Environmental Center, Report ENAEC-EC-CR-93064, 141 p.

Dockery, D.T., 1981, Stratigraphic column of Mississippi: Jackson, Mississippi Bureau of Geology, 1 sheet.

Environmental Laboratory, 1987, Corps of Engineers wetland delineation manual: Vicksburg, Mississippi, U.S. Army Engineer Waterways Experiment Station, Technical Report Y-87-1, 165 p.

Foster, V.M. and McCutcheon, T.E., 1941, Forrest County mineral resources: Jackson, Mississippi Geological Survey, Bulletin 44, 87 p.

Kusler, J.A., 1987, Hydrology: An introduction for wetland managers, *in* Kusler, J.A., and Brooks, G., eds., Proceedings National Wetlands Symposium: Berne, New York, Association of Wetland Managers, p. 4–25.

Law Engineering Testing Company, 1982, Gulf Coast Salt Domes geologic area characterization report: Columbus, Ohio, Office of Nuclear Waste Isolation, Battelle Memorial Institute, ONWI-120, 499 p.

May, J.H., Harrelson, D.W., Moore, W.H., Patrick, D.M., Cameron, C.P., and Schmitz, D.W., 1995, Post-Oligocene, stratigraphy and mapping considerations: Jackson, Miss., Mississippi Office of Geology, Mississippi Geology, v. 16, p. 1–7.

Meylan, M.A., and Li, Z., 1995, Geologic mapping of south-central Mississippi: A model for the distribution of Neogene and Quaternary sediments: Transactions, Gulf Coast Association of Geological Societies, v. 45, p. 435–440.

Miller, B.J., 1991, Pedology, *in* Morrison, R.B., ed., Quaternary nonglacial geology: Boulder, Colorado, The Geological Society of America, Geology of North America, v. K-2, p. 565–567.

Minkin, P., Packer, W., Gravid, D., Bishop, M., and Bishop, A., 1998, Delineation of wetlands and other regulated waters, Camp Shelby: Report to the National Guard Bureau: Vicksburg, Mississippi, U.S. Army Engineer Waterways Experiment Station, 10 p.

Misch, W.J., and Gosselink, J.G., 1993, Wetlands: New York, Van Nostrand-Reinhold, 172 p.

Munsell Soil Color Charts, 1994, Revised edition: New Windsor, New York, Macbeth Division of Kollmorgan Instruments Corporation, 10 p.

National Research Council, 1995, Wetland characterization: Washington, D.C., National Research Council, 268 p.

Patrick, D.M., 1990, Geologic mapping issues in southern Mississippi, *in* Bograd, M.B.E., and Dockery, D.T., III, eds., Geologic mapping in Mississippi, Proceedings MISGEOMAP Conference: Jackson, Mississippi Department of Environmental Quality, Bureau of Geology, Circular 3, p. 31–32.

Patrick, D.M., Corcoran, M.K., Albertson, P.E., and Smith, L.M., 1994, Earth resources stewardship at Department of Defense installations: Interim report of the Earth Resources Task Area, Legacy Resources Management Program: Vicksburg, Mississippi, U.S. Army Engineer Waterways Experiment Station, Technical Report GL-94-9, 143 p.

Patrick, D.M., Smith, L.M., and Whitten, C.B., 1982, Methods for studying accelerated fluvial change, *in* Hey, R.D., Bathurst, J.C., and Thorne, C.R., eds., Gravel-bed rivers: Chichester, U.K, John Wiley and Sons, Ltd., p. 783–815.

Reed, P.B., 1988, National list of plant species that occur in wetlands: National summary: Washington, D.C., U.S. Fish and Wildlife Service, Biological Report 88(24), 209 p.

Sharif, M., and Engel, B., 1995, Watershed monitoring study at Camp Shelby, Mississippi, Informal Report to Mississippi Military Department: Champaign, Illinois, U.S. Army Engineer Construction Engineering Research Laboratory, 30 p. plus appendices.

Siehl, G.H., 1991, Natural resource issues in national defense programs: Washington, D.C., Library of Congress, Congressional Research Service, Report for Congress, 91-781 ENR, 13 p.

Smith, L.M., and Patrick, D.M., 1991, Erosion, sedimentation and fluvial systems, *in* Kiersch, G.A., ed., The heritage of engineering geology; The first hundred years: Boulder, Colorado, Geological Society of America, Centennial (DNAG) Special Volume 3, p. 169–181.

U.S. Department of Agriculture, Soil Conservation Service, Forest Service, Mississippi Agricultural and Forestry Experiment Station, 1979, Soil Survey of Forrest County, Mississippi: Washington, D.C., U.S. Government Printing Office, 103 p.

U.S. Department of the Army, National Guard Bureau, Mississippi Army National Guard, 1994, Final environmental impact statement: Military training use of forest service lands, Volume. 1, Washington, D.C., 522 p.

MANUSCRIPT ACCEPTED BY THE SOCIETY OCTOBER 27, 2000

Geological Society of America
Reviews in Engineering Geology, Volume XIV
2001

Sustainability of military lands: Historic erosion trends at Fort Leonard Wood, Missouri

Paul E. Albertson
U.S. Army Engineer Research and Development Center, Geotechnical Laboratory
Waterways Experiment Station, Vicksburg, Mississippi, USA

ABSTRACT

Military land managers are faced with questions of landscape stability and sustainability. Fort Leonard Wood, Missouri, was selected to test these concerns because it has been the site of engineering training for over 50 years. Prior to U.S. Army occupancy, the landscape was undergoing disequilibrium resulting from historic land use activities. An integrated approach was used to examine landscape changes using existing information and technologies to answer geomorphic inquiries of equilibrium and recovery. The lack of a long-term sediment record was supplemented by performing soil-loss modeling. Soil simulations were done using the Revised Universal Soil Loss Equation (RUSLE) to simulate the effect of changing land use and land cover on soil loss. The aerial photographic record offered a means to create land cover for RUSLE simulations. The sustainable or acceptable soil-loss rate is known as the soil loss tolerance. Simulation of soil loss using 1938, 1955, 1976, and 1997 aerial photographs identified "hot spots" where soil loss was greater than tolerance. The results show that past Army training activities caused more soil loss than did presettlement activities, but that estimated soil loss from current training is less than loss rates before military occupancy of the landscape. Current best management practices are leading to landscape restoration within accepted soil loss tolerance. This study supports the U.S. Army's commitment to landscape stewardship, which is essential for land-use sustainability.

INTRODUCTION

Problem

The United States as a whole, and specifically the U.S. Army, faces the challenge of operating within the sustainable limits of natural systems in the twenty-first century. The challenge cuts across both civil works and military operations. In terms of military operations, U.S. Army trainers are faced with questions concerning landscape carrying capacity. The Deputy Chief of Staff for Operations and Plans emphasized the need to sustain the Army's lands and considered land to be one of the Army's most valuable resources (Macia, 1995). He went on to define a greater challenge: objective prediction of impacts and effects on the

Army (Macia, 1995). In general, land managers and trainers are faced with questions such as the following:

• How much stress from troop activities can the land sustain?

• How can training be optimized with minimum environmental impact?

• Are conservation programs sufficient to allow for landscape recovery?

The research presented here was directed toward examining sustainability questions within the context of erosion and soil-loss tolerance. Sustainability means different things to different people. The confusion comes because, according to Sitarz (1998), literally hundreds of definitions have been suggested. With regard to soil loss for this research effort, threshold of sustainability is defined as soil tolerance as recognized by the soil

Albertson, P.E., 2001, Sustainability of military lands: Historic erosion trends at Fort Leonard Wood, Missouri, *in* Ehlen, J., and Harmon, R.S., eds., The Environmental Legacy of Military Operations: Boulder, Colorado, Geological Society of America Reviews in Engineering Geology, v. XIV, p. 151–161.

science community (NRCS, 1997). There is a need to understand the landscape processes to minimize military-induced impact and increase environmental management to stewardship status while at the same time maintaining mission readiness requirements.

Fort Leonard Wood was selected as the study area for a number of reasons. The first was because it is the largest training center for U.S. Army Engineers. The training of combat engineers involves interaction with and disturbance of the ground. Military missions on the fort have the potential to adversely impact the landscape. On the surface, erosion or soil loss and resulting stream sedimentation are obvious potential problems. In addition, the fort is targeted for expansion under the Base Realignment and Closure (BRAC) Act. According to the Environmental Impact Statement (EIS) associated with this BRAC expansion, additional activities will increase erosion, soil loss, and sedimentation (U.S. Army, 1997). However, the EIS only states the problem qualitatively. Commanders and resource managers need to understand the causes and effects in quantitative terms.

The purpose of this research was to examine sustainability of military lands quantitatively using soil-loss estimates within the recent geomorphic history of Fort Leonard Wood's landscape. The knowledge gained will aid future land management and training to work within the limits of the system. The two specific objectives were to model soil-loss processes to predict the stability and sensitivity of the landscape within the recent geomorphic history of the Fort, and to determine if the landscape has recovered from historic disturbance and if current land-use practices are within the landscape's sustainable limits.

History of Fort Leonard Wood

What is now known as Fort Leonard Wood was once Ozark farm and timberland (Welfare Department, 1940). In May 1940, the local population of 300 became overwhelmed by more than 30 000 construction workers. Groundbreaking for the Seventh Corps Training Area began on 3 December 1940. In April 1943, the 75th Infantry was activated, which caused the population to rise to a daily average of 40 000. The following year witnessed the addition of 5000 German prisoners of war.

After World War II, the training center was literally "put out to pasture." The Bar-O-Bar Ranch of Oklahoma leased the entire acreage for cattle range from 1946 to 1950. The post was reactivated on 1 August 1950 because of the Korean War. Troops began arriving a month later and troop activities have continued ever since. The Sixth Armored Division arrived for training in September 1950. The post became a U.S. Army reception center (Basic Training Center) in 1953. Additional troops arrived in 1955 for the new six-month active duty program because of the Reserve Forces Act. On 16 March 1956, the Sixth Armored Division was inactivated. A few days later, 21 March 1956, the post officially was designated Fort Leonard Wood. The building of permanent facilities followed in the fall of 1956. The "building boom" consisted of 33 family quarters. The summer of 1958 saw the first permanent troop housing.

The population of the Fort grew to a peak of 123 000 soldiers in 1967 with the increase of troops training for Vietnam. In 1975, $60 million was spent in construction and expansion. In February 1985, the Secretary of the Army decided to move the engineering center to Fort Leonard Wood. The move took place in June 1988. The Military Police and Chemical Schools arrived in 1999.

The number of people on post is directly correlated to the land-use load on the landscape. The population data for the military installation is based on open file information (Roberts, 1997, personal and written commun.). Figure 1 graphically presents census values gleaned from open files at the fort. Population varied through time but a certain peak period of land-use loading can be inferred. The subsequent soil loss analyses will examine effects of the peak loading on the landscape.

Fort Leonard Wood thus offers a setting to examine a mid-continent landscape with a history of land use change and five decades of military training. The study area is located in south central Missouri (Fig. 2). The fort is 193 km southwest of St. Louis, Missouri, and 117 km northeast of Springfield, Missouri. Fort Leonard Wood Military Reservation covers 68 564 acres, or approximately 277 km^2, and is situated primarily in Pulaski County, Missouri. The Army inherited a landscape in disequilibrium due to a history of land-use stress. This analysis will first look beyond the Fort boundaries and back into time to establish the geological and geomorphic background conditions before modeling the historic soil loss.

Geological background

Fort Leonard Wood is located within the Salem Plateau portion of the Ozark Plateaus Province of the Interior Highlands. The bedrock underlying and outcropping on the military reservation consists of Ordovician-age cherty dolomite and sandstone. The rock units are essentially flat lying with a regional dip to the northwest of approximately one meter every kilometer. The bedrock units exposed on the Fort consist of the Gasconade Dolomite, Roubidoux Formation, and the Jefferson City Dolomite Formations (Greenhorne and O'Mara, 1982). Differences among these formations have traditionally been based upon the relative amounts of chert and sandstone, the type of dolomite, and the type of chert (Thompson, 1991).

Physical and chemical weathering have altered the near-surface bedrock units into a residual soil. Dolomite weathers into a reddish silty clay residuum or "terra rosa." Chert and sandstone, resistant to weathering, form angular fragments in the matrix of the red clay. Relict bedding structures are visible in soil where no major mass wasting has occurred. Generally, the residual soil is thinnest on the steep hill slopes and thickest on the broad ridges.

Colluvium is found on toe slopes in the landscape. It consists of gravelly sand and clay derived from adjacent slopes formed of sandy and cherty dolomite and sandstone. The silty portion of the colluvium originates largely from reworked loess. Aeolian silt occurs as a thin (<1 m) veneer on the uplands. The gravel portion of the colluvium consists of chert and sandstone fragments.

Alluvium is found in the flood plains of the fort. It consists of a gravelly basal unit overlain by finer-grained sand, silt, and clay units. The gravel is predominantly chert derived initially from the weathering of cherty dolomite and later reworking of the colluvium. Sand is derived from the sandy dolomite and sandstone, and from reworked colluvium and older alluvium. The silt is derived from the loess-capped Ozark uplands. The sediment record contained in the alluvial fill of the valleys offers evidence of both geomorphic stability and disequilibrium of the landscape (Albertson, 1998).

Geomorphic background

Previous studies conducted on the Ozark Plateau offer insight toward understanding the geomorphic development of Fort Leonard Wood. Schoolcraft (1819) provided descriptions that served as initial conditions for soil loss modeling. He defined a dualistic scene of bottomland, cliff, prairie, or barren in harmony or in equilibrium (Schoolcraft, 1819). Bretz (1965) described the Ozark Plateau as a peneplain. Reams (1968) tested Bretz's Davisian paradigms and found that the concept of a peneplain did not explain the evolution of the Ozarks. Reams's calculations did support Bretz's (1965) conclusions that the plateau and residuum probably were Tertiary in age. Thus, there is evidence of a stable landscape when viewed over long time scales.

Rath (1975) defined two loess sheets in the Ozarks. Some colluvium could be relatively dated based on overlying loess deposits. The loess veneer has been an easily eroded sediment supply on this Ozark landscape. Brackenridge (1981) and Haynes (1976, 1985) differentiated the alluvium of the Pomme de Terre River, within 200 km of the Fort, providing a regional geochronologic framework for the last 130 000 years. Johnson (1983) concluded that the older Holocene alluvium is reworked loess. Landscape instability associated with the older alluvium is linked to possible climatic change. He postulated that the younger charcoal-rich alluvium was related to slash and burn technology of late Holocene Indians.

Pugh (1992) deduced that stream disturbances, such as increased sedimentation, were caused by a complex interaction between changing climatic trends and changing land use. Jacobson and Primm (1994) presented evidence that stream disturbances in Ozark streams are a complex process-response system of natural and anthropogenic forces.

The alluvial framework developed by Albertson et al. (1995) established a local Holocene geomorphic reconstruction for the Fort Leonard Wood landscape. Calculation of sedimentation rates throughout the Holocene based on alluvial deposition indicates an increase by two orders of magnitude accompanying Euro-American settlement (Albertson, 1998).

SOIL-LOSS SIMULATIONS

Soil-loss modeling was performed to fill in gaps in the historic sediment record. Actual sediment data derived from selected training areas (Southard, 1998) were collected during only four events for one year. Using just four events during one water year is not representative of the geomorphic system's variability but it was the best data available for this study. Therefore, simulations were needed to estimate soil loss further back into the historic past.

Soil-loss models can back-calculate the effects of land use activities over the previous decades and centuries. However, what model to use was a matter of debate because each approach has advantages and limitations. Numerical methods can estimate the physical reality of a phenomenon. Revised Universal Soil Loss Equation (RUSLE) was selected because it is an accepted analytical tool for the engineering and natural resources community. However, it is an empirical equation derived from agricultural experiments and refined by experience. Collectively, all numerical analyses are based on assumptions. At best, the supposedly quantitative methods only yielded qualitative results.

Despite the promise of new and better models, and criticism of empirical models such as RUSLE, a recent review of soil loss models available to the U.S. Army still recommended using RUSLE (USACE, 1997). Simulations were made using only the RUSLE model. Modeling was intended to simulate the effects of changing land use on landscape development. Until recently, erosion and sedimentation assessments (Profitt, 1994; U.S. Army, 1997) have been chiefly qualitative. Efforts to monitor the sediment in streams by the U.S. Geological Survey (USGS) (Southard, 1998) were good steps leading to a quantitative understanding of the problem. The results from RUSLE modeling of the Fort Leonard Wood landscape were compared to sediment studies and produced results acceptable to the natural resource community. Modeling results were compared to the sediment-sampling program (Southard, 1998) to validate the simulations. The simulations used *ArcView spatial analyst* to estimate the soil-loss distribution across the military reservation through time.

The Revised Universal Soil Loss Equation is:

$$A R \bullet K \bullet LS \bullet C \bullet P,$$

where A = estimated annual soil loss (tons /acre/year); R = rainfall factor of energy and intensity; K = soil erodibility; LS = topographic factor, slope length (L) and slope steepness (S); C = crop management or cover class; and P = practice or conservation class.

Essential to understanding the soil loss simulations is the selection process for the values of the variables. The R factor of 225 for rainfall energy was obtained from the Field Office Technical Guide (Natural Resource Conservation Service, 1997). During these simulations, R was held constant at 225 ft tons/ acre to represent average annual conditions in the study area. The soil erodibility (K) and the length-steepness (LS) values for each soil series were obtained from Lamb (1998, written commun.) and detailed in Albertson (1998). Land managers have some control over the other two factors, C and P. The C factors were selected from a review of literature (Jacobson and Prime, 1994; Natural Resource Conservation Service, 1997) and consultation with a local soil scientist (Lamb, 1998, written commun.). Land cover for circa 1800 was derived from a presettlement vegetation GIS

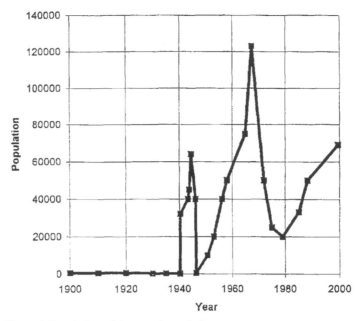

Figure 1. Population of the post through time.

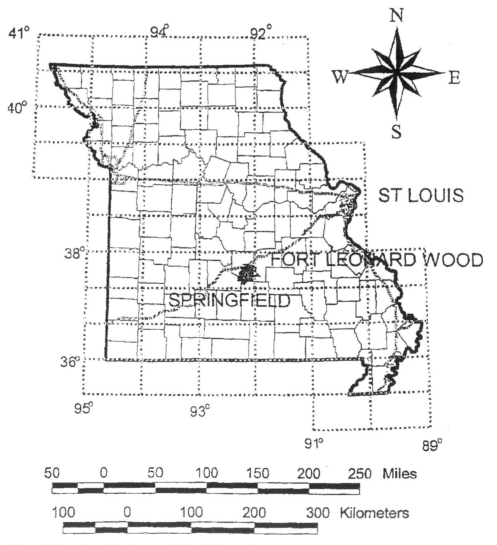

Figure 2. Location of Fort Leonard Wood, Missouri.

TABLE 1. LAND COVER CIRCA 1980 FROM 1:250 000 LAND USE/LAND COVER CLASS; MILITARY LAND USE; *C* FACTOR (U.S. Geological Survey, 1990)

Class number and name		Military land use	*C* Factor
11	Residential	Cantonment	0.100
12	Commercial services	Training area	0.500
14	Transportation, communication, and utilities	TA 244	1.00
17	Other urban or built-up land	Training ranges	0.500
21	Cropland and pasture	Mowed grass	0.050
41	Deciduous forestland	Reservation	0.005
43	Mixed forestland	Reservation	0.005
53	Reservoir	Sediment ponds	0.000
76	Transitional areas	Quarry	1.000

coverage (Jones, 1995, written commun.). The *C* factor was assigned based on land cover. The presettlement (prior to 1800) land cover from Jones (1995, written commun.) portrayed essentially two land-cover types, the Post Oak flat, which was assigned 0.003, and thinner slope woods, which were assigned 0.05. A modem simulation used 1980 land cover derived from the U.S. Geological Survey (1990). Land cover was differentiated by using the USGS 1990 land use/land cover classification. Table 1 presents the classes, military land use, and the assigned *C*-factors.

The land cover based on 1:250 000 data generalized the landscape too much to produce meaningful results. An automated aerial photographic technique was employed to derive more detailed and distributed land cover. Photos flown in 1938, 1955, 1976, and 1997 were selected. Pre-army conditions are displayed on the earliest 1938 photos. Thus, land use in 1938 served as a reference for pre-military conditions. The 1942 coverage was examined but the flight lines did not cover the study area completely. Post World War II and Korean War conditions were represented by the 1955 photo series. The 1976 coverage showed post-Vietnam conditions. The recent 1997 flights were the most up-to-date aerial photo coverage available.

Transforming the aerial photos to usable digital data was tedious and time consuming. Therefore, the study was limited to the vicinity of Smith Branch basins (Fig. 3). The photos were scanned, georeferenced, and mosaicked for later comparison and processing. *ERDAS IMAGINE* software was used to perform supervised classification. The scenes were separated into four classes, and *C* factors were assigned during a reclassification procedure. The four land cover classes are: (1) bare ground, (2) 10 to 50 percent cover, (3) 50 to 90 percent cover, and (4) greater than 90 percent cover. Table 2 shows the classes and *C* factors used during each RUSLE run. The RUSLE model was run with R, *LS*, and *K* held constant for each time simulation. Once the *C* factors were set for each of the land-cover classes for the 1997 RUSLE run (Fig. 4), they were held constant for the subsequent 1976, 1955, and 1938 simulations (Figs. 4B, 4C, and 4D). The *P* factor was adjusted to reflect the degree of land stewardship in each time interval. The *P* factor is usually 1.0, but if soil conservation practices are installed, the *P* factor can

be less than 1.0 (Hausenbuilder, 1985). The 1997 RUSLE results were validated to reflect the 1997 sediment data. The monitored basins collectively produced an estimated 0.6 to 0.66 tons/acre/year.

ASCE (1977) suggested a basin of this size would have a sediment delivery ratio of about 20%. Therefore, a soil loss of 0.6/0.2 to 0.66/0.2 would be expected to be about 3.0 to 3.3 tons/acre/year. The basin also contained sediment ponds that will reduce sediment delivery. The 1997 aerial photos were examined to estimate the pond size/basin size ratio. Consulting the ASCE (1977) sediment pond trapping curves suggested that the ponds would trap about 30% in Smith Branch basin. Therefore, the 3.0 to 3.3 tons/acre/year translates to 4.3 to 4.7 tons/acre/year. The 1997 RUSLE model was run varying *P* between 0.1 and 0.9 as recommended by NRCS (1997). When a *P* factor of 0.5 was used, the model produced a mean soil-loss over Smith Basin of 4.59 tons/acre/year. The RUSLE results were then considered reasonable because the input used accepted *C* factors and the mean was within the range of soil loss estimated from the sediment sampling (4.3 to 4.7 tons/acre/year). The *P* factor for the 1976 simulation was changed to 0.75. The higher *P* factor was used to reflect less soil conservation. The rationale was based on examination of 1976 aerial photos, which revealed that the major sediment pond, Bloodland Lake, was not built yet. Following similar rationale, a *P* factor of 1.0 was used for the 1938 and 1955 simulations to reflect the level of soil conservation at those times.

RESULTS

The RUSLE model runs were conducted to simulate the effect of changing land use and land cover on soil loss over time. The selected simulations corresponded to time periods when land cover could be assumed, for example, 1800 for presettlement conditions. Land cover was also estimated from aerial photographs. Table 3 presents the results of the RUSLE simulations. Figure 5 presents the results as a graph of soil loss verses time. Examining the mean values on Figure 5 and in Table 3 reveals an increase in soil loss during the first 100 years of settlement.

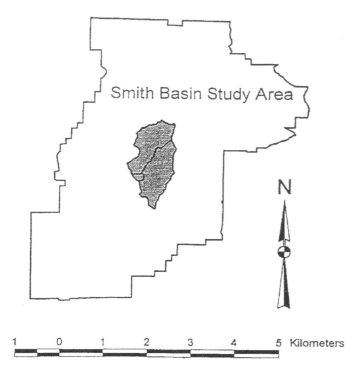

Figure 3. Location of Smith Branch basins sediment and soil loss studies.

TABLE 2. LAND COVER *C* FACTOR CLASSIFICATION

Class	Land cover	*C* factor
1	Bare ground; 0 to 10% cover	1.000
2	10% to 50% cover	0.180
3	50% to 90% cover	0.050
4	Woodland; 90% to 100% cover	0.003

These analyses temporally indicate the general sediment yield trends over time. GIS analysis with *ArcView* portrays the specific areas of spatial change (Fig. 4). The simulations indicated that land use activities induced high soil loss through the first half 1900s until conservation practices were implemented in the 1970s, continuing through the present.

DISCUSSION

Once human activities upset the balance where the landscape is adjusted to climate and vegetation with the minimum erosion, the processes reestablishing equilibrium are slow (Reesman and Godfrey, 1981). The steep change in sediment loss rates (Fig. 5) reflects the geomorphic system undergoing a threshold response followed by a reaction of increased soil loss, then a relaxation indicated by a reduction in soil loss.

The following examples compare the simulated soil loss estimates to soil loss values associated with cited land use activities to place the results in a broader context. The American Society of Civic Engineers (1977) manual suggested that 0.3 tons/acre/year is a normal geological rate of soil loss. Simulation of the presettlement soil loss (Table 3) resulted in a mean of 0.24 tons/acre/year, which is similar to the 0.3 tons/acre/year cited by ASCE. Therefore, the RUSLE results for presettlement conditions were considered reasonable. The sustainable or acceptable soil loss rate is known as the soil loss tolerance or *T* factor. Wolf (1989) reported *T* factors of 3 to 5 tons/acre/year for the soils on site. The RUSLE results are presented in Figures 4A, 4B, 4C, and 4D in tons/acre/year categories of 0 to 3, below *T*; 3 to 5, within *T*; 5 to 10, "Twice *T*" and greater than 10, beyond 2T.

Reported erosion rates (American Society of Civic Engineers, 1977) for urban construction were recorded as 10 to 50 tons/acre/year. Both active mining and military heavy equipment training, which equates to ongoing construction, have the potential to increase erosion two to three orders of magnitude (American Society of Civic Engineers, 1977). Simulation of soil loss in 1938, 1955, 1976, and 1997 (Fig. 4) showed "hot spots" with soil loss greater than 10.

Figure 6 presents the RUSLE results as percentage of the basin in the four classes for the four time periods. Class 1 (below tolerance [<*T*; 0 to 3 tons/acre/year]) showed an increase in time except for the 1955 time step. Class 2 (at tolerance [within *T*; 3 to 5 tons/acre/year]) increased in 1955 and 1976 to about 10 percent and then decreased. Class 3 (twice tolerance [2*T*; 5 to 10 tons/acre/year]), showed a decrease after the peak in 1955. Class 4, (beyond twice tolerance [>2*T*; 10 to 70 tons/acre/year]), increased from 1938 to 1955 and then decreased and has remained constant since then. Collectively, Figure 6 reveals a landscape healing from past land-use stresses, but one that still has some "hot spots" that exceed the suggested soil-loss tolerance. Present conditions (1997) are the land is either below tolerance or beyond twice tolerance. The analysis shown in Figure 6 reflects conservation and concentrated land use with containment. Thus, from a military planner's point of view, the land is hot or it is not.

Table 4 presents the change compared to presettlement and pre-military conditions. After considering the soil simulations, impacts caused by army training resulted in the following soil loss increases: (a) 30 to 40 times increase from presettlement, (b) an initial increase over 1930s agriculture, but (c) less than or equal to the pre-military soil after soil conservation implementation.

The 1997 RUSLE results show mean soil loss within tolerance. Obviously, present land use generates more soil loss than presettlement conditions but estimates of present soil loss are less than during pre-military times.

The RUSLE simulations were simplified by several assumptions. For example, the *R* factor was held constant from 1938 to 1997. The *K* and *LS* factors were attributes assigned based on the digital soil survey coverage. The *C* factors were assigned to land cover files that were derived by supervised remote-sensing techniques. The land cover classes were visually validated. The *P* factor was selected to calibrate the results within physically reasonable soil-loss values and degree of soil conservation practices.

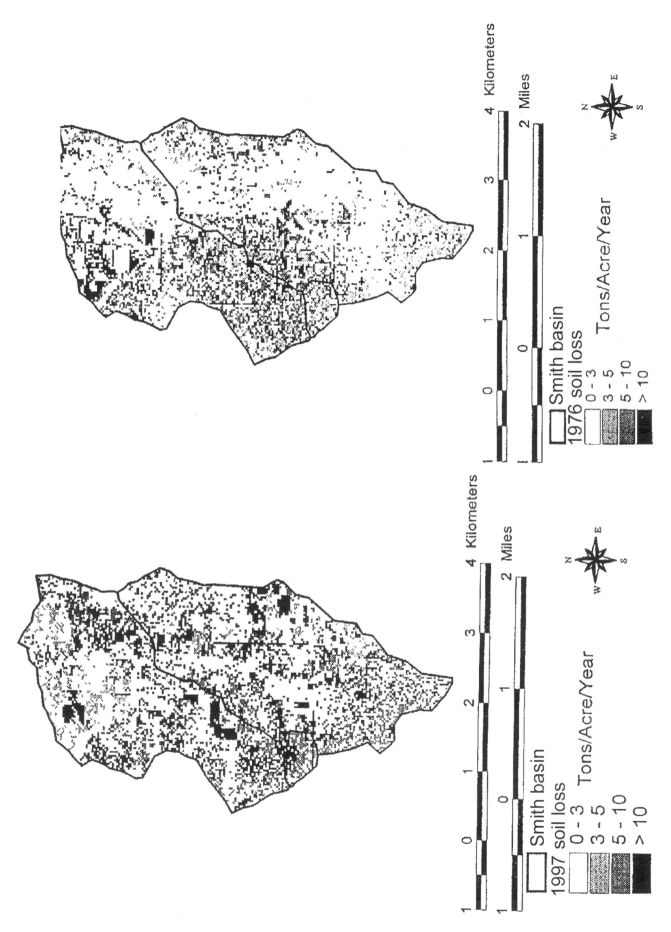

Smith basin

1997 soil loss

0 - 3   Tons/Acre/Year
3 - 5
5 - 10
> 10

Figure 4A. RUSLE soil loss simulation for Smith Branch in 1997.

Smith basin

1976 soil loss

0 - 3
3 - 5   Tons/Acre/Year
5 - 10
> 10

Figure 4B. RUSLE soil loss simulation for Smith Branch in 1976.

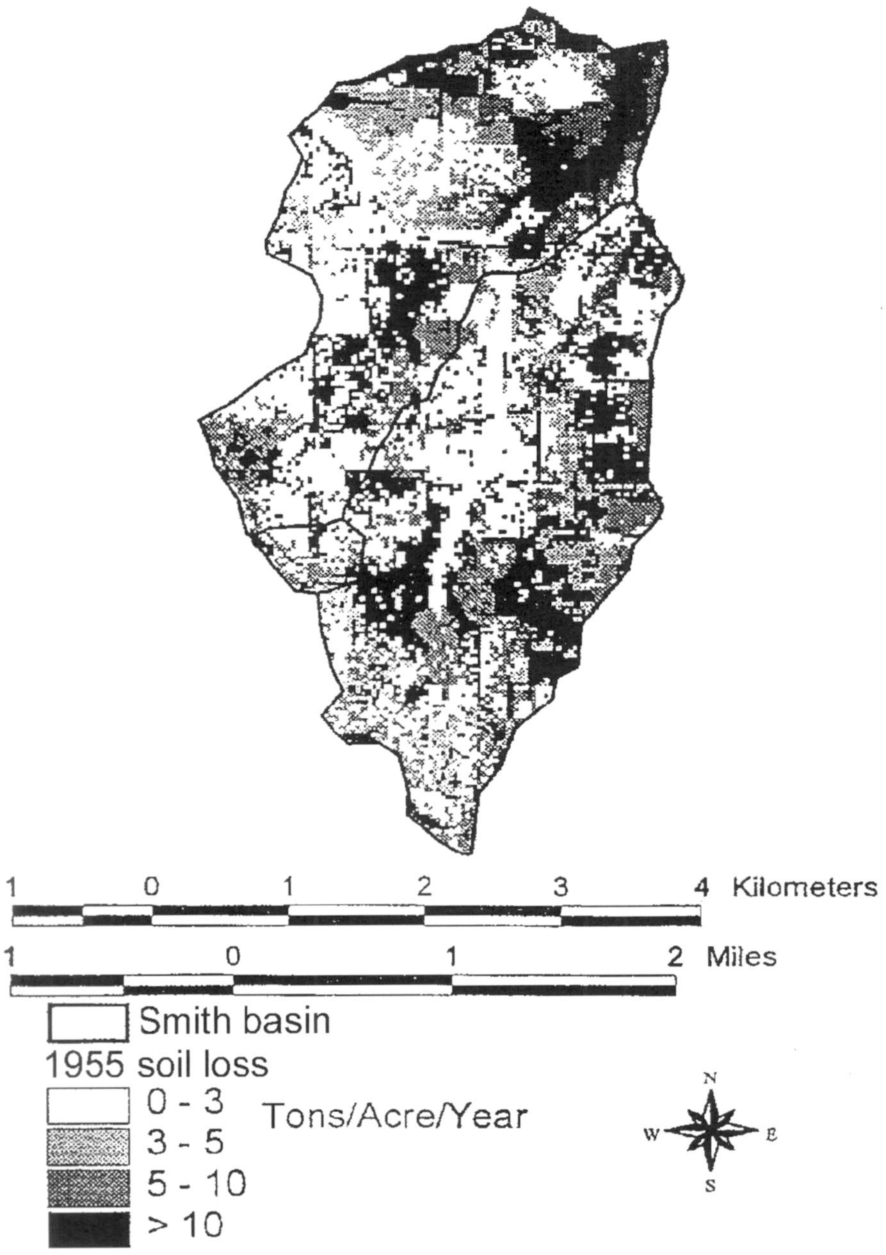

Smith basin
1955 soil loss

Tons/Acre/Year
0 - 3
3 - 5
5 - 10
> 10

Figure 4C. RUSLE soil loss simulation for Smith Branch in 1955.

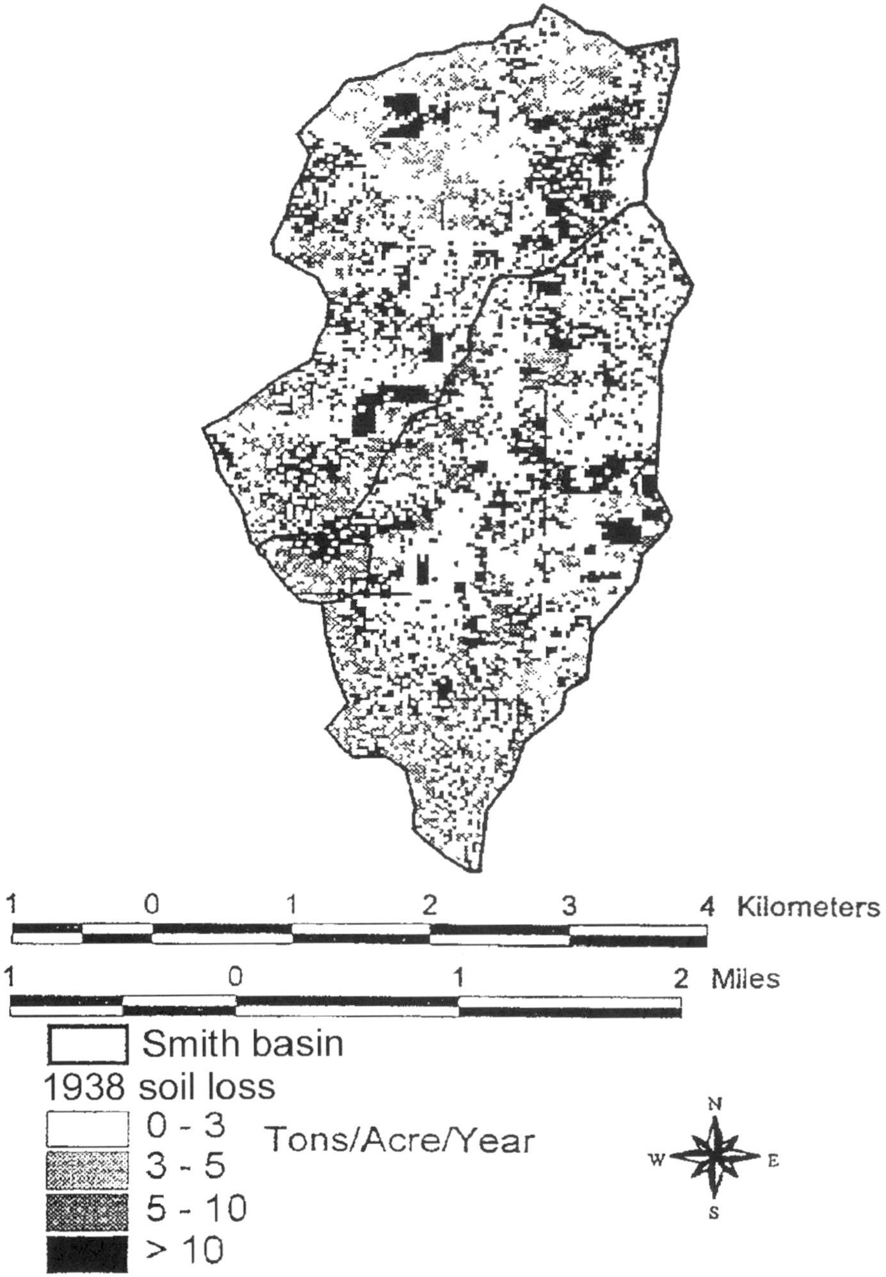

Smith basin
1938 soil loss

Tons/Acre/Year
0 - 3
3 - 5
5 - 10
> 10

Figure 4D. RUSLE soil loss simulation for Smith Branch in 1938.

**TABLE 3. RUSLE SOIL-LOSS ESTIMATES
IN TONS/ACRE/YEAR FOR SELECTED DATES**

Year	1800	1938	1955	1976	1977
Mean	0.24	8.40	11.90	6.70	4.57
Standard deviation	0.17	17.97	18.40	16.32	9.84
Mean + standard deviation	0.41	26.37	30.30	23.02	14.41
Mean + standard deviation/2	0.33	17.39	21.10	14.86	9.49
Twice the mean	0.49	16.80	23.80	13.40	9.14

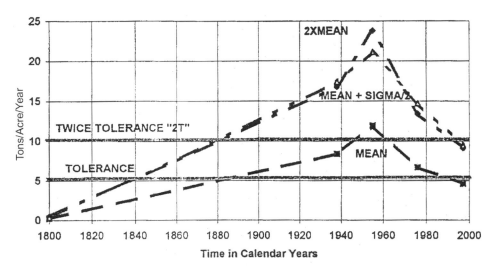

Figure 5. RUSLE soil loss results through historic time.

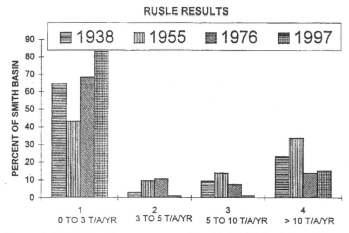

Figure 6. RUSLE results, percentage of land in Smith Basin in soil loss classes. T/A/YR is tons/acre/year.

**TABLE 4. COMPARISON OF SOIL LOSS WITH PRESETTLEMENT
1800 REFERENCE AND PRE-MILITARY 1938 REFERENCE**

Year	Mean (tons/acre/year)	Change since 1800	Change since 1938
1800	0.24	—	—
1938	8.40	34.57	—
1955	11.90	48.97	1.42
1976	6.70	27.57	0.80
1997	4.57	18.81	0.54

CONCLUSIONS

The landscape was examined using existing data sets and available information from different temporal and spatial scales. Acknowledging the limits caused by scale and the existing data sets, the following conclusions were drawn.

Examinations of the aerial photographic record offered qualitative evidence that conservation practices implemented in the late 1970s have resulted in landscape restoration. The aerial photographic record offered a means to create landcover for RUSLE simulations. Using RUSLE and varying land cover based on aerial photos indicated that soil loss has been reduced in the last two decades. Present best management practices are leading to landscape restoration within accepted soil loss tolerance (T factors). Average soil-loss estimates are near to tolerance, but some "hot spots" still need additional erosion-control efforts. Thus, the recovery trend requires that a stewardship commitment be continued to reverse previous land use impacts. The landscape development of Fort Leonard Wood was examined by Albertson (1998) using multiple lines of inquiry over multiple timescales. Deposition rates showed an increase in response to climatic forces, but a sharp increase in sediment load in transition from prehistoric to the historic period. The major threshold jump in sediment corresponds to about the time of European-American settlement of the land. RUSLE simulations estimated landscape system response to land use change. Figure 5 reflects the marked increase in sediment load over time since human settlement. Viewed in these terms, the geomorphic system was stressed and the response to historic land use change was an increase in sediment load by two orders of magnitude. Simulated erosion rates indicate that the system is recovering.

The working hypothesis based on the few actual measurements and the RUSLE simulations is that the land was stressed, but due to conservation and land stewardship, the system is beginning to recover. The decrease in sediment load during the army's ownership in the last two decades reflects the implementation of stewardship principles.

ACKNOWLEDGMENTS

Two anonymous reviewers are acknowledged for their careful reading, review, and helpful comments. The author wishes to thank three institutions. First thanks go to my employer, the U.S. Army Corps of Engineers Waterways Experiment Station, for supporting this geomorphic research. Second, Fort Leonard Wood is acknowledged for providing me with the data and access to examine landscape recovery. Third, the University of Missouri, Rolla, is recognized for providing the fruitful place to complete my research. Citation of commercial product brand names does not constitute an official endorsement or approval of the use of such commercial products by the Army.

Following the tragic death of Paul E. Albertson, this manuscript was revised for publication by Judy Ehlen and Lillian Wakeley, U.S. Army Engineer Research and Development Center.

REFERENCES CITED

Albertson, P.E., 1998, Geomorphic development of Fort Leonard Wood [Ph.D. thesis]: Rolla, University of Missouri, 155 p.

Albertson, P.E., Meinert, D., and Butler, G., 1995, Geomorphic evaluation of Fort Leonard Wood, Missouri: Vicksburg, Mississippi, U.S. Army Corps of Engineers Waterways Experiment Station, Technical Report GL-95-19, 380 p.

American Society of Civil Engineers (ASCE), 1977, Sedimentation engineering manual: New York, American Society of Civil Engineers, n. 54, 745 p.

Brackenridge, G.R., 1981, Late Quaternary floodplain sedimentation along the Pomme de Terre River, southern Missouri: Quaternary Research, v. 15, p. 62–76.

Bretz, J.H., 1965, Geomorphic history of the Ozarks of Missouri: Rolla, Missouri Geological Survey and Water Resources, v. 41, Second Series, 147 p.

Greenhorne and O'Mara, 1982, Terrain analysis of Fort Leonard Wood: Fort Belvoir, Virginia, U.S. Army Engineer Topographic Engineering Laboratories, scale 1:50 000, 65 p.

Hausenbuilder, H.L., 1985, Soil science principles and practices (third edition): Dubuque, Iowa, William C. Brown Publishers, 610 p.

Haynes, C.V., Jr., 1976, Late Quaternary geochronology of the lower Pomme de Terre Valley, *in* Wood, W.R., and McMillan, R.B., eds., Prehistoric man and his environments: A case study in the Ozark Highland: New York, Academic Press, p. 47–61.

Haynes, C.V., Jr., 1985, Mastodon-bearing springs and late Quaternary geochronology of the lower Pomme de Terre Valley, Missouri: Geological Society of America Special Paper 204, 35 p.

Jacobson, R.B., and Primm, A.T., 1994, Historical land-use changes and potential effects on stream disturbance in the Ozark Plateaus, Missouri: U.S. Geological Survey Open-File Report 94-333, 95 p.

Johnson, D.L., 1983, Cultural resources survey, Harry S. Truman Dam and Reservoir Project, Missouri. 4. Soils and soil-geomorphic investigations of the lower Pomme de Terre Valley: Columbia, University of Missouri, for the U.S. Army Corps of Engineers, Kansas City District, Environmental Study Papers, v. 10, 164 p.

Macia, T.E., 1995, The U.S. Army's Integrated Training Area Management (ITAM) Program, *in* Proceedings of the Department of Defense /Interagency Workshop on Technologies to Address Soil Erosion on Department of Defense Lands, Little Rock, Arkansas: Vicksburg, Mississippi, draft report prepared by FTN Associates Ltd. for U.S. Army Corps of Engineers Waterway Experiment Station, p. 183–186.

Natural Resource Conservation Service (NRCS), 1997, Field office technical guide, General resource reference, erosion prediction: Section 1-4.

Profitt, R.J., 1994, Land condition–trend analysis (LCTA) data summary and analysis report for Fort Leonard Wood, Missouri: ATZT-DPW-EE, 61 p.

Pugh, A.L., 1992, Recent geomorphic evolution of the Little Piney Creek, Phelps County, Missouri, [M.S. thesis]: Rolla, University of Missouri-Rolla, 84 p.

Rath, D.L., 1975, A study of Middle to late Quaternary sediments in a karst trap [M.S. thesis]: Rolla, University of Missouri, 91 p.

Reams, M.W., 1968, Cave sediments and geomorphic history of the ozarks [Ph.D. thesis]: St. Louis, Missouri, Washington University, 167 p.

Reesman, A.L., and Godfrey, A.E., 1981, Development of the central basin of Tennessee by chemical denudation: Zeitschrift für Geomorphologie, v. 25, p. 437–451.

Schoolcraft, H.R., 1819, A view of the lead mines of Missouri: New York, John Wiley and Sons, 299 p.

Sitarz, D., 1998, Sustainable America, America's environment, economy and society in the 21st century: Carbondale, Illinois, Earth Press, 312 p.

Southard, R.E, 1998, Sediment data collection for the Normandy training area at sites Smith 1, Smith 2, and Smith 3 during 1997 calendar year [Fort Leonard Wood]: Rolla, Missouri, U.S. Geological Survey, Water Resources Division, Missouri District Data Report (variously paged).

Thompson, T.L., 1991, Paleozoic succession in Missouri, 2. Ordovician system: Rolla, Missouri Department of Natural Resources, Division of Geology and

Land Survey, Report of Investigations, n. 70, 282 p.

U.S. Army, 1997, Main report: Environmental impact statement: Relocation of U.S. Army Chemical and U.S. Army Military Police School to Fort Leonard Wood, Missouri: Kansas City, Missouri, U.S. Army Corps of Engineers Kansas City District, 746 p.

U.S. Army Corps of Engineers, 1997, Evaluation of technologies for addressing factors related to soil erosion on Department of Defense lands: Champaign, Illinois, U.S. Army Construction Engineering Research Laboratory, Technical Report 97/134, 100 p.

U.S. Geological Survey, 1990, Land use and land cover digital data from 1:250 000 and 1:100 000 scale maps: U.S. Geological Survey National Mapping Program Technical Instructions, Data Users Guide 4, 44 p.

Welfare Department, 1940, When the Army came to the Ozarks: Washington, D.C., U.S. Government Report, 74 p.

Wolf, D.W., 1989, Soil survey of Pulaski, Missouri: Washington, D.C., United States Department of Agriculture, Soil Conservation Service, 120 p.

MANUSCRIPT ACCEPTED BY THE SOCIETY OCTOBER 27, 2000

Geological Society of America
Reviews in Engineering Geology, Volume XIV
2001

Freeze-thaw–induced geomorphic and soil changes in vehicle ruts and natural rills

Lawrence W. Gatto
Environmental Sciences Branch, U.S. Army Cold Regions Research and Engineering Laboratory,
Hanover, New Hampshire 03755-1290, USA

Jonathan J. Halvorson
Appalachian Farming Systems Research Center, U.S. Department of Agriculture Agricultural Research Service,
Beaver, West Virginia 25813-9423, USA

Donald K. McCool
Land Management and Water Conservation Research Unit, U.S. Department of Agriculture Agricultural Research Service,
Washington State University, Pullman, Washington 99164-6420, USA

ABSTRACT

Land managers of military training lands must conserve the soil to ensure that training can continue on those lands. However, military maneuvers damage vegetation, break up soil crusts, loosen the surface soil, change soil-surface geometry, compact the soil, and often form ruts in which runoff is concentrated. The constrained flow in ruts can detach and transport far more sediment than can unchanneled, overland flows. Rills often form in ruts as a result. However, natural processes in the soil alter the impacts of maneuvers over time, and our objectives were to measure how soil freeze-thaw (FT) cycling changes compacted soil and the geometry of military-vehicle ruts and how these changes compare to those in natural rills. We established research sites at Yakima Training Center (YTC) in south central Washington and Ethan Allen Firing Range (EAFR) in northwestern Vermont and made field observations and measurements at these sites over two winters. The cross sections of tank ruts at YTC became smoother as soil from rut crests slid into the rut during thaw. Tank ruts at EAFR were shallower than those at YTC and smoothed over the winter, but rills also formed in the ruts over one winter. Scattered soil slumps occurred along the sides of deeper rills at EAFR during spring thaw, but the slumped sediment was removed by subsequent flows. FT at both sites reduced the mean penetration resistance and bulk density of the top 5 cm of soil in ruts. Below 5 cm, resistance and density were statistically greater in than out of ruts at YTC, especially where the soil contained 15% water by volume during maneuvers. Saturated hydraulic conductivity in and out of ruts at YTC was not statistically different when ruts were formed in soil that contained 5% water, was lower in 75% of straight ruts made in soil containing 15% water, and was lower yet in curved ruts. Surface-water runoff at YTC began sooner in ruts than on adjacent, unrutted soil, and runoff rates were 67% to 77% higher due to the persistence of subsurface soil compaction in ruts. Incipient rills formed in tank ruts at EAFR after one winter on the 7% and 18% slopes. In-rut rills up to 11-cm deep formed on the 21% and 31% slopes. The adjacent, untrafficked soil on any of the slopes showed no new rills. These results can be used to parameterize soil-erosion models used by land managers of military-training lands in cold regions.

Gatto, L.W., Halvorson, J.J., and McCool, D.K., 2001, Freeze-thaw–induced geomorphic and soil changes in vehicle ruts and natural rills, *in* Ehlen, J., and Harmon, R.S., eds., The Environmental Legacy of Military Operations: Boulder, Colorado, Geological Society of America Reviews in Engineering Geology, v. XIV, p. 163–175.

INTRODUCTION

Maneuver impacts

The Army is responsible for over 4.8×10^4 km^2 of land that is used principally for training to maintain the military readiness of its units (Doe, 1992). Trainers must ensure that maneuvers are realistic, but the goals of readiness and realism often conflict with environmental requirements. Army land managers are required to minimize vegetation damage and soil disruption, which are inevitable during training, to preserve natural resources on training lands. In addition, damage to vegetation and soils often leads to accelerated soil erosion (Dregne, 1983).

An armored unit composed of tracked and wheeled vehicles damages vegetation; breaks up soil crusts; loosens surface soil; damages the soil structure; changes soil-surface roughness, shape, and depressions; and compacts the soils as it moves overland (Gatto, 1997a). Soil compaction reduces infiltration and hydraulic conductivity in soils (Horton et al., 1994) which increases the volume and length of time of surface water runoff (Hinckley et al., 1983; Mathier and Roy, 1993). Iverson (1980) found that more sediment eroded from hillslope plots trafficked by off-road vehicles than from untrafficked plots. Voorhees et al. (1979) reported that ruts could channel surface runoff and increase the sediment transport capacity of runoff. Foltz (1993) determined that 200%–400% more erosion occurred on rutted roads than unrutted roads. In addition, Morgan (1977) reported that rill flows carry far more sediment from a hillslope than unchanneled flows.

Freeze-thaw effects

Ice that forms in soil can push soil grains apart and reduce soil density. The amount of soil expansion depends on the soil-water content, soil texture, the volume of water drawn to the freezing zone, the rate of frost penetration, and the number of FT cycles (Miller, 1980). A frozen soil with ice in its voids often has low cohesion on thawing because it is saturated, which reduces particle attachment, interlocking, and friction. Thus, a recently thawed soil can easily flow and slide downslope because of the water content. This weakened state persists until the excess water drains and cohesion is reestablished (Formanek et al., 1984).

Schumm (1956, 1964) reported that frost-induced soil creep could obliterate natural rills over one winter. Gatto (1997a, 1997b, 1998, 2000) found in controlled laboratory experiments reduced soil strength and hydraulic radius in a rill and wheel ruts after cycles of FT and also found differences in the rates of freezing and thawing in and out of ruts. Frame et al. (1992) reported that the final shape of V-shaped rills in frozen soil in laboratory troughs was deeper and narrower throughout the slope than that of rills in nonfrozen soil. However, detailed studies of the effects of FT on ruts and rills in the field have not been done. Kok and McCool (1990a) report that the effects of soil FT on soil-erosion mechanics are poorly understood in spite of extensive research on FT

physics. The inability to model seasonal soil erodibility associated with these effects impedes improvements in soil-erosion predictions (Nearing et al., 1994; VanKlavern and McCool, 1998).

The specific objectives of our field experiments were (1) to measure the FT-induced changes in the geometry, soil density, and infiltration of vehicle ruts in two different hydro-climatic regions, (2) to measure the differences between compacted and uncompacted soil in terms of frost penetration, thaw progression, and soil-water redistribution during FT cycles, and (3) to compare over-winter changes to vehicle ruts and natural rills at EAFR. The characteristics of ruts and rills affect the velocity and volume, and thus the erosivity, of water flowing in them, and partially determine the amount of soil eroded from trafficked areas.

APPROACH

Research sites

We established three vehicle plots at Yakima Training Center (YTC) in south central Washington (Fig. 1A) and five vehicle plots at Ethan Allen Firing Range (EAFR) tank range 6-6 in northwestern Vermont (Fig. 1B). Twelve variably sized, naturally formed rills were present on the land in five separate areas near the EAFR vehicle plots. These rill locations are marked as rill plots on Figure 1B. No natural rills were present at the YTC sites.

The YTC sites receive about 20–30 cm of precipitation annually with about 45 cm of snow, EAFR about 60–70 cm precipitation with about 215 cm of snow. At YTC, the air temperature cycles above and below 0 °C an average of 90 times a year and on average the mean daily air temperature is less than 0 °C for 55 consecutive days. In contrast, at EAFR, there is an average of 100 air temperature FT cycles and 115 consecutive days when mean daily air temperature is less than 0 °C (Haugen, 1997 personal commun., Cold Regions Research and Engineering Laboratory). Soil temperature, however, does not fluctuate below and above 0 °C as often as air temperature, so the number of soil FT cycles at the sites would be less than the number of air temperature FT cycles.

The Badger Gap and C sites at YTC have a silty clay loam soil and site E has a slightly coarser soil; the slope at the three sites is 0–3%, and vegetation is big sagebrush and perennial bunchgrass. The EAFR sites have a silty sand soil, slopes from 7 to 31%, and vegetation is grass and small brush interspersed with unvegetated areas (some of which are covered with cryptogamic crust).

Ruts at YTC Sites C and E were formed by one to eight passes of an M1A2 Abrams combat tank in July 1994, at a time when the soil-water content was 0-5% by volume (dry) in the top 10 cm, and in April 1995, when water content was about 15% (moist). Most of the measurements, which form the database for the present study, were made from December 1995 to July 1996 in ruts formed in April 1995 because few distinct ruts formed in the dry soil in July 1994. Tank ruts at the Badger Gap site (Fig. 1) were made in April 1997 and April 1998 when the soil moisture was about 20% and the 1997–1998 YTC measurements were

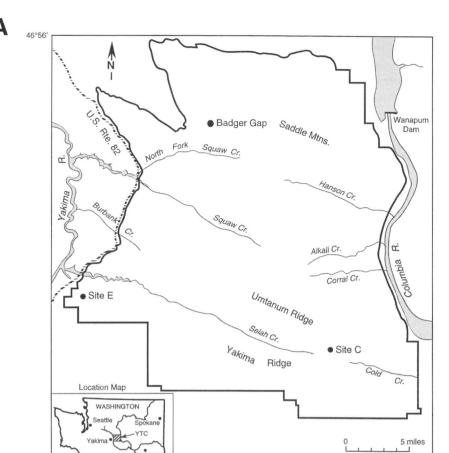

Figure 1. Research sites. A: Yakima Training Center, B: Ethan Allen Firing Range.

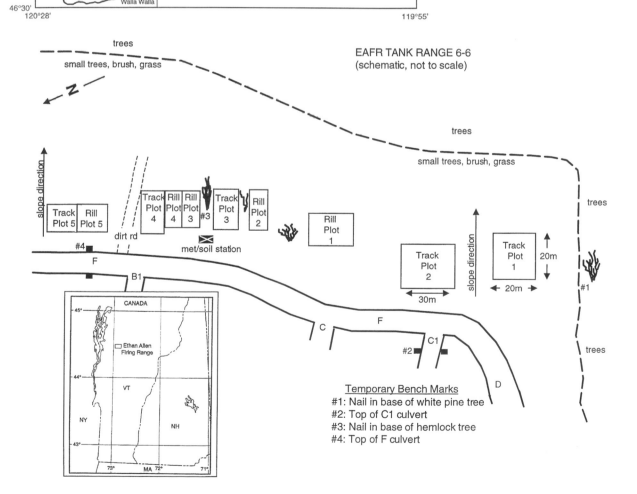

made in these ruts. At EAFR, an Abrahms tank produced 20 distinct, shallow ruts perpendicular to the hillslope contours and a wheeled High Mobility Multipurpose Wheeled Vehicle (HMMWV) formed 18 compacted paths, but no measurable rut, in October 1996. Volumetric soil-water content at the time of trafficking was 15–38% (33–76% saturation). The EAFR observations reported herein were made from October 1996 to December 1998.

Methods

Rut and rill cross sections were measured to determine changes in the geometry of the soil surface within them over time. At YTC only rut cross sections were measured using a sliding-pin meter (see Halvorson et al. [1998b] for details on the meter and its use). At EAFR we measured rut and rill cross sections by using a millimeter stick to measure the vertical distance between the soil surface and a bar mounted over the rut or rill. The bar rested on rebar driven into the soil on either side of the rill or rut. Vertical measurements were made horizontally along the bar as often as was necessary to adequately define cross-sectional geometry. That horizontal distance varied depending on the complexity of that geometry. The tops of the rebar were surveyed to be sure that they did not move over the winter so that the datum bar was in the same position for each cross-sectional survey. Figure 1B shows the locations of the four temporary benchmarks used to check for rebar movement.

Soil frost depth was measured out of ruts at the YTC sites C and E using frost tubes during the 1995-1996 winter and in and out of ruts at the Badger Creek site using resistivity probes during the 1997-1998 winter (Halvorson et al., 1998a, 1998c). A resistivity probe was used out of ruts at EAFR during the 1996-1997 and 1997-1998 winters. The probes determine soil resistivity when soil water changes to ice during FT cycles (Atkins, 1979). Air temperature and soil temperatures in and out of ruts at both YTC and EAFR were measured with thermistors and thermocouples. Precipitation, wind speed and direction, relative humidity, and solar radiation at EAFR were measured with standard meteorological instruments.

At YTC, saturated hydraulic conductivity was determined with a Guelph permeameter; soil penetration resistance with a hand-operated, cone-type, Bush recording soil penetrometer; and soil bulk density from 5 × 2.5 cm cores following standard methods. At EAFR, penetration resistance was measured with a pocket penetrometer similar to that described by Kok and McCool (1990b). These measurements were made in compacted rut soil and in adjacent, uncompacted soil about 1 m from the center of ruts. A rainfall simulator specifically designed for the low-intensity rains characteristic of the Palouse region of Washington was used to apply rainfall and measure runoff in ruts and out of ruts at YTC (Bubenzer et al., 1985). No rainfall simulator experiments were done at EAFR. Additional details on the site characteristics and methods employed at YTC are given in Halvorson et al. (1998a, 1998b, 1998c) and at EAFR in Gatto (1998).

RESULTS AND DISCUSSION

Yakima Training Center, 1995–1996

Soil FT regime. All work during this period was done at YTC; the EAFR research plots were not established until October 1996. Table 1 gives the snow accumulation and frost depths at YTC sites C and E at various times during the winter of 1995-1996. Because frost depths were not read daily, these data do not show the number of FT cycles at the two sites. However, the data indicate that the soil at site C froze deeper than that at E, although this difference diminished later in the winter; deeper frost at site C was expected because it is cooler than site E. Sites C and E had days when a thawed layer of soil was observed between two frozen layers, indicating periods of partial, shallow thawing followed by refreezing.

Soil conditions after thaw. The general changes in penetrometer resistances with depth in the in- and out-of-rut soils at sites C and E in May 1996 after FT cycling had stopped were similar (Fig. 2). Average resistance was low near the surface, increased to a maximum of about 4.0 MPa inside ruts and 2.0 MPa outside ruts between 10- to 15-cm depth, and decreased to 30-cm depth. However, the average resistances at specific depths were significantly greater in ruts than out at all depths below 5 cm at site C and at depths between 7.5 and 22.5 cm at site E.

These averages are useful for statistically comparing sites, but they do not describe the intersite variation that was observed. For instance, resistances at some places within both YTC sites showed little change with depth or little difference between rutted and unrutted soil within a plot, whereas resistances elsewhere within a plot varied greatly with small increments of depth or across short horizontal distances (Halvorson et al., 1998b).

Soil bulk densities (Fig. 3) were measured in May 1996 in and out of ruts that were made in July 1994 (Fig. 3A) and in April 1995 (Fig. 3, B–E). The distribution of densities suggests that changes in density due to vehicle compaction are affected by soil water content at the time of compaction, soil texture, and vehicle direction. Soil bulk densities through the soil profile below a straight rut made in dry soil (<5% water) at site C were similar to those outside that rut and averaged about 1.3 g/cm³ (Fig. 3A). However, densities below a straight rut made in moist soil (~15%) at site C were very different (Fig. 3B). They were consistently greater than those in the uncompacted soil below the 2.5-cm depth, they varied more down the soil profile, and their profile average was between 1.5 and 1.6 g/cm³ (Fig. 3B). In the coarser soils at site E, when the rut was made in moist soil, the in-rut bulk densities were also higher than the out-of-rut throughout the profile (Fig. 3D), but the along-profile variability was less than at C and the average density over the profile was between 1.3 and 1.4 g/cm³ (Fig. 3D).

The bulk densities in single-pass, curved ruts made during a tank turn in moist soil at sites C and E were generally less than those in straight ruts and were less than uncompacted soil at some depths. At C (Fig. 3C), where the profile average was between

TABLE 1. SNOW AND FROST DEPTH
(HALVORSON ET AL., 1998b)

Date	Snow depth (cm)		Frost depth* (cm)	
	Site C	Site E	Site C	Site E
12-11-95	6	0	0.0–18.2	0.0
12-15-95	0	0	5.5–17.5	0.0
12-19-95	3	0	0.0–3.5, 6.0–15.5	0.0–3.7
12-21.95	0	0	0.0–4.0, 5.5–13.0	0.0
12-28-95	0	2	0.0–23.0	0.0–10.0
01-02-96	0	1	1.5–26.5	0.0–9.5
01-03-96	0	0	4.0–26.0	1.5–9.0
01-04-96	0	0	0.0–2.0, 5.0–26.0	0.0–9.0
01-05-96	0	trace	0.0–26.0	0.0–1.5, 3.0–9.0
01-09-96	0	4	4.5–24.5	0–7.5
01-11-96	0	4	5.0–23.0	0–7.5
01-12-96	0	4	5.0–23.0	0–7.5
01-16-96	0	0	0.0	7.0–7.5
01-17-96	0	0	0.0–1.5	0.0
01-18-96	0	0	0.0–6.5	0.0
01-22-96	10	9	0.0–12.0	0.0–6.2
01-23-96	10	9	0.0–12.5	0.0–6.8
01-24-96	14	14	0.0–13.0	0.0–13.0
02-27-96	7	2	0.0–13.0	0.0–5.5
03-01-96	0	0	0.0–11.0	0.0–10.0

* Readings indicate the range of depths for frozen soil as recorded by a frost tube. Thus a reading of 0.0–3.7 indicates the soil was frozen from the surface to a depth of 3.7 cm. A reading of 0.0–1.5, 3.0–9.0 indicates the soil was frozen from the surface to a depth of 1.5 cm, unfrozen from 1.5 to 3.0 cm, and frozen from 3.0- to 9.0-cm depth.

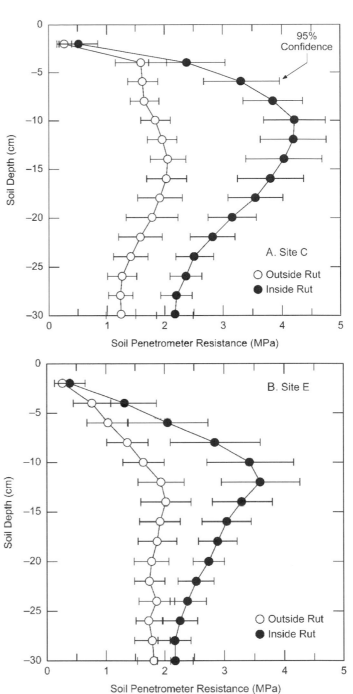

Figure 2. Average soil penetrometer resistances measured in May 1996 at YTC. A: $n = 17$ at Site C, B: $n = 18$ at Site E.

1.4 and 1.5 g/cm³, the in-rut density at the 5-cm depth was less than that out of the rut, but was higher through the rest of the profile. At E (Fig. 3E), which averaged about 1.1 g/cm³, the in-rut density was greater than the out-of-rut density in the upper 20 cm and was less in the lower 10 cm. These distributions in curved ruts suggest that the added shearing forces applied to the soil by a tank during a turn tend to loosen the soil particles more than when moving straight and that the loosening action is manifest deeper in coarser soil.

Figure 3F shows that there was no statistical difference between the densities if the data for straight and curved ruts made on moist soil at both sites are combined (Fig. 3B–E). The validity of combining these different data sets may be questioned, but it permitted a statistical comparison which otherwise was not possible.

Table 2 shows that the saturated hydraulic conductivity (K_{fs}) in ruts at four of five locations at sites C and E was lower than that observed in adjacent unrutted soil; at one Site E location the out-of-rut K_{fs} was less than that in the rut, although this difference was so small as to be of questionable significance. Although there was no significant difference between the in- and out-of-rut K_{fs} measurements, the data in Table 2 suggest that (1) K_{fs} is more spatially variable at site E, (2) the difference between in- and out-of-rut K_{fs} is partially determined by soil moisture at the time of rutting, and (3) the K_{fs} of straight ruts differs from that of curved ruts.

The K_{fs} for ruts formed in moist soil in Site C was less than half that in adjacent uncompacted soil, while K_{fs} for ruts formed on dry soil was nearly identical to the out-of-rut value. Figure 3 shows the moist, rutted soil to be denser. In addition, the differences between the K_{fs} in the curved ruts versus that in adjacent unrutted soil were much greater; thus the shearing and vertical forces generated when a tank turns may decrease the potential for water movement in soil in a curved rut more than in straight ruts.

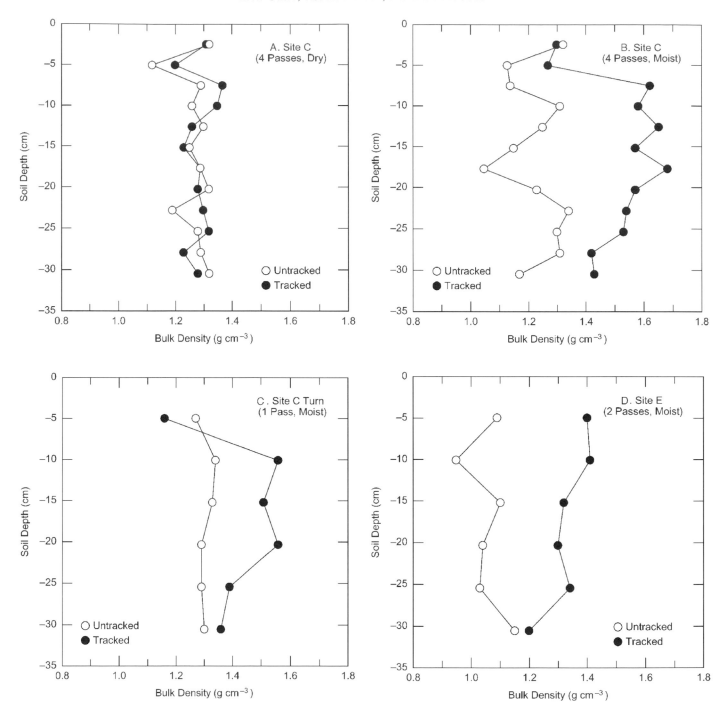

Figure 3. Soil bulk density with depth at YTC; in 3A to 3E, each point is a single measurement; in 3F, each point is an average of the four measurements made at each corresponding depth in the moist ruts shown in 3B to 3E.

Rut geometry. Rut cross sections were measured on 8 December 1995, 27 March 1996, and 16 July 1996. Tank ruts at YTC plots C and E had a depressed, compacted zone about 64 cm wide, 2 to 15 cm deep, often with imprints of the tank tread, and had relatively steep sidewalls bordered by a lip raised as much as 10–20 cm above the adjacent, unrutted soil (Fig. 4). Ruts from turning the vehicle sometimes exhibit asymmetric cross sections with one lip more pronounced than the other (Halvorson et al., 1998b).

A two-way analysis of variance was used to test if there were overall cross-sectional differences between sites or between straight and curved ruts that were measured first on 8 December 1995. The average overall standard deviations of cross-sectional elevations, 4.16 cm at site C and 4.38 cm for E,

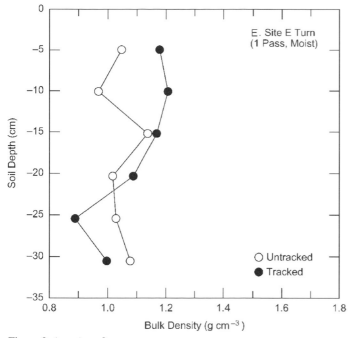

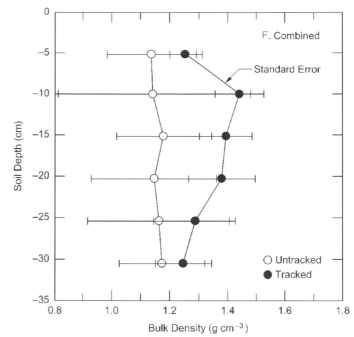

Figure 3. (*continued*)

were not significantly different ($P = 0.35$). However, curved-rut cross sections had significantly larger average standard deviations than those for straight ruts at both sites ($P < 0.001$), 5.26 cm for curved ruts and 3.15 cm for straight ones at C; 6.44 cm for curved ruts and 3.26 cm for straight ones at E. The interaction term between site and rut type was not significant ($P = 0.52$), indicating that both sites demonstrated about the same degree of difference between curved and straight ruts, i.e., that individual comparisons of curved and straight ruts between the sites did not differ from the combined analysis, so individual analysis of each rut was not needed.

Analysis of the combined data over time with the Friedman test, a nonparametric analog of a repeated-measures analysis of variance, indicated that the average standard deviations for the combined data decreased significantly during 1996 ($P < 0.001$). The standard deviations were 4.31 cm on 8 December 1995, 4.03 cm on 27 March 1996, and 3.77 cm on 16 July 1996. However, changes in individual ruts during 1996 varied from slight to significant (Halvorson et al., 1998b). The Kruskal–Wallis one-way analysis of variance and the Kolmogorov–Smirnov two-sample test indicated that curved ruts changed significantly more than straight ones ($P < 0.01$). In other words, curved ruts with the greatest amount of initial disturbance (largest average standard deviations in December 1995) had the greatest decrease in standard deviation over time. These statistics show that the cross section of the rut tends to smooth with time, i.e., the high points become lower and the lows fill in. Much of this smoothing originated from rapid erosion of the thin edges of asymmetric rut lips and subsequent infilling of the compacted channels near the center of the ruts.

TABLE 2. FIELD SATURATED HYDRAULIC CONDUCTIVITY, K_{fs}, MEASURED 1–3 MAY 1996 (HALVORSON ET AL., 1998b)

Plot*	Out-of-rut K_{fs} (cm/sec)	In-rut K_{fs} (cm/sec)
Plot C, M1, x 4, moist, straight	4.14×10^{-4}	1.52×10^{-4}
Plot C, M1, x 4, dry, straight	4.68×10^{-4}	4.04×10^{-4}
Plot C, M1, x 1, moist, turn	4.29×10^{-4}	2.22×10^{-6}
Plot E, M1, x 2, moist, straight	1.86×10^{-4}	2.09×10^{-4}
Plot E, M1, x 1, moist, turn	1.91×10^{-3}	3.79×10^{-4}

* Plot nomenclature syntax is in the form of plot location, vehicle type, number of passes, antecedent soil moisture at time of tracking, and track path. Plots C and E are shown in Figure 1A.

As suggested above, changes in the cross sections did not occur uniformly within the same rut. In general, the greatest changes during 1996 occurred at the highest or lowest parts of the rut cross section. A net loss of height was most often measured at the rut lip. In contrast, the base of the sidewalls of the ruts were the zones of deposition or infilling. Little change was detected along the steep sidewalls. However, the profile meter records only cross-sectional changes that lie in an unobstructed vertical pin path. Careful inspection in the field showed that soil slumping sometimes resulted in concave or undercut rut sidewall geometry that was not detectable with the sliding pin meter. Gatto (1998) observed similar changes in the cross-sectional geometry of wheel ruts and of rills (2000) during laboratory experiments.

Summary. The soil at YTC froze to 30-cm depth during the winter of 1995–1996 with periods of partial, shallow thawing and

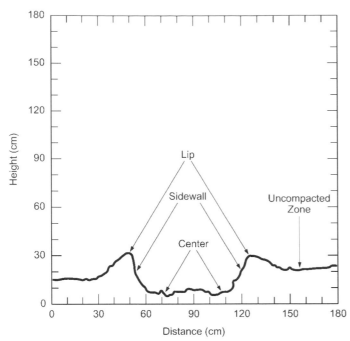

Figure 4. General cross-sectional geometry of a tank rut at YTC plots C and E.

refreezing. The mean standard deviation of rut cross sections decreased significantly, indicating that the smoothing occurred as soil at the rut crest consolidated and slid into the rut during thaw. Cross-sectional changes were highly variable within and between ruts, suggesting that FT-induced degree of soil wetting and drying were also variable. Mean penetration resistance and bulk density values in rutted and unrutted surface soil were similar, but statistically larger in ruts below 5-cm depth. This difference was especially obvious when the soil contained 15% water by volume when ruts were made. Compaction in ruts does not persist in the surface soil because FT-induced wetting and drying and ice forming in the soil loosened the particles of the surface soil. Saturated hydraulic conductivity was less in 75% of straight ruts made on soil with 15% water and was reduced even more in curved ruts. Conductivity was not statistically different in and out of ruts when ruts were made on soil with 5% water.

EAFR, 1996–1998

Soil FT regime. During the 1996–1997 winter the soil at EAFR froze to 14 cm by late December, to 40 cm by mid-late January, and remained frozen except for seven thaws of the soil from 0 to 6 cm deep from 16 January to 2 March 1997. The final spring thaw began on 27 March. In the winter of 1997–1998, the soil started to freeze by mid-January, froze to 30 cm by mid-February, and thawed by late March.

Soil conditions after thaw. On 25 October 1996, a tank and HMMWV were driven on the plots, making two passes at each location. Penetration resistance was measured in the tank ruts,

wheel paths, and adjacent untrafficked soil on the same day and on three subsequent dates after the soil had thawed. The average soil resistance, or compressive strength, was greatest in the tank ruts immediately after they were made (Fig. 5A). Over the winter the resistance of the compacted soil in the tank ruts decreased by 60% and by 50% in the wheel paths (Fig. 5A and 5B). The untrafficked soil was 29% less resistant to penetration in April after thaw and generally regained strength as the soil dried in June (Fig. 5C). The soil FT cycling had reduced the compaction in the upper centimeter of soil as was suggested by the previous measurements at YTC and observed by Gatto (1997b) in laboratory experiments.

Rut and rill geometry. Ruts made by the tank were generally about 5 cm deep (Fig. 6), with some up to 7 cm deep. Portions of some rut cross sections studied over the winter heaved 2 to 3 cm because of ice formation in the soil, but the two rill cross sections monitored exhibited little to no frost heave. Most of the rills were filled with snow during the winter, which both insulated the soil in the rills from the cold air temperatures and reduced the frost penetration into the rills and, therefore, also reduced the likelihood of frost heave.

However, the rills in rill plot 5 (Fig. 1B) were on a 21% slope and up to 60 cm deep so that snow did not completely fill these rills. Frost penetration was likely in these rills, and a few scattered soil slides were observed along the rill sidewalls during spring thaw. The slumped soil was removed by subsequent rill flows. The downslope end of rill 5-2 in rill plot 5 had an elevated surface on 15 December 1998 that may have resulted from frost heave and also exhibited areas where erosion and deposition had dramatically changed the rill cross section (Fig. 7).

In contrast, the cross sections of most of the rills in the other rill plots did not change during the 2-year period, even the ones on the 31% slopes at rill plots 2, 3, and 4 (Fig. 1B). Many of these other rills were between 5 and 10 cm deep, had side slopes between 10 and 40°, and were either completely or partially covered with cryptogamic crusts or with coarse-grained sediments left as lag deposits that served to armor the rill soil surface against flows.

On several occasions during the spring thaw at EAFR, 1- to 5-mm-deep flows of water were observed in the ruts when there was no surface flow on the adjacent unrutted soil. This suggests that infiltration into the ruts was less than into the untrafficked soil because the density of the subsurface soil remained greater in the ruts even after FT cycling; a similar finding to that at YTC. This reduced infiltration resulted in more runoff in the ruts, which, in turn, contributed to substantially more changes to the cross sections of the ruts than the rills.

Some track ruts, especially those in track plots 1 and 2 (Fig. 1B) with slopes of 7% and 18%, respectively, showed rills up to 2 cm deep through the track pad depressions (Fig. 8A). The tank ruts, especially those on the 31% slopes in track plots 3 and 4 (Fig. 1B), had pockets of sediment deposited in their depressions (Fig. 8B) that resulted from the intermittent flows within the ruts. By the spring of 1997, a distinct V-shaped, 11-cm-deep rill (Fig. 9)

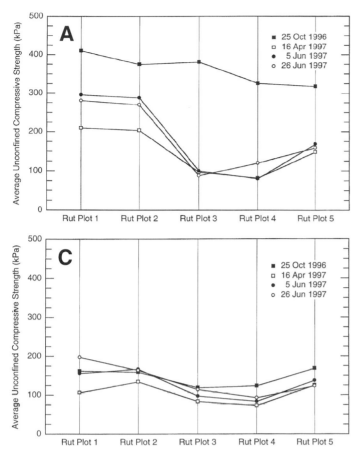

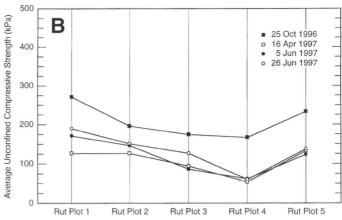

Figure 5. Over-winter soil-strength changes in track ruts (A), wheel paths (B), and untrafficked soil (C) at EAFR.

Figure 6. Typical tank rut made at EAFR on 25 October 1996; this one is tank rut 2 in track plot 1, which has a 7% slope.

had formed in a track rut in track plot 4 (Fig. 1B), whereas adjacent untrafficked soil showed no evidence of rill initiation. The cross-sectional geometry of the wheel path surfaces did not change over the winter or during the entire 1996-1998 period.

Summary. The results of the EAFR observations and measurements are summarized as follows. Soil-FT cycling over one winter reduced soil resistance in soil compacted by tanks and HMMWVs. Scattered sidewall soil slumps occurred along some of the deeper rills when soil thawed in the spring, changing the cross-sectional geometry of the rills. Small rills and pockets of deposited sediment developed within some ruts due to intermittent flows. A distinct V-shaped, 11-cm deep rill formed in a tank rut, while soil adjacent to that rut showed no evidence of rill initiation. Wheel-path surface geometry did not change over the winter. These data suggest that FT cycling loosens compacted surface soil in ruts, making it more erodible, while subsurface compaction persists, which leads to greater runoff in ruts than in adjacent untrafficked soil and exacerbates surface soil erosion.

YTC, 1997–1998

Soil FT regime. Average soil temperatures in the rut were significantly warmer than those out of it, –1.4 °C and –0.2 °C at 5- and 30-cm depths inside, respectively, –1.6 °C and –0.5 °C outside. Soil from 3 to 5 cm depth in the rut froze the earliest and remained frozen longer than deeper soil, whereas the soil from 11 to 13 cm depth froze earlier and remained frozen for longer than that at 23 to 25 cm depth. Outside the rut, the soil at 3 to 5 cm froze at about the same time as soil at a depth of 11 to

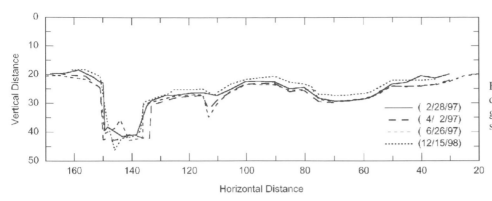

Figure 7. Changes in the EAFR rill 5-2 at the downhill cross section (lines define the geometry of the soil surface in the rill measured with the mm stick and datum bar).

Figure 8. Small rills through tank-track pad depressions in EAFR tank rut 2 in track plot 1, 16 April 1997 (A) and deposited sediment in tank rut 1 in track plot 3, 28 February 1997 (B) after one winter.

Figure 9. V-shaped rill formed in tank rut 1 in EAFR track plot 4, which has a 31% slope, 28 February 1997.

13 cm. Soil from the 23 to 25-cm depth both inside and outside the rut froze later than the overlying soil, but that in the rut underwent several large FT cycles during the season while that out of the rut did not thaw in mid-season. This deeper out-of-rut soil remained frozen until late January, when thawing occurred in all frozen soil at about the same time. Temperatures in and out of the

rut at the 30-cm depth were only slightly below 0 °C and soil may or may not have frozen. Gatto (1997a, 1997b, 1998) also measured similar temperature patterns within in-rut and out-of-rut soils in laboratory experiments; the differences in the temperature regimes suggest that the thermal conductivity of compacted and uncompacted soil is different.

Soil temperature fluctuations were suppressed with depth in and out of the rut. The lowest temperatures at the 5 cm depth were –6.4 °C inside the rut and –7.2 °C outside of it on 11 January. At the 30-cm depth, the low temperature was –1.7 °C inside and –2.8 °C outside on 13 January. Several fluctuations of electrical resistivity were observed at the 3 to 5 cm depth in and out of the rut, suggesting a diurnal FT cycling between partially thawed and frozen states, but these resistivity fluctuations, like temperature fluctuations, diminished with depth.

Soil conditions after thaw. A comparison was made at the Badger Creek site (Fig. 1A) of soil penetration resistances near the resistivity probe in and out of the tank rut formed in April 1997, and in and out of a rut formed in April 1998. The soil-water content at the time the ruts were made was 20% by volume (Halvorson et al., 1998c). Figure 10 shows the average penetration resistance (±95% C.I.) for the three sampling dates.

Resistance from the 2–10 cm depth in the rut about one month after the April 1997 rutting was significantly greater than

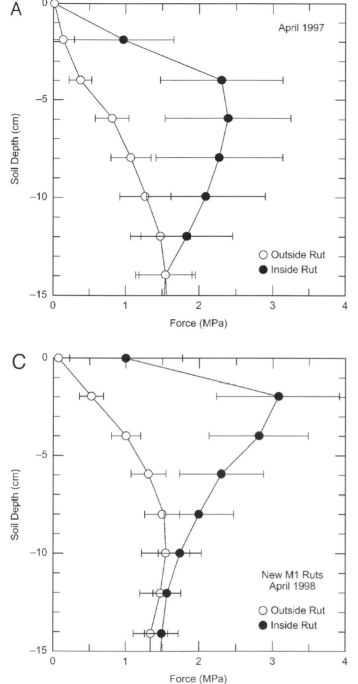

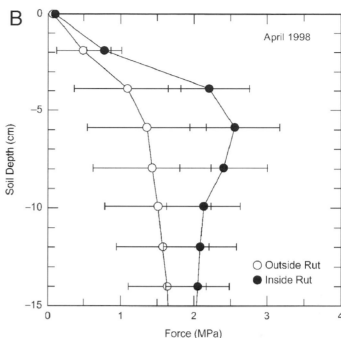

Figure 10. Penetration resistances in and out of a one-month-old rut in April 1997 (A)(*n* = 26), the same rut in April 1998 (B) (*n* = 13), and a new, two-week-old rut in April 1998 (C) (*n* = 26) at YTC (Halvorson, 1998c).

showed much greater differences between tracked and untracked soil near to the surface (Fig. 10C) than were observed in the one-month old rut (Fig. 10A).

Runoff. Steady-state runoff rates produced with a rainfall simulator in recently rutted and unrutted soils also were measured at the Badger Creek site in August 1997 and May 1998 (Fig. 11). Rainfall was applied with a rotating disk-type simulator developed to mimic the low intensity and small drop size rainfall that is typical of the Pacific Northwest. Average steady-state runoff in two different tank ruts was about 75% of the water application rate (35 mm/hour) compared to about 19% for uncompacted soil in August 1997 (Fig. 11A). About 90 minutes were required to reach steady-state flow in tank ruts as compared with almost twice as long for uncompacted soil. Average steady-state runoff rates in three different tank ruts and adjacent uncompacted soil were slightly lower in May 1998, 66% and 8%, respectively (Fig. 11B). The observations noted more variation in final runoff rates and less synchronicity among the individual tank ruts measured in May than in the previous August. Two of the three tank ruts measured in May did not approach steady-state runoff until about 150 minutes of simulated rainfall, the same time needed for uncompacted soil.

Summary. Soil in ruts had a different FT regime than soil outside ruts. The FT patterns in near-surface soils in and out of ruts were similar. At greater depths, freezing in ruts either did not occur or occurred later than that out of ruts. The differences between in-rut and out-of-rut soil penetration resistances decreased near the surface over a single winter. Steady-state runoff rates were much greater in tank-compacted soil than in uncompacted soil. Steady-state runoff rates were slightly lower and more variable in spring than the previous summer.

in unrutted soil (Fig. 10A). Resistances in the same rut one year later (April 1998) indicated that the differences between rutted and unrutted soil had diminished, especially near to the surface (Fig. 10B). In comparison, data collected in April 1998 in a new rut formed about two weeks earlier, again near to the probe rut,

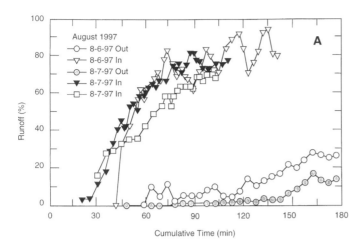

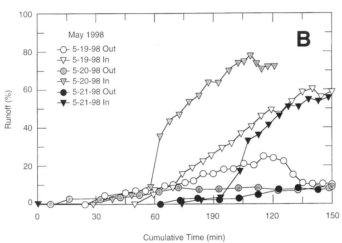

Figure 11. Runoff (% of total water applied) in ruts (In) and out of ruts (Out) in August 1997 (A) and May 1998 (B) at YTC (Halvorson, 1998c).

FUTURE RESEARCH

This study has improved the current understanding of the relationships between FT cycling and rut and rill soil erosion but much remains unclear. Future research will be directed toward: (1) rainfall-simulator experiments on newly thawed soil, (2) determination of the effects of different soil FT regimes in tank and wheel ruts and untrafficked soil, (3) assessment of the spatial and temporal variation of FT at different landscape positions, (4) determination of the relative importance of FT cycling compared to other soil-modifying processes, i.e., wetting and drying, expansion and contraction, and (5) measurement of the impact of soil moisture on FT-induced soil deformation along ruts and rills.

ACKNOWLEDGMENTS

The U. S. Army Corps of Engineers Research and Development Office funded this research under the BT25 Environmental Quality Technology Program. We thank Mike McLane, Warren Bordine, and Kurt Knuth for setting up the meteorological station and soil sensors at EAFR; William Bowe, Russell Fitzgerald, Paul Mutch, and Christopher Pannkuk for field assistance at YTC; Tim Cary and Nick Goodman for field assistance at EAFR; and Peter Nissen (YTC) and Major Don Lynaugh (EAFR) for assistance in coordinating fieldwork. We also thank two anonymous reviewers for valuable comments and suggestions. Citation of commercial product brand names does not constitute an official endorsement or approval of the use of such commercial products by the U.S. Army.

CONCLUSIONS

Vehicles traveling overland compact and often rut the soil, which can increase overland flow, spatially concentrate those flows, and exacerbate natural soil erosion. Results of field research described in this study demonstrate that FT processes reduce near-surface soil density in compacted tank ruts and wheel paths and also induce significant geometric changes in rut cross-sectional profiles and minor changes in rills through soil flows and slides along rut and rill sidewalls. Such geomorphic changes could reduce the velocity of water flows in ruts. However, the reduced soil strength in the rut surface soil could make the soil more erodible and increase its erosion potential.

The persistence of subsurface compaction below the zone of significant ice formation in the soil during freezing results in increased surface runoff in ruts, which has important implications for potential erosion and its prediction because surface and subsurface soil density could be different and affect runoff erosivity. This suggests that Army land managers might underestimate erosion based on the condition of the surface soil alone.

REFERENCES CITED

Atkins, R.T., 1979, Determination of frost penetration by soil resistivity measurements: Hanover, New Hampshire, U.S. Army Cold Regions Research and Engineering Laboratory Special Report 79-22, 24 p.

Bubenzer, G.D., Molnau, M., and McCool, D.K., 1985, Low intensity rainfall with a rotating disk simulator: Transactions of the American Society of Agricultural Engineers, v. 28, p. 1230–1232.

Doe, W.W., III, 1992, Simulation of the spatial and temporal effects of Army maneuvers on watershed response [Ph.D. thesis]: Fort Collins, Colorado State University, 287 p.

Dregne, H.E., 1983, Soil and soil formation in arid regions, *in* Webb, R.H., and Wilshire, H.G., eds., Environmental effects of off-road vehicle impacts and management in arid regions: New York, Springer-Verlag, p. 15–30.

Foltz, R.B., 1993, Sediment processes in wheel ruts on unsurfaced forest roads [Ph.D. thesis]: Moscow, University of Idaho, 177 p.

Formanek, G.E., McCool, D.K., and Papendick, R.I., 1984, Freeze-thaw and consolidation effects on strength of a wet silt loam: Transactions of the American Society of Agricultural Engineers, v. 27, p. 1749–1752.

Frame, P.A., Burney, J.R., and Edwards, L.M., 1992, Laboratory measurements of freeze/thaw, compaction, residue and slope effects on rill erosion: Canadian Agricultural Engineering, v. 34, p. 143–149.

Gatto, L.W., 1997a, Ground freezing effects on soil erosion of Army training lands. 1. Initial test results: Hanover, New Hampshire, U.S. Army Cold Regions Research and Engineering Laboratory Special Report 97-15, 32 p.

Gatto, L.W., 1997b, Freeze-thaw effects on the hydrologic characteristics of rutted and compacted soils, *in* Iskandar, I.K., et al., eds., International Symposium on Physics, Chemistry, and Ecology of Seasonally Frozen Soils:

Hanover, New Hampshire, U.S. Army Cold Regions Research and Engineering Laboratory Special Report 97-10, p. 189–198.

Gatto, L.W., 1998, Freeze-thaw effects on vehicular ruts and natural rills: Importance to soil-erosion and terrain modeling, *in* Summer, W., et al., eds., Modelling soil erosion, sediment transport and closely related hydrological processes: International Association of Hydrological Sciences Publication 249, p. 71–79.

Gatto, L.W., 2000, Soil freeze-thaw-induced changes in a simulated rill: Potential impacts on soil erosion: Geomorphology, v. 32, p. 147–160.

Halvorson, J.J., King, L.G., McCool, D.K., Pannkuk, C., Gatto, L.W., and Nissen, P., 1998a, Monitoring soil freeze-thaw dynamics in tank-compacted and uncompacted soil at Yakima Training Center, Washington: Yakima, Washington, Annual Department of Army–Integrated Training Area Management Workshop, 7th, Abstracts, p. 63.

Halvorson, J.J., McCool, D.K., King, L.G., and Gatto, L.W., 1998b, Ground freezing effects on soil erosion of Army training lands. 2. Overwinter changes in tracked-vehicle ruts, Yakima Training Center, Washington: Hanover, New Hampshire, U.S. Army Cold Regions Research and Engineering Laboratory Special Report 98-8, 47 p.

Halvorson, J.J., McCool, D.K., Pannkuk, C.D., Gatto, L.W., King, L.G., and Nissen, P.E., 1998c, Soil freezing and changes to near-surface bulk density, penetration resistance and infiltration rates in tank-compacted soil at Yakima Training Center, Washington: Baltimore, Maryland, 1998 Annual Meeting, American Society of Agronomy, Abstracts, p. 10.

Hinckley, B.S., Iverson, R.M., and Hallet, B., 1983, Accelerated water erosion in off-road vehicle use areas, *in* Webb, R.H., and Wilshire, H.G., eds., Environmental effects of off-road vehicle impacts and management in arid regions: New York, Springer-Verlag, p. 81–96.

Horton, R., Ankeny, M.D., and Allmaras, R.R., 1994, Effects of compaction on soil hydraulic properties, *in* Soane, B.D., and van Ouwerkerk, C., eds., Soil compaction in crop production: Developments in agricultural engineering 11: Amsterdam, Elsevier, p. 141–165.

Iverson, R.M., 1980, Processes of accelerated pluvial erosion on desert hillslopes modified by vehicular traffic: Earth Surface Processes and Landforms, v. 4, p. 369–388.

Kok, H., and McCool, D.K., 1990a, Freeze thaw effects on soil strength, *in* Cooley, K.R., ed., International Symposium on Frozen Soil Impacts on Agricultural, Range, and Forest Lands: Hanover, New Hampshire, U.S. Army Cold Regions Research and Engineering Laboratory Special Report 90-1, p. 70–76.

Kok, H., and McCool, D.K., 1990b, Quantifying freeze/thaw-induced variability of soil strength: Transactions of the American Society of Agricultural Engineers, v. 33, p. 501–506.

Mathier, L., and Roy, A.G., 1993, Temporal and spatial variations of runoff and rainwash erosion on an agricultural field: Hydrologic Processes, v. 7, p. 1–18.

Miller, R.D., 1980, Freezing phenomena in soils, *in* Hillel, D., ed., Applications of soil physics: New York, Academic Press, Inc., p. 254–299.

Morgan, R.P.C., 1977, Soil erosion in the United Kingdom: Field studies in the Silsoe area, 1973–1975: National College of Agricultural Engineering Silsoe Occasional Paper 4, 41 p.

Nearing, M.A., Lane, L.J., and Lopes, V.L., 1994, Modeling soil erosion, *in* Lal, R., ed., Soil erosion research methods: Ankeny, Iowa, Soil and Water Conservation Society, p. 127–156.

Schumm, S.A., 1956, Evolution of drainage systems and slopes on badlands at Perth Amboy, New Jersey: Geological Society of America Bulletin, v. 67, p. 597–646.

Schumm, S.A., 1964, Seasonal variations of erosion rates and processes on hillslopes in western Colorado: Zeitschrift für Geomorphologie, Supplement band 5, p. 215–238.

Van Klaveren, R.W., and McCool, D.K., 1998, Erodibility and critical shear of a previously frozen soil: Transactions of the American Society of Agricultural Engineers, v. 41, p. 1315–1321.

Voorhees, W.B., Young, R.A., and Lyles, L., 1979, Wheel traffic considerations in erosion research: Transactions of the American Society of Agricultural Engineers, v. 22, p. 786–790.

MANUSCRIPT ACCEPTED BY THE SOCIETY OCTOBER 27, 2000

Geological Society of America
Reviews in Engineering Geology, Volume XIV
2001

Unsurfaced road investigation and management plan, Fort Leonard Wood, Missouri

Jon B. Isaacson
A. Elaina Hurst
Department of Geological and Petroleum Engineering, University of Missouri, Rolla, Missouri 65409, USA

Danny L. Miller
U.S. Geological Survey Mid-Continent Mapping Center, Rolla, Missouri 65401, USA

Paul E. Albertson
U.S. Army Engineer Research and Development Center, Waterways Experiment Station, Vicksburg, Mississippi 39180, USA

ABSTRACT

Unsurfaced roads, common throughout both private and public sectors, are the source of engineering, economic, and ecological concerns. The U.S. Army currently maintains a large number of unsurfaced roads on its training and testing installations. These road networks must be maintained in a safe and serviceable condition to sustain training and testing requirements. Fort Leonard Wood's (FLW) road network was examined to identify present problems and future engineer training requirements so that a proper maintenance plan could be recommended. Standard U.S. Army methods were used. A road management system was developed using a dynamic digital database of road conditions linked to the FLW Geographic Information System (GIS). The field data, the extent of road distresses and severity level measurements, were used to determine the unsurfaced road condition index (URCI). A repair budget was estimated for road segments with a URCI value below an established threshold. GIS analyses correlated URCI values to physical and operational conditions. Well-graded soils with a low plastic index were correlated to high URCI values. Operations data were examined to identify types of use, requested maintenance, and the resulting road condition. URCI values were higher for frequently traveled and maintained roads. Continuation of current reductions in maintenance will result in higher repair costs and possible road closures. Road rehabilitation to accommodate future traffic volume and increased vehicle loads will require proper selection of geometric design parameters, aggregate type, gradation, and layer thickness.

INTRODUCTION

Background

Unsurfaced roads account for approximately 80% of worldwide road networks. Nationally, the U.S. Forest Service (USFS) operates the largest unsurfaced road network consisting of approximately 415 000 km (260 000 miles). The construction, maintenance, and reconstruction budget for this network is approximately $500 million/yr. In consideration of such a large budget, Luhr and McCullough (1983) suggested conducting economic analyses of these low-volume roads. In addition to economic issues, low-volume roads cause environmental concerns (Beachy and Eck, 1995). The USFS, by considering road location

Isaacson, J.B., Hurst, A.E., Miller, D.L., and Albertson, P.E., 2001, Unsurfaced road investigation and management plan, Fort Leonard Wood, Missouri, *in* Ehlen, J., and Harmon, R.S., eds., The Environmental Legacy of Military Operations: Boulder, Colorado, Geological Society of America Reviews in Engineering Geology, v. XIV, p. 177–190.

and minimizing alteration of drainage, is reducing the impact of low-volume roads on the environment. Locating roads for minimal impact requires planning expertise such as design, cost estimation, construction, maintenance, drainage design, materials, engineering, and soil mechanics.

Although unsurfaced roads are an issue of international importance that faces road managers around the world, this chapter only addresses some of the Department of Defense's (DoD) concerns. It is estimated that the DoD is responsible for 25 million acres of land containing about 160 000 km (100 000 miles) of roads. In 1991, the Legacy Resource Management Program raised the DoD environmental programs to a level of leadership, partnership, and stewardship (Patrick et al., 1994a). The Legacy program fostered an integrated management approach of natural and cultural resources with mission readiness. As an outgrowth of Legacy demonstration projects (Patrick et al., 1994b), the U.S. Army Engineer Waterways Experiment Station (WES) was requested to examine road management concerns at Eglin Air Force Base (AFB). Following the USFS multi-discipline experience, WES responded to Eglin AFB's request to assist in road management planning with an integrated approach (Albertson et al., 1995). The WES research team, sent to address the unsurfaced road problem, consisted of road engineers, geomorphologists, and a recreational planner. Working with the many users of Eglin's road network, a consensus was reached for criteria to determine rehabilitation or road closure. The criteria incorporated engineering, economic, ecological, and mission concerns. The approach suggested a GIS procedure to prioritize road segments. The workshop, which led to the consensus and plan for Eglin AFB unsurfaced road management, is described by Albertson et al. (1995).

Fort Leonard Wood

Fort Leonard Wood (FLW), Missouri, requested assistance from WES in evaluating its unsurfaced road network based on the WES's demonstrated ability in the arena of road management. FLW is located in south central Missouri. The Fort's range roads are used as driver training courses for many vehicle types and by all branches of the U.S. military. The condition of the range roads on FLW was questionable with respect to sustaining training needs. Management concerns included maintenance economics, safety, and environmental impacts. A multidisciplinary team addressed the situation. In addition to Geotechnical Laboratory of WES, the FLW Directorate of Public Works (DPW); U.S. Army ROTC at University of Missouri, Rolla (UMR); Geological Engineering Department, UMR; and U.S. Geological Survey Mid-Continent Mapping Center were actively involved in the investigation.

Scope of work

The goal of the work was to undertake an inventory and analysis of road conditions at FLW to identify present problems and future requirements. The management system developed to meet this objective consists of a dynamic digital database of road conditions linked to the FLW Geographic Information System (GIS) to assure mission readiness while providing the best maintenance schedule.

METHODS

Survey

The unsurfaced roads at FLW were surveyed using standard U.S. Army methods as outlined in Eaton et al. (1987). Seven different distress types were defined, quantified, and used to calculate the unsurfaced road condition index (URCI) of each representative road segment. The severity of the seven distresses (Fig. 1)—improper cross section, drainage, corrugations, potholes, dust, ruts, and loose aggregate—were measured and recorded in the field. The field data-collection procedure entailed evaluating the seven distresses found on representative road segments at one-half mile distances for multiple roads at FLW. Each surveyed area was 30 m in length times the width of the road segment. The severity of each of the observed distresses was classified as low, moderate, or high. The field measurements were entered into a database and locations were geo-referenced by a Global Positioning System (GPS).

The data collection procedure consisted of several steps. First, one-half mile was measured out using the vehicle odometer. The road evaluator measured the width of the road segment and then analyzed each distress type, its relative severity, and the number of square or lineal feet covered by each distress in the representative 30-m segment. The following data were recorded using a laptop computer: the GPS point, the road name, and the station number to create a new entry beginning with those coordinates into the database. The procedure was repeated at the next representative segment a half mile down the road. Detailed measurements are necessary to assign URCI ratings to the unsurfaced roads and are required at least once every three years (Eaton and Beaucham, 1992).

Seven distresses. Seven distresses of unsurfaced roads were measured. Each distress was measured separately. A description of each distress and its severity level is as follows (Eaton et al., 1987):
1. Improper cross section. A proper cross section is defined as the presence of constant downward slope away from the centerline of the road to the shoulder edge; the cross section is considered improper when a road surface is not shaped or maintained to carry incident surface water to ditches. Each road should have enough gradient from the centerline to the shoulder to remove water from the road surface. Low severity has evidence of small amounts of standing water on the road surface or the road is completely flat (no slope). Moderate severity has evidence of moderate amounts of ponding water on the road surface. The road is bowl shaped. High severity has evidence of large amounts of ponding water on the road surface. The road has large and severe depressions.

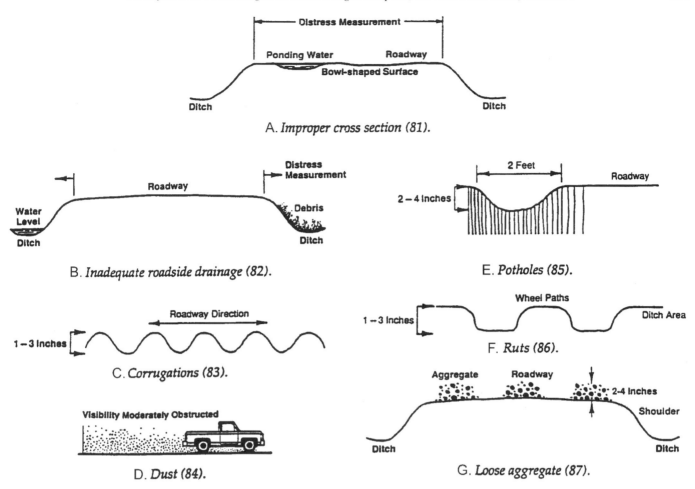

Figure 1. Sections showing moderate severity of each of the seven road distresses.

2. Inadequate roadside drainage. This condition occurs when culverts and ditches are not adequately prepared or maintained to direct or carry runoff water due to the road surface maintenance or geometric shape. Ponding water results from poor drainage along the roadsides. Low severity is evidenced by small amounts of standing water and the presence of small amounts of overgrowth or debris in the ditches. Moderate severity is characterized by a modest amount of ponding water in the ditches. High severity is identified by large amounts of ponding water in the ditches. Clues to this condition are washouts and other signs of large amounts of water running across or down the road. Other signs are large amounts of overgrowth or debris in the ditches or significant ditch erosion into the roadway and shoulders.

3. Corrugations. Commonly called "washboarding," corrugations are described as closely spaced ripples and ridges that occur at fairly regular intervals along a road. These distresses are perpendicular to the direction of traffic. Corrugations usually occur on hills or on curves, in areas of vehicle acceleration or deceleration. Washboarding often occurs in areas of loose aggregate or potholes. Low severity corrugations are less than 2.5 cm (1 in.) deep, moderate severity are between 2.5 and 7.5 cm (1 and 3 in.), and high severity are 7.5 cm (3 in.) or deeper.

4. Potholes. Concave depressions in the road surface are referred to as potholes. Ponded water in a pothole loosens the surface material or creates low strength areas in the subgrade, causing the holes to enlarge at a faster rate. A chart (Table 1) is helpful in measuring the severity of the potholes, which is determined by average diameter and depth.

5. Dust. Dust is defined as the release of fine particles from the road surface, as a result of wind and dry conditions, caused by the wear and tear of vehicular traffic. Dust clouds are potential hazards to trailing or passing vehicles and cause environmental problems for wildlife. The severity of dust was determined by observing the dust cloud produced by a vehicle driving 25 mph. Dust severity was recorded as low, medium, or high for each sample unit. Low severity consists of thin dust clouds, lower than 1 m, which do not obstruct visibility. Moderate severity consists of a moderately thick cloud, between 1 to 2 m in height, which causes traffic to slow due to partially obstructed visibility. High severity consists of very thick clouds that are greater than 2 m in height, which cause traffic to slow significantly or stop because of severely obstructed visibility.

**TABLE 1. POTHOLE DETERMINATION CRITERIA
(MODIFIED AFTER EATON ET AL., 1987)**

Maximum depth cm (in.)	Average diameter			
	Less than			More than 90 cm (3 ft)
	30 cm (1 ft)	30–60 cm (1-2 ft)	60–90 cm (2-3 ft)	
1–5 (1/2–2)	Low	Low	Moderate	Moderate
5–10 (2–4)	Low	Moderate	High	High
10+ (4+)	Moderate	High	High	High

6. Ruts. Linear surface depressions parallel to the centerline of the road in the wheel path resulting from deformation of the road surface or subgrade are known as ruts. Repeated vehicle passes over low-strength road materials cause rutting. Low severity ruts are less than 2.5 cm (1 in.) deep, moderate severity ruts are between 2.5 and 7.5 cm (1 and 3 in.), and high severity ruts are 7.5 cm (3 in.) or deeper.

7. Loose aggregate. Berms of loosened aggregate build up on the road centerline and on shoulders away from the wheel paths. Large particles are loosened due to wear and tear and loss of fines. Low severity is defined as a berm of aggregate less than 5 cm deep. Berms of aggregate between 5 and 10 cm deep, and large amounts of aggregate on the road surface with berms greater than 10 cm in depth, constitute moderate severity and high severity conditions, respectively.

Global Positioning System. The use of a Global Positioning System (GPS) was essential for georeferencing the field data to specific segments of roads. The surveyed segments were displayed on GIS maps, with specific road segment information and URCI ratings (Fig. 2).

The laptop computer used for the project was equipped with an internal *Trimble* GPS receiver and software. During field operations, *FieldNotes GPS* software was used to convert positional data into Universal Transverse Mercator (UTM) coordinates, which were stored in the database. The GPS unit tracked as many as eight satellites simultaneously, which allowed for positioning calculations accurate to within 1 m. However, due to selective availability of the satellite signals, nonmilitary personnel can expect varying accuracy within 30 m. This level of accuracy was sufficient to record representative road segments.

ANALYSIS

Database

The *FieldNotes* database, which resulted from the georeferenced collection of field information, was downloaded into an *Excel* spreadsheet (Table 2). This enabled the conversion of the field data to URCI ratings to be automated utilizing the prototype calculations developed by Hurst et al. (1998) to automate the conversion of distress data to usable URCI ratings, rather than using graphs, following the methods and calculations of Eaton et al. (1987). The field information contained the areal or linear

extent of each type of road distress and its corresponding severity level. The total area of each segment, its designation, GPS location, and date of inspection were also contained in the database. This information was used later in the GIS analysis of the information (Table 2).

First, the density of each distress was calculated by dividing the total areal or linear extent of each severity and type of distress by the total area or linear value of the road segment. These densities were then used to determine the deduction values for each distress and severity level from the deduction graphs provided by Eaton et al. (1987). This procedure was automated by using the *Excel* spreadsheet by selecting points from the graphed curves used by Eaton et al. (1987) to extrapolate polynomial equations to closely approximate these curves. The resulting polynomial equations were then used to calculate the corresponding deduct values. The deduct values for all seven distresses noted for each segment were added and the sum then plugged into another set of polynomial equations derived to mimic the graphs from Eaton et al. (1987). The use of specific polynomial equations depended on the number of distresses found in each particular road segment. Conditional "if, then" statements were employed to ensure the proper polynomial was used for the URCI calculation. The result of the proper polynomial equation was the URCI rating for each road segment.

Once the prototype was developed, all field data from the road survey were entered into the spreadsheet and URCI values were automatically calculated for all road segments. A maximum URCI rating was established for sections to be repaired. Road segments with ratings that fell below this established URCI rating threshold were examined in detail.

The spreadsheet was expanded to include recommended repair procedures corresponding to specific distresses (Table 3) so that a user can interactively examine the segments to determine which distresses caused the road to fall below the threshold value. The recommended repair procedures are those given by Eaton and Beaucham (1992). Estimated costs for each type of repair, based on a statewide unit-bid database (Missouri Department of Transportation, 1997), were calculated and entered into the spreadsheet, so that each distress could be examined and its corresponding severity calculated for segments below the threshold URCI value. The costs of repair for those segments falling below the established threshold rating were then totaled to provide estimated budget to repair the road network (Table 3).

GIS

The GIS at FLW is still under construction in 2001. Prior to this project, the unsurfaced road data were only CADD files without feature attribution and the FLW GIS contained information about topography and derived slope, hydrology, geology, and soil. Geospatial analyses of URCI of themes such as slope, hydrology, geology, soil properties, equivalent axle load, and distance were conducted as discussed below. Spatial analysis also

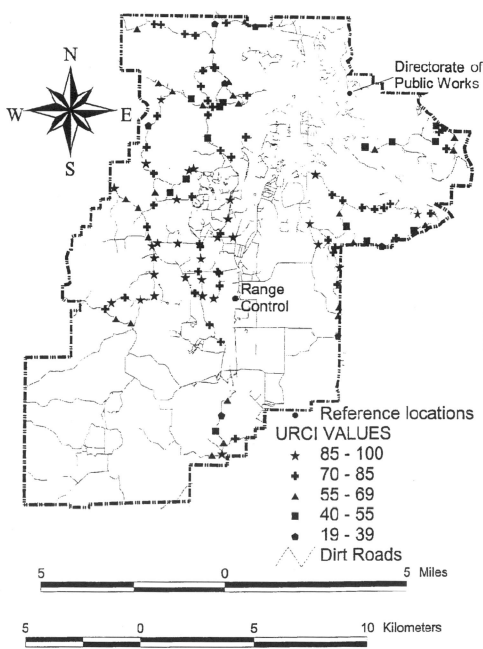

Figure 2. Fort Leonard Wood GIS map displaying unsurfaced road network with georeferenced road survey points superimposed.

revealed that the convoys could be rerouted to distribute the loads more evenly throughout the range road network.

Slope. A comparison of the topographic slope relationship to URCI values was conducted. Figure 3, which is a plot of URCI values versus a slope file derived from a digital elevation model (DEM), shows a very weak tendency for lower URCI values to correspond to road segments with steeper slopes. Intuitive correlation of low URCI values with steeper slope values was suggested.

Hydrology. The road URCI values were also compared to the FLW GIS stream network coverage, with no apparent relationship evident. The database lacked information about culverts and low water crossings. Thus, without knowledge of engineered water routings, no geospatial relationship between road stress and surface runoff could be practically evaluated. However, during the data collection phase of the project, it was noted that inadequate roadside drainage led to the road being damaged during precipitation events. Thus, drainage and hydrology are related causes of road distress, even if available GIS data do not capture the correlation.

Geology. The road segment URCI values were then compared to available geology data to determine if there were any geologic causal relationships. The geology at FLW consists of five mappable engineering geologic units (Greenhorne and

TABLE 2. SUMMARY OF SPREADSHEET DATA TYPES AND LABELS

Column	Data field	Explanation
A	ROAD	Road number of letter label
B	SAMPLE	Representative 1/2 mile sample
C	X	UTM Easting
D	Y	UTM Northing
E	AREA	Length of 100 feet X width
F	INSPECTOR	Initials of inspector
G	DATE	Month/Day/Year of inspection
H	XSECTIONL	Length of low severity cross section
I	XSECTIONM	Length of medium severity cross section
J	XSECTIONH	Length of high severity cross section
K	DRAINL	Length of low severity inadequate drainage
L	DRAINM	Length of medium severity inadequate drainage
M	DRAINH	Length of high severity cross section
N	CORRUGL	Square area of low severity corrugation
O	CORRUGM	Square area of medium severity corrugation
P	CORRUGH	Square area of high severity corrugation
Q	DUSTL	Length of low severity dust
R	DUSTM	Length of medium severity dust
S	DUSTH	Length of high severity dust
T	POTL	Number of low severity potholes
U	POTM	Number of medium severity potholes
V	POTH	Number of high severity potholes
W	RUTSL	Square area of low severity ruts
X	RUTSM	Square area of medium severity ruts
Y	RUTSH	Square area of high severity ruts
Z	AGGRGTL	Length of low severity loose gravel
AA	AGGRGTM	Length of medium berms of loose gravel
BB	AGGRGTH	Length of high berms of loose gravel

O'Mara, 1982). The three bedrock units outcropping on FLW are the Gasconade Dolomite, Roubidoux Sandstone, and Jefferson City Dolomite Formations. The remaining two units are unconsolidated materials mapped as alluvium and colluvium. Comparison of the geology grid file with the URCI data file demonstrated only general trends (Fig. 4). Field examinations revealed that the silty alluvial units required building up the subbase to provide a road foundation. Thus, the road segments measured on the alluvium (Qal) had a median URCI of 70 and only a minimum of 60 because of their engineered design. The colluvium (Qc) mapped by Greenhorne and O'Mara (1982) has the same median URCI value as Qal, but a lower minimum value of 50. However, the range is based on only three records; thus, no definite correlation can be made. Comparison of roads on the residuum of the Ordovician rock units (Ojc, Or, and Og) revealed that the best road conditions were sustained by the Jefferson City Dolomite (Ojc), based on 25 records, and the worst on Gasconade Dolomite (Og), based on 20 records. The variability of the URCI values on the Roubidoux Formation (Or) may be due to the fact that a greater number of surveyed road segments (65 records) were on this geological unit.

Soil properties. The influence of soil type on road conditions at FLW was explored by correlating URCI ratings with GIS cov-

erage of soil series. Figure 5 presents a comparison of road conditions to soil series (Wolf, 1989). Soil series with only one data point, such as Moniteau, Gatewood, and Kickapoo, do not have enough information to make a definitive correlation. Figure 5 shows a wide variability for most series. For example, URCI values for roads on Cedargap soils range from 39 to 98; those for Clarksville soil roads, from 31 to 100; and for roads on Lebanon soils, from 22 to 97. Judging by the series median URCI, and using a URCI of 70 as a threshold, soil series such as Cedargap, Clarksville, Viraton, and Lebanon apparently contain better subgrade soil material. In contrast, the Nolin and Clarksville-Gepp soil series, which exhibit medians below 70, are less desirable subgrade soil materials for road construction.

In Table 4, the soil data are regrouped using different classification systems such as the American Association of State Highway and Transportation Organization (AASHTO), the United States Department of Agriculture (USDA) texture, and the Unified Soil Classification System (USCS). Lumping data into USDA texture classes revealed a wide range of variability for soils such as cherty silt loam and silt loam, which is probably due to the variable nature of silt. However, because the class of cherty clay has only two data points and sandy loam has only one, no definitive correlation could be made based on these values.

A comparison of road conditions as a function of the AASHTO classification (Table 4) revealed that A-2, A-2-4, and A-2-6 were generally better than A-4, A-6, and A-7. The A-4 soils are silty and reflected the generally poor construction properties of silt. The wide ranges of results for all the soil classes reflected the large variability of the roads as a function of design and maintenance rather than subgrade conditions. The narrow range of the A-2 soil class reflects only two measured road segments.

Comparison of road conditions as a function of the USCS classification shows that the URCI median values for clayey soils (GC and CL) were higher than for silty soils (GM and ML). The silty sand (SM) reflects only one data point and thus does not permit correlation. All other soil types exhibited wide ranges of URCI values.

Road segments with well-graded soil and a low plastic index generally had higher URCI values. It is thought that well-graded soils allowed for greater compaction and also lowered the hydraulic conductivity of the roadbed. The low plasticity index (PI) indicated reduced potential for shrinking and swelling of the soil even under saturated conditions. The correlation of well-graded, low PI soils to high URCI values was thus established (Table 4). As expected, soils with excessive amounts of fines and higher PIs exhibit lower URCI ratings (Table 4 and Fig. 5).

Traffic. The vehicle load is a primary factor in conducting road evaluations. The vehicle load can be expressed in terms of equivalent axle load (EAL) in order to compare segments subjected to varying traffic types. The equivalent axle loading of each segment was determined based upon traffic type and volume. The routes with low, medium, and high EALs were shown on an overlay of FLW roads. Then, symbols indicating low to high URCI values for individual road segments were overlaid

TABLE 3. RECOMMENDED REPAIRS (MODIFIED AFTER EATON AND BEAUCHAM, 1992)

Distress	Severity	Action	Cost with overhead included
Improper cross section corrugation, potholes, ruts or, loose aggregate	Low	Grade	Labor and equipment
	Medium	Grade, add aggregate and water, and compact	Labor, material, and equipment
	High	Cut to base, add aggregate, shape, water, and compact	Labor, material, and equipment
Inadequate drainage	Low	Clear ditches	Labor
	Medium	Clean ditches and culverts	Labor and equipment
	High	Install culvert or alternative engineering	Labor, material, and equipment
Dust	Low	Spread water	Labor and equipment
	Medium	Spread stabilizer	Labor, material, and equipment
	High	Increase stabilizer, water, and compact	Labor, material, and equipment

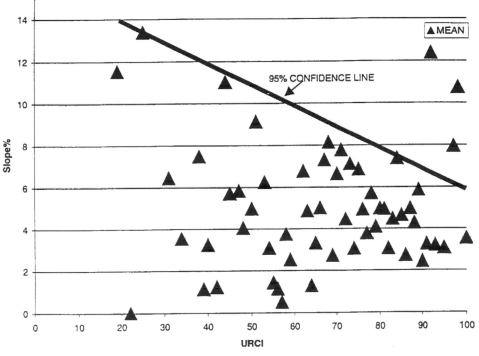

Figure 3. Plot of percent slope versus URCI rating showing 90 percent confidence line.

on that figure. Visually, there seemed to be no indication that EAL correlated with low URCI values. Visual observation of the figure indicated that road segments with high EALs had some of the better URCI ratings compared to the group. Those roads with high EALs may just represent better maintenance due to relative priority of usage. Increased loads provide more compaction effort to the road base. This, in turn, would increase the density of the road base and cause the ratings to be high on these road segments. It appears that EAL is correlated with higher URCI values. Where roads are generally used more often, maintenance is more routinely requested and the resulting road condition (URCI) is higher.

Distance. Examination of the relationship of road conditions to distance from the nearest inspector station revealed that URCI ratings were inversely related to the distance from Range Control. Simply, the further one goes from Range Control, the greater likelihood that the road will be in worse shape.

Cost analysis

Past spending. Review of the maintenance budget (from DPW records) for the unsurfaced road system on the Fort revealed reduction in maintenance spending over time (Fig. 6). A review of the types of maintenance performed indicated that only problems with the roads were addressed and repaired. There was little indication that the underlying causes of the problems were investigated or corrected. As a result, much of the maintenance budget was spent on grading and applying more aggregate. Cursory review of maintenance records indicated that spending had been cut in half twice over the last ten years. At the same time, the convoy traffic increased tenfold (Fig. 6). The combined effect of budget cuts and increasing usage is that maintaining the operational capacity of the FLW road system is nearly impossible. The present trend of reducing maintenance dollars and increasing traffic (Fig. 6) cannot continue without impacting mission readiness.

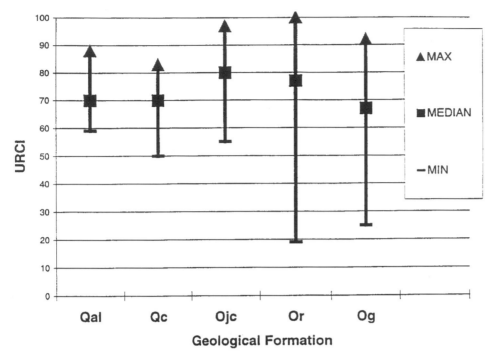

Figure 4. URCI rating related to engineering geologic units.

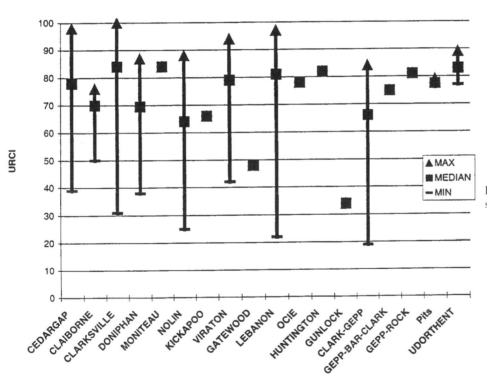

Figure 5. Comparison of road conditions to soil series.

Estimated repair costs. In order to bring the FLW road system back to its full operational capacity, more labor and materials will be required in the short term. The entire system must be examined for the causes of failure and these causative factors must be corrected. This also entails repairing all damaged road segments to restore their operational capacity. The initial cost to return the system to full operational capacity will be greater than the annual long-term cost of maintaining the road system.

In the recent past, budget constraints have caused a reduction in road maintenance. For example, current spending is only half that of 1993 expenditures. Although the number of repairs has stayed fairly constant over that time, the amount of money spent

TABLE 4. SELECTED SOIL SERIES, SOIL PROPERTIES, AND CORRESPONDING URCI VALUES

Soil series	Texture	USCS	AASHTO	PI	Fines (% passing #200 sieve)	URCI median	URCI (min)	URCI (max)
Cedargap	Cherty silt loam	GM	A-2-4	3-9	15–40	78	39	98
Clarksville	Cherty silt loam	GC	A-2-6	5-15	5–35	84	31	100
Viraton	Silt loam	CL	A-6	8-15	45–75	79	42	94
Lebanon	Silt loam	CL	A-6	5-15	60–75	82	22	97
Claiborne	Silt loam	ML	A-4	8-20	55–80	70	50	76
Doniphan	Cherty silt loam	GM	A-4	15-25	50–70	70	38	87
Clarksville-Gepp	Cherty silt loam	CL	A-6	8-20	51–90	67	19	84
Nolin	Silt loam	ML	A-4	5-23	75–100	64	25	88

for each repair has been reduced approximately 50%. The current repairs are not adequate to maintain the road network at acceptable levels. It has also been noted that repair work has shifted from FLW personnel to private contractors over the last ten years.

The current FLW road survey indicates that only 62% of the segments surveyed have URCI ratings above 70. Due to the reduction of maintenance spending over the past five years, the percentage of road segments having URCI ratings above 70 has probably decreased over time due to lack of proper maintenance. Assuming that in 1988, based on anecdotal information, 100% of the FLW road segments had URCI ratings above 70, then the amount of roads above that rating has decreased by over 4% per annum.

ROAD CONDITION: DESIGN AND CONSTRUCTION

Present conditions

The road network was surveyed from a slowly moving vehicle by the principal investigator and range control rover (a person tasked specifically with the visual inspection of road conditions at FLW). As described by Hurst et al. (1998), a survey team examined the roads in detail, occasionally assisted by FLW DPW personnel. The survey efforts created a database of 131 sample road sections. Analysis of the survey data indicates that 38% of the unsurfaced roads have a URCI value lower than 70 and, thus, need some maintenance and repair.

During the field phase of the project, surveyors noticed that drainage problems were the common factor in most road segments that received low ratings. Often, standing water was present in areas where the drainage ditches had become choked with debris and granular material. Unable to carry water away from the road, the adjacent road-base material became saturated. This saturation moved the material toward liquid behavior. Upon loading, the road-base material would pump and deform, damaging the integrity of the road surface and decreasing its URCI rating. Under such poorly drained conditions, the vehicles that use the roads most often transfer loads that are greater than the effective strength of the road. Other areas where drainage was a key factor in low URCI ratings resulted from steep slopes or the absence of roadside drainage. The lack of conduits for water to flow through and away from the road base allowed the water to spill over the roadway and remove some of the road material. This damaged

the geometry of the road and lowered URCI values for those road segments. Since inadequate roadside drainage can (and did) lead to many of these other damages, it was concluded that drainage was the key factor controlling the URCI value of a road segment.

Design

The present unsurfaced road network at FLW evolved over time without any set design criteria. New road construction now has specific design specifications. Road rehabilitation should follow the design specifications of TM 5-822-12 (Department of the Army, 1990). A traffic category and a California Bearing Ratio (CBR) value are needed to determine a design thickness of aggregate. Roads required to carry convoys are categorized as class IV. Through consultation with DPW Fort personnel, the design value for FLW was estimated to be a CBR of 3.5. The design nomograph (TM5-822-12) recommends a design gravel thickness of 27.9 cm (11 in.) for these convoy routes and 22.9 cm (9 in.) for lower volume roads (under 70 vehicles per day). Testing of the road subbase to determine a potentially higher design CBR will reduce the required aggregate thickness. Soil stabilization such as lime or fly ash treatment, as specified in TM 5-822-14 (Departments of the Army and the Air Force, 1994), will also increase the CBR strength and thus reduce the required aggregate thickness. Regardless of the alternative engineering solutions, large volumes of aggregate will be needed to rehabilitate the roads.

Aggregate

The locally available aggregate sources are of two varieties. The cheaper and more common is known as river rock. The more expensive and better engineering material is crushed dolomite stone. Field observations revealed that loose aggregate problems were more common with river wash gravel than crushed dolomite stone.

River rock. The type of aggregate used on the majority of the FLW roads is siliceous river gravel. This material, which is easily mined from the river valleys that surround FLW, consists predominately of subangular to subrounded chert gravel ranging in size from 7.6 cm (3 in.) to sand-sized particles. Fragments of dolomite and sandstone are included in lesser amounts. This river chert gravel meets hardness requirements.

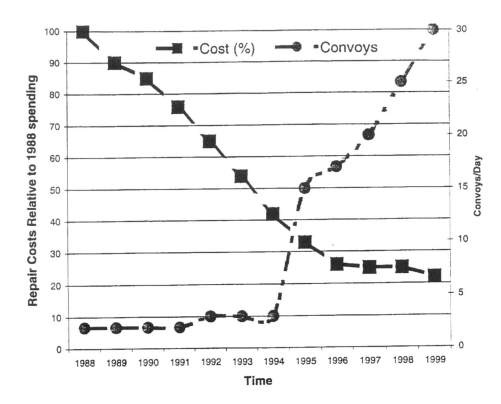

Figure 6. Maintenance spending and convoy volume through time.

Road aggregate specifications require that the selected gravel should also have good gradation. Rollings and Rollings (1996) suggested that angular aggregate, containing significant fines, should be used when designing and constructing unsurfaced roads. Decades earlier, Dake (1918) warned that, "the extreme variation in composition of stream gravel from the Ozarks... would demand screening to guarantee the right proportions of sand and pebbles for the best grade of product."

Well-graded and angular material will attain a higher state of compaction than rounded aggregate, particularly aggregates containing few fines. Angularity helps the gravel to interlock and therefore improves stability. Compaction of angular aggregate leads to higher strength than a rounded-rock aggregate. Dake (1918) notes that, unfortunately, very little angular gravel occurs naturally in Missouri. This is one of the causes for the poor road conditions at FLW. The rounded aggregate does not contain enough fines to readily compact and, as a result, rolls under vehicle loading because the larger, rounded particles do not have the angularity to interlock and spread point loads. The result is roads that have a short duration during which URCI ratings fall above the 70 level. Roads constructed with this aggregate type are susceptible to distress failures such as potholes, loose aggregate, ruts, and corrugations. It is also suggested that, if round chert gravel continues to be used as road aggregate, it should be crushed so as to create some angularity and fines in the aggregate, making it more suitable for road construction purposes.

Crushed dolomite stone. Angular dolomite aggregate is currently being used in repair work and new construction; however, few areas were observed on the FLW road networks where angular dolomite aggregate had been used. This aggregate type contained enough fines to be readily compacted. The segments of road with this aggregate type exhibited fewer distresses than their round aggregate counterparts. The crushed dolomite aggregate, both angular and well graded, compacted well under load and could distribute point loads sufficiently enough to avoid most distresses. This aggregate type was recommended for unsurfaced road use by Rollings and Rollings (1996).

FLW contains a large dolomite quarry that is used for the training of military personnel. It is suggested that, with such a large quarry already on site, it be utilized as a source of the angular, well-graded, dolomite aggregate that is recommended for road surfacing. The quarry has the capability of crushing and screening aggregate to the Army's specifications.

Compaction

Compacting the subbase and base of a road is an accepted engineering practice. However, compaction is not commonly conducted or only halfheartedly performed during construction at FLW, resulting in distressed roads and high long-term repair costs. Upgrading the roads to meet present and future training requirements will require 90% compaction of road courses (Department of the Army, 1990).

RECOMMENDATIONS

Maintenance plan

It was recommended that repair protocols at FLW be modified to optimize the use of the local resources in maintaining its unsurfaced road system. By first addressing the causes of a problem, and then fixing the effects, the FLW DPW would be proactively preventing future expenditures to correct the same problems at a later time. Such an approach would optimize the budget to maintain full operational capacity.

Repairs should follow the appropriate methods for each type of distress and its relative severity, as outlined by Eaton and Beaucham (1992). The unsurfaced road network needs to be upgraded to accommodate the traffic volume and loads of present and future training needs. The rehabilitation operation should upgrade all unsurfaced roads to a URCI rating of 70 or above. An alternative approach would be to upgrade roads used only for convoys and heavy traffic (>200 vehicles/day) to a URCI rating above 70 (Fig. 7). Following this alternative plan, other unsurfaced roads with low traffic volumes would be upgraded only to a URCI value of 55. All roads deemed mission essential should be graded every year. Roads deemed nonessential could be closed following procedures described by Albertson et al. (1995).

The road repairs and closures need to be agreed upon by the Directorate of Public Works and Directorate of Plans, Training, and Mobilization. The selection process should use information about vehicular traffic at FLW to delineate usage and to prioritize the repair scheme. After a consensus is reached, a more rigorous cost estimate should be conducted. Once funding is secured, the roads should be rehabilitated and the network resurveyed to determine benchmark URCI ratings.

The GPS georeferencing of road data should be continued to provide critical information for maintaining the operational capacity of the FLW road system. Georeferenced digital data eases mapping problem areas and also facilitates the causes of damaged areas to be determined and addressed. This will provide for the most efficient use of funds spent to maintain the road system.

Design

It was recommended that future roads be situated on soils and slopes that are conducive to high URCI values and that drainage issues be addressed during construction to ensure long-term performance of these new roads. Areas with chronic maintenance and repair problems should be treated with alternative engineering designs. Soil stabilization techniques, such as lime and fly ash treatment, are often used to improve soils with high Plastic Indexes usually, which exhibit shrink-swell problems. Geotextiles serve to distribute loads over soft soil subgrades and reduce pumping of subgrade fines into the overlying aggregate layer.

Proper selection of design aggregate type, gradation, and layer thickness are required to rehabilitate roads to accommodate the future increase in traffic volume and loads expected at FLW.

Crushed rock with angularity is the aggregate of choice. Therefore, placing crushed dolomite stone or crushed river rock will ensure interlocking angularity, which will improve the stability of the roadbed. The gradation of the aggregate should follow the specifications stated in TM-5-822-12 (Department of the Army, 1990). A well-graded material will achieve higher compacted strengths needed to support the applied traffic loads. The thickness of the aggregate should be determined based upon the traffic category and soil subgrade strength as outlined in TM-5-822-12 (Department of Army, 1990). By using the correct aggregate type, gradation, and design thickness, long-term maintenance costs will be reduced for the road network.

Economics of maintenance

Since unsurfaced roads are used to meet specific training needs, a separate budget for their construction and maintenance is warranted. It is therefore recommended that a larger budget be allocated solely for the purpose of road system maintenance. If protocols are changed to optimize the benefits of every dollar spent in repair, the overall cost in the long term will be lower than the current costs of maintaining the system as a whole. However, the initial cost will be higher and, thus, budgets in the short-term will need to be larger to upgrade the entire system. Once the entire system has been reviewed and upgraded, the costs will decline significantly. Currently, money is spent to address problems rather than causes. Such an approach would serve mission readiness by optimizing the budget for the road system and focusing on long-term objectives. Without a larger short-term budget, the road system at FLW will continue to degrade.

Considering the large estimated short-term costs, some of the rehabilitation could be accomplished as troop-training exercises. Engineering units and the on-post quarry operation could be used in concert with contract services to accomplish rehabilitation in a timely and cost-effective manner. Engineering units could use the opportunity to practice design, construction, and maintenance planning of the road network. Quarry materials present at FLW could be used on selected road segments to supplement off-post aggregate obtained to repair the road network. Trainees would benefit from the experience of controlling gradation. Transportation units could practice hauling aggregate materials to experience driving with loaded vehicles. Through coordinated effort, engineering and transport trainees would benefit from increased mission readiness while aiding in maintaining the road network.

Future studies

Future road management will require updated information. Therefore, while the roads are being rehabilitated and maintained, it is important to maintain records of where, when, what, and how much work is done. This study revealed that the location, size, and condition of culverts were not documented. Thus, a culvert inventory needs to be conducted to address road-drainage

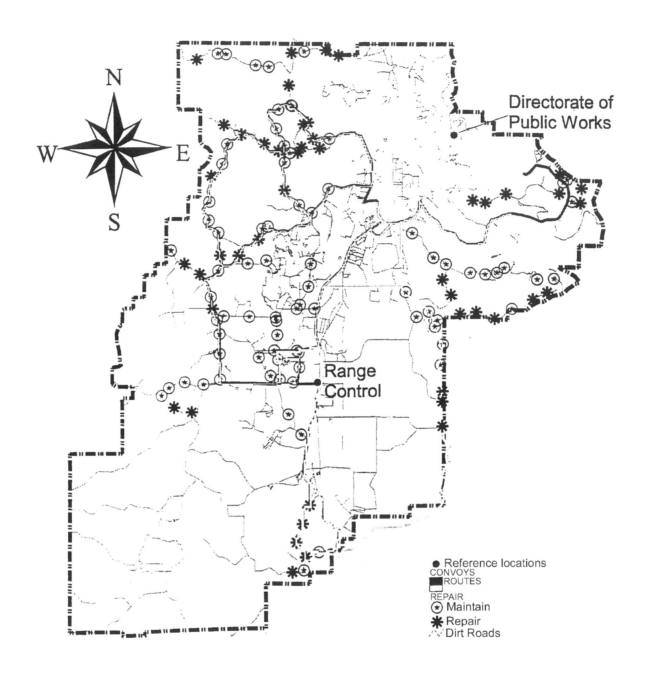

Directorate of
Public Works

Range
Control

● Reference locations
CONVOYS
■ ROUTES
REPAIR
⊛ Maintain
✳ Repair
⩘ Dirt Roads

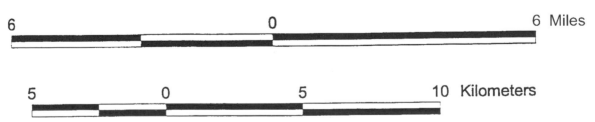

6   0   6 Miles

5   0   5   10 Kilometers

Figure 7. GIS analysis output portraying convoy routes and road segments with URCI<70.

issues. The culvert inventory should be done with GPS to facilitate integration into the FLW GIS. In addition, areas with obvious washouts should be noted for the future installation of culverts. Planning and prioritizing where to place additional aggregate would be assisted by an existing aggregate inventory. By noting the aggregate types and thicknesses present on the road network, areas of greater need could be determined. If desired, selected test sections could be monitored to observe aggregate wear performance. Every two to three years, URCI surveys should be conducted to gauge the condition of the road network and the effectiveness of the maintenance program.

SUMMARY AND CONCLUSIONS

Unsurfaced roads present specific economic, engineering, and ecological concerns around the world. DoD is responsible for many miles of unsurfaced roads on its millions of acres. DoD's commitment to mission readiness and environmental stewardship led WES to address road-management issues in general at Eglin AFB (Albertson et al., 1995) and then in greater detail at Fort Leonard Wood (this study). The present road systems at both installations were inherited from previous private owners, the U.S. Forest Service, and previous mission requirements. Specifically, the unsurfaced road network at FLW has evolved over time from the rural road system inherited in the 1940s to a network of many roads added to meet mission needs during World War II, the Korean War, Vietnam Era, and subsequent training. Over time, the traffic volumes and loads have increased dramatically. The vehicles that now use the roads often transfer loads that are greater than the effective strength of the roads.

The logical starting point when addressing unsurfaced road problems is an inventory of the road system. A GIS containing an inventory of the road system in terms of mission needs, traffic volume, maintenance conditions (URCI), and environmental concerns was developed. A systematic approach to inventory, categorize, and rate the roads was adapted from the U.S. Army (Eaton et al., 1987) and automated (Hurst et al., 1998).

Unsurfaced roads generally suffer from seven distresses—improper cross section, drainage, corrugations, potholes, dust, ruts, and loose aggregate (Fig. 1). The road condition survey of the unsurfaced road network at FLW revealed that most of the problems are caused by only a few of these distresses. Commonly, inadequate drainage and poor surface aggregate appeared to be the primary cause of problems.

Inadequate roadside drainage led to roads being damaged through erosion during precipitation events. Drainage also directly affects the moisture content of the road subgrade. It was observed that many roads were driven upon while subgrade soils contained moisture contents beyond their optimum moisture content (OMC). Spring thawing is a particularly problematic time for conditions higher than OMC.

Many roads appeared to have poor or nonexistent subbases, which did not allow them to support heavy axle weights. Road condition is often a function of the type and quality of aggregate used for the subbase and base. Although local chert river gravel was a low-cost approach to road construction, it has generated high maintenance costs in the long term because the gravel tends to roll off the road surface under vehicular loading. Thus, if round chert gravel continues to be used as road aggregate, it should be crushed so as to create some angularity and fines, making the aggregate more suitable for road construction purposes. Crushed dolomite aggregate, both angular and well graded, is the aggregate of choice because it compacts well under load.

Both fieldwork and computer analysis suggested that road condition is a site-specific phenomenon depending on design and past maintenance. Data collected during fieldwork were used to determine the unsurfaced road condition index (URCI). GPS coordinates tied the road measurement to geographic space. Road CADD files were attributed with convoy route names. Then records of convoy types and numbers were converted into equivalent axle loads (EAL). GIS overlay procedure calculated EAL for road segments. The GIS portrayed the areas of greatest distress and maximum use (Fig. 3). Spatially defining the areas of greatest concern allowed prioritization of the repairs in order to upgrade the road network. Road rehabilitation should follow the design specifications of TM 5-822-12 (Department of the Army, 1990). Upgrading the roads to meet present and future training requirements will require 90% compaction of road courses.

Failure to rehabilitate and maintain the unsurfaced road network will result in higher repair costs and possible road closures. In specific circumstances, closing a road is an economic alternative to investing in maintenance or reconstruction. However, decisions involving road closure need to be made based on road mission requirements, maintenance condition, and environmental considerations. The GIS-based approach employed in this study allowed for standard expeditious information sharing between road users and managers. Maintenance and operation decisions were aided by querying the GIS database for the road segments with the greatest training requirements and need of repair. Without roads in safe and suitable condition, mission readiness will not be possible.

DoD is addressing its unsurfaced road concerns to meet its specific needs. For example, the actions taken at Eglin AFB addressed the economics and ecological criteria of road closure. More recently, Corps of Engineer methods were adapted and automated to inventory roads at Fort Leonard Wood. The actions taken at Eglin AFB and the procedures developed for Fort Leonard Wood can serve as models for other military installations faced with the problems of road management. The insights learned from these case studies can benefit road managers of county, state, and federal lands or other communities around the world.

ACKNOWLEDGMENTS

The following institutions are acknowledged for their support of this research: U.S. Army Engineer Waterways Experiment Station (USAEWES); Fort Leonard Wood Directorate of Public Works (DPW); U.S. Geological Survey Mid-Continent

Mapping Center; and the Department of Geological and Petroleum Engineering, University of Missouri, Rolla (UMR). The authors would like to personally thank the following persons for their contributions: Bryson Burton and Cory Reiter of the UMR Senior Design Team for their contribution to the senior design project; Allen W. Hatheway (UMR) for his guidance throughout this research; Angie Rolufs, Chief of Planning Division, DPW, Fort Leonard Wood for project direction; and Travis Lynch (DPW) for his help providing vital information and field logistical support. The authors are grateful for the rigorous review by the following colleagues: Jeb Tingle of the Pavement Division, Geotechnical Laboratory, USACEWES; Robert A. Larson of Materials Engineering Division, Los Angeles County Public Works, California; Valerie Morrill, Natural Resources Manager, Yuma Proving Ground; and Sally A. Shoop, USACRREL. The first author (JBI) would also like to thank the last author (PEA) for his mentoring during this study and writing of this chapter. Following the tragic death of Paul Albertson, this manuscript was revised for publication by Russell Harmon, Army Research Office; Lillian Wakeley, U.S. Army Engineer Research and Development Center (Waterways Experiment Station); and Judy Ehlen, U.S. Army Engineer Research and Development Center (Topographic Engineering Center).

REFERENCES CITED

Albertson, P.E., Bush, A.J., Webster, J., Titre, J.P., Patrick, D.M., and Brown, J.W., 1995, Road management plan and workshop, Eglin Air Force Base, Florida: Vicksburg, Mississippi, U.S. Army Engineer Waterways Experiment Station, Miscellaneous Paper GL-94-12, 40 p.

Beachy, K.T., and Eck, R.W., 1995, Environmental dilemma of administering and maintaining low-volume roads, *in* Proceedings, International Conference on Low-Volume Roads, 6th: Washington, D.C., National Academy Press, p. 88–98.

Dake, C.L., 1918, The sand and gravel resources of Missouri: Rolla, Missouri Bureau of Geology and Mines, ser. 2, v. 15, 274 p.

Department of the Army, Headquarters, 1990, Design of aggregate surfaced roads and airfields: Washington, D.C., Technical Manual TM 5-822-12, 14 p.

Departments of the Army and the Air Force, Headquarters, 1994, Soil stabilization for pavements: Washington, D.C., Technical Manual TM 5-822-14/AFJMAN 32-1019, 57 p.

Eaton, R.A., and Beaucham, R.E., 1992, Unsurfaced road maintenance management: Hanover, New Hampshire, U.S. Army Cold Regions Research and Engineering Laboratory, Special Report 92-26, 61 p.

Eaton, R.A., Gerard, S., and Cate, D.W., 1987, Rating unsurfaced roads: A field manual for measuring maintenance problems: Hanover, New Hampshire, U.S. Army Corps of Engineers Cold Regions Research and Engineering Laboratory, Special Report 87-15, 34 p.

Greenhorne and O'Mara, 1982, Terrain analysis of Fort Leonard Wood: Fort Belvoir, Virginia, U.S. Army Topographic Laboratory: scale 1: 50 000, 65 p.

Hurst, A.E., Burton, B., Isaacson, J.B., Reiter, C., and Albertson, P.E., 1998, Geospatial evaluation of range roads on Fort Leonard Wood, Missouri: Seattle, Washington, Association of Engineering Geologists Annual Meeting, 41st, Abstracts, p. 99.

Luhr, D.R., and McCullough, B.F., 1983, Economic evaluation of pavement design alternatives for low-volume roads, *in* Low-volume roads: Proceedings, International Conference, 3rd, Transportation Research Record 898, p. 24–29.

Missouri Department of Transportation (MODOT), 1997, Unit bid prices: Jefferson City, Missouri Department of Transportation, 27 p.

Patrick, D.M., Corcoran, M.K., Albertson, P.E., and Smith, L.M., 1994a, Earth resources stewardship at Department of Defense installations: Interim report of the Earth Resources Task Area, Legacy Resources Management Program: Vicksburg, Mississippi, U.S. Army Engineer Waterways Experiment Station, Technical Report GL-94-9, 143 p.

Patrick, D.M., Albertson, P.E., and Smith, L.M., 1994b, Legacy Earth Resource Workshop, Proceedings of the March 1993 Earth Resource Workshop, Eglin Air Force Base, Florida: Vicksburg, Mississippi, U.S. Army Engineer Waterways Experiment Station, Miscellaneous Paper GL-94-12, 40 p.

Rollings, M.P., and Rollings, R.S., 1996, Geotechnical materials in construction: New York, McGraw-Hill, 525 p.

Wolf, D.W., 1989, Soil survey of Pulaski, Missouri: Washington, D.C., U.S. Department of Agriculture, Soil Conservation Service, 120 p.

Manuscript Accepted by the Society October 27, 2000

Geological Society of America
Reviews in Engineering Geology, Volume XIV
2001

Geology without borders: A conceptual model for Aberdeen Proving Ground

Joseph B. Dunbar
Lillian D. Wakeley
S. Paul Miller
Stanley M. Swartzel
U.S. Army Engineer Research and Development Center, Waterways Experiment Station, Vicksburg, Mississippi, 39180, USA

ABSTRACT

Research by the U.S. Army Corps of Engineers at numerous military facilities has shown that a regional geologic approach is the key to cost-effective risk assessment and environmental remediation. This approach addresses the needs of the facility by placing it directly in the larger framework of the land, water, and the people off post who comprise potential contaminant receptors. Application of a regional geologic framework to a large military facility requires extensive research and focused study to establish the overall picture.

A regional geologic and geomorphic model was developed for the Aberdeen Proving Ground (APG), located in the headwaters of Chesapeake Bay near Aberdeen, Maryland, USA. Regional geologic information and interpretation of data from over 2000 geologic and water well borings indicate that APG is situated upon Pleistocene terraces of the ancestral Susquehanna River, which unconformably overlie Cretaceous unconsolidated sediments. Pleistocene terraces represent estuarine and fluvial filling of an earlier manifestation of Chesapeake Bay during interglacial periods of high sea level during the past 1.5 m.y. During episodes of low sea level, corresponding to glacial maxima, the Susquehanna River downcut into Pleistocene and Cretaceous deposits. The remnants of at least three and possibly four separate filling cycles, ranging from middle Wisconsin to early Pleistocene in age (youngest to oldest), are present at APG. The geologic and geomorphic model of APG is being used to define aquifer limits and to assess the movement of groundwater for potential impacts to public drinking water supplies on the Aberdeen Peninsula and to Chesapeake Bay.

A GEOLOGIC CONCEPTUAL MODEL

Everyone has a conceptual model of the geology underlying any place. A conceptual model is the mental picture of what is in the subsurface or how a surface feature formed, based upon available information. Non-geologists may have a conceptual model of the place they live that consists of a layer of soil over different types of rock, with water present below ground in open tubes and pools. Changes in the water table may be attributed to puncturing of such underground fluid reservoirs. This would be an example of a geologic conceptual model based on very limited data.

The work of many earth scientists consists of building and refining geologic conceptual models using information and interpretation of data that can be defended. As more data are acquired, one modifies and refines a mental picture and uses visual images, such as cross sections, maps, and three-dimensional (3-D) visualization. A conceptual model will explain more of the geologic setting and history as the quantity of data increases and interpretation

Dunbar, J.B., Wakeley, L.D., Miller, S.P., and Swartzel, S.M., 2001, Geology without borders: A conceptual model for Aberdeen Proving Ground, *in* Ehlen, J., and Harmon, R.S., eds., The Environmental Legacy of Military Operations: Boulder, Colorado, Geological Society of America Reviews in Engineering Geology, v. XIV, p. 191–202.

is refined. The ultimate aim is to understand factors that contribute to current and future conditions, to identify inconsistencies or gaps in the data, and to explain the causes of geologic features and phenomena to others.

GEOLOGIC SETTING OF ABERDEEN PROVING GROUND

Aberdeen Proving Ground (APG), located on the Chesapeake Bay (Fig. 1), is an area of interest to military and engineering geology. A first-order geologic conceptual model of the Aberdeen Proving Ground (APG) is fairly simple. From the Fall Line, which is the boundary between the Piedmont and Coastal Plain physiographic provinces (Fig. 2) northwest of APG, Precambrian basement rocks dip toward the southeast and are overlain by Atlantic Coastal Plain strata of Cretaceous and Pleistocene ages, separated by unconformities. The depth of the Precambrian bedrock surface increases from its exposure at the surface at the Fall Line toward the Atlantic Ocean (Richards,

1948; Owens, 1969); the surface is situated at a depth of well over 1000 m in eastern Maryland (Fig. 3). Deposits of sands, silts, clays, and gravels overlie the Precambrian rocks. These sediments, which dip and thicken eastward and southeastward, are the evidence of fluvial, deltaic, and nearshore deposits from late Mesozoic to Cenozoic sea-level changes (USGS, 1967; Vroblesky and Fleck, 1991). Upper Cretaceous sediments are absent at APG, but are present throughout much of the Coastal Plain. Lower Cretaceous beds (Potomac Group) at APG are unconformably overlain by Quaternary sediments that accumulated during the Pleistocene in the highly variable depositional conditions of fluvial and estuarine environments associated with interglacial sea-level changes (Owens, 1969; Owens and Denny, 1979). A generalized stratigraphic section for the Coastal Plain near APG is shown in Table 1.

Previous work on the Coastal Plain has defined the regional geologic framework for APG and its surroundings. Detailed data specific to APG only recently became available to provide a useful level of detail to this regional conceptual model. Security and

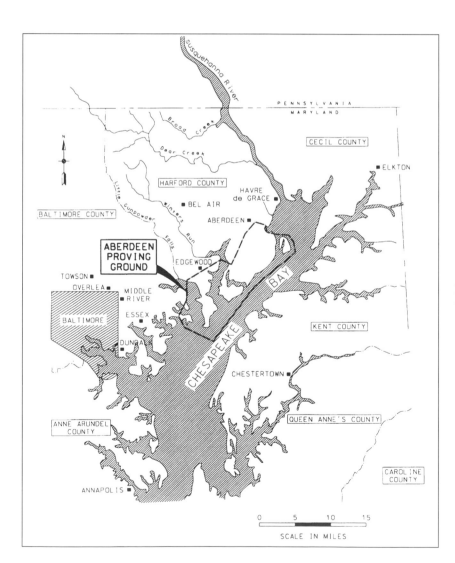

Figure 1. Location of Aberdeen Proving Ground (APG), Maryland, USA.

safety considerations nearly precluded access for research during much of the 80 years of APG operation.

EARLY AND RECENT APG HISTORY

At the outset of World War I, the existing ordnance testing facility in northeastern New Jersey was considered by the U.S. government to be too close to large population centers for its anticipated increased use. APG was established in 1917, within six months of the entry of the United States into the war, for acceptance testing of new and experimental munitions. Regional geology probably was not a factor in site selection, although officials at the time may have had some kind of geologic conceptual model. Reasons for locating a proving ground on a peninsula in Chesapeake Bay were largely economic and geographic. The Aberdeen Peninsula was at a safe but convenient travel distance from Philadelphia and Washington, D.C., and accessible by ship and railroad. The fact that it was a peninsula provided increased public safety. Open water on three sides, rather than settled land, would minimize the detrimental effects of unexpected or uncontrolled explosions. The economic impact of removing all the inhabitants from this area of farmland and swamp was considered by the government to be justified by national need.

Acceptance testing of munitions and military vehicles began almost immediately after the facility opened (Fig. 4) and continues to the present. Soon, the nearby Edgewood Peninsula was acquired for chemical weapons research, development, and testing, for all the same reasons of geographic location and transportation infrastructure. The two areas, joined administratively in 1971, have been used for most of a century for Department of Defense (DoD) activities that inevitably introduced contaminants into the subsurface at some locations.

The geology became increasingly important as big east-coast cities spawned suburbs and land prices rose. Over several decades, people moved out of the cities and close to the boundaries of APG (Fig. 5), and demands on domestic water supplies increased concomitantly. The widespread sandy sediments exposed east of the Fall Line and the piedmont crystalline rocks were reliable sources of high-quality groundwater. Aquifers were readily recharged by abundant rainfall. Groundwater was plentiful and population growth continued. DoD environmental investigations of the long history of military land use at APG identified contaminants that resulted from long-term past activities, some of which were not well documented. DoD concern and study increased as land use changed rapidly and the demand for domestic water supplies grew.

Once there was awareness of the contaminant problem, an environmental infrastructure grew quickly at APG and throughout DoD. Initially, environmental management was based on defining contaminated sites as individual solid-waste-management units (SWMUs). The apparently arbitrary surface geographic boundaries of SWMUs were zones of a fixed radius

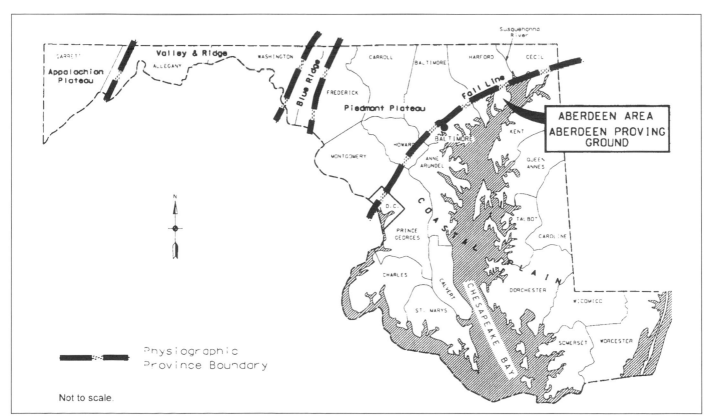

Figure 2. Physiographic provinces in the Chesapeake Bay region.

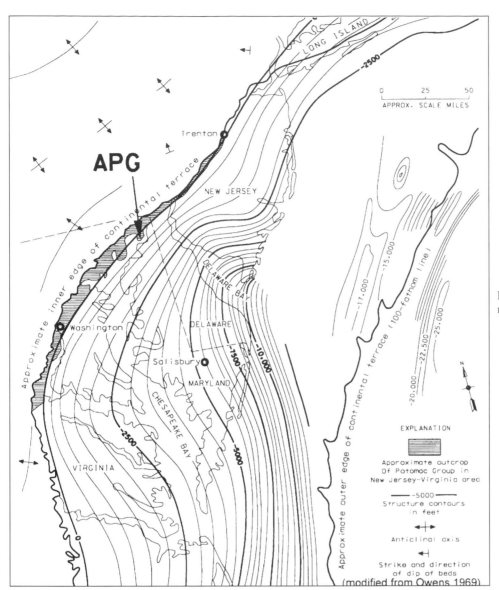

Figure 3. Surface of Precambrian basement rocks beneath the Atlantic Coastal Plain.

TABLE 1. GENERALIZED LITHOLOGY OF THE COASTAL PLAIN IN HARFORD COUNTY, MARYLAND

System	Series	Group	Formation	Generalized lithology	Water-bearing properties
Quaternary	Holocene			Clay, sand, silt, and gravel	May yield large quantities of water where recharge can be induced from nearby streams
	Pleistocene		Talbot	Fine to medium silty sand with mixtures of fine gravel and lenses of silt and clay; localized areas of marine silty clay unit	Water-table aquifer where composed of coarse-grained water-bearing materials as in Aberdeen and Havre de Grace areas; yields up to 500 gal/min.
Cretaceous	Lower Cretaceous	Potomac	Patapsco	Fine to medium sand, silt, and clay	Yields some water to domestic wells in Harford County
			Arundel	Silty clay to clayey silt with lenses of organic silty clay and traces of lignite and ironstone nodules	Not a water-bearing formation except where penetrated by a few wells in outcrop area
			Patuxent	Fine to medium sands and gravels intercalated with silt and clay lenses	Source of water for numerous domestic and small commercial groundwater supplies along U.S. Highway 40; thickens rapidly toward southeast and becomes an excellent aquifer yielding up to 1000 gal/min.
Precambrian	Glenarm		Wissahickon and others	Bedrock	Not a water-bearing formation

Note: Modified from Bandoian and Waldrop (1985).

Figure 4. Aberdeen Proving Ground, munitions and military vehicles during World War I.

surrounding historic hazardous land-use features such as known landfills or buried trenches. On maps, these SWMUs were considered independent of each other. Their shape in the third dimension, vertically into geologic units, was not part of their definition. The infrastructure for detailed environmental study and remediation of contaminated sites grew up around these groups of geographic locations, which from the surface appeared to be totally separate. Studies were site specific and did not address a regional hydrogeologic model or framework.

A REGIONAL GEOLOGIC STUDY

The focus on SWMUs created the opportunity for geologists to influence regulatory thinking about a regional approach and to refine the initial geologic conceptual model of APG, which led toward regional thinking about contaminant migration and risk. Geologic features within the Aberdeen and Edgewood areas were correlated to layers and features identified or defined elsewhere on the Coastal Plain. Data about subsurface features were available from nearly 2000 borings, spanning 25 years of characterization of discrete sites (Whitten et al., 1997; see Appendix for a list of data sources). These data originated from diverse sources in activities ranging from logging water wells to detailed geotechnical exploration for construction of new facilities.

Site characterization activities, performed by federal and state agencies and contractors, used different sampling methods and inconsistent or incompatible location systems and naming strategies. Boring depths and spacing were determined over the years in response to concerns about individual SWMUs, leaving large areas underrepresented or unrepresented in the data sets. Because of the differences in their history and purpose, the Aberdeen and Edgewood areas had been managed and regulated separately, resulting in groups of separate data sets. A large part of fitting these data sets together into a comprehensive and comprehensible

picture was quality assurance to establish which borings had adequate positional accuracy and which data were defensible.

A unique opportunity for geologic study was almost missed during excavation of the Underwater Explosive (UNDEX) facility "superpond," constructed for underwater testing of munitions on a narrow neck of land between the Bush River and Romney Creek. Dry excavation to a depth of about 17 m below mean sea level (MSL) exposed a high area on the Cretaceous surface and characteristics of the Cretaceous-Quaternary unconformity (Fig. 6). The Quaternary sediments provided wood and shell samples to confirm landform age, as well as pollen samples for regional correlation. This excavation provided a rare opportunity to study the Coastal Plain sediments of upper Chesapeake Bay. It was quickly lost when the facility was flooded for its intended purpose. Geologic studies were conducted during the brief time of accessibility and confirmed some of the geologic interpretations from borings and other less direct data sources.

Review of the extensive data available for APG focused on determining the age and the subsurface characteristics of the sedimentary units, which underlie the installation and host wells for public drinking water supplies. Each boring log was evaluated to correlate Cretaceous sediments, and identify characteristics and depositional environments of Pleistocene sediments. From these data, 18 geologic cross sections were constructed across the Aberdeen and Edgewood Peninsulas. An example of one of these cross sections is given in Figures 7A and 7B. These sections also allowed correlation with units identified in previously published studies (Table 1). Regional correlation is difficult owing to facies changes within all formations, a paucity of deep boring data, and the lack of data from active ordnance ranges or Chesapeake Bay, both of which preclude extensive drilling or study.

Quaternary landforms were identified in the sediments above the Cretaceous contact. Ancient landforms present at APG are directly related to the Susquehanna River and its response to

Figure 5. 1971 aerial photograph showing suburban growth at APG boundary.

eustatic changes in sea level or base level during the Pleistocene. These ancient river courses also partly eroded the Cretaceous strata and completely removed the Tertiary stratigraphic record, further complicating correlation. Generalized regional correlation is shown in Figure 8.

ENVIRONMENTS OF DEPOSITION AND RESULTING STRATIGRAPHY

Cretaceous and Pleistocene strata at APG are largely unlithified and laterally discontinuous. Understanding the geologic processes and Quaternary history that produced these units is the key to correlating widely varying data into a regional geologic model.

Cretaceous units

Examination of Cretaceous stratigraphy in the cross sections revealed several local and regional trends in lithology. Near the Fall Line and along the northwest boundary of both the Aberdeen and Edgewood areas, boring data indicate a predominantly clay lithology (although there are water-bearing sands along the northwest boundary of the Aberdeen area). Solely on the basis of distance and relationship to the crystalline basement rock, the thick clay sequence is correlated to the Lower Potomac Group (the Arundel Formation). Pollen data obtained by Cleaves (1968) during construction of the Susquehanna Aqueduct support this age and formation assignment.

Between the Fall Line and somewhere near the APG boundary, there is a transition from the Arundel Formation into the overlying Patapsco Formation (Table 1). Quaternary sediments are present at the surface and mask this contact, and the Arundel Formation is discontinuous throughout the Upper Chesapeake Bay region. Therefore, recognition of the contact between the Lower Potomac Group (Arundel and Patuxent Formations) and Upper Potomac Group (Patapsco Formation) is extremely difficult in the APG area. This contact has been tentatively identified on the cross sections in both the Edgewood and Aberdeen areas (Fig. 8).

The contact between Lower and Upper Potomac Group on the cross sections is based on the interpretation of lithology by Drummond and Blomquist (1993). Their study defined the contact between the Patapsco and Patuxent Formations on several test borings in the Aberdeen and Edgewood areas. They located the contact at the top of a thick sand sequence, regarded as being generally continuous along the regional strike of the Potomac Group stratigraphy.

Farther to the south on the Edgewood Peninsula, the Patuxent sand occurs downdip at about 160 ft below MSL. This sand sequence has been termed the Lower Confined Aquifer in the Edgewood area by Oliveros and Vroblesky (1989a, 1989b). Because of the lack of data downdip, the limits of the Lower Confined Aquifer in the southern Edgewood Peninsula are unknown.

Use of the Patuxent sand contact at APG established by Drummond and Blomquist (1993) for the boundary between Lower and Upper Potomac Group sediments permits a general

Figure 6. Excavation to –17 m below MSL and UNDEX facility showing Cretaceous-Quaternary unconformity.

310 m

regional correlation of the Cretaceous stratigraphy in the Upper Chesapeake Bay area. In the Aberdeen area, this sand sequence continues along the strike. Eventually, this sand pinches out, and the Arundel clay is encountered adjacent to the Fall Line. In the Aberdeen area, the contact between the Patapsco Formation, and the Arundel and Patuxent Formations is just below the Quaternary deposits. Northward, the lithology changes toward Arundel clay. Southward, the Patuxent sand thickens toward the Edgewood area. Within the central part of the Aberdeen area, the Lower Potomac Group (Arundel and Patuxent Formations) contact is downdip at ~220 ft below MSL. At the UNDEX site, this sand contact is much shallower, occurring farther updip in the section at ~160 ft below MSL.

Along the regional dip, it becomes difficult to follow this sand body in the subsurface because of the lack of boring data downdip. Additionally, there is a well-defined Quaternary contact where much of the Cretaceous sediment has been removed. This buried contact is the western edge of the Pleistocene Susquehanna River valley.

Sections that run parallel with the dip in the Aberdeen and Edgewood areas identify the contact between the Upper (Patapsco Formation) and Lower (Arundel and Patuxent Formations) Potomac Group sediments as being a highly variable surface, rather than a smooth or planar boundary. This variability is probably due to a combination of differential weathering, erosion, and stratigraphic interbedding caused by postdepositional reworking of the underlying sediments. Other possible contributors to a highly variable surface involve the quality of the boring logs. The quality can be influenced by the sampling interval and sampling methods (i.e., drill cuttings, split spoon, undisturbed). All of these factors can cause irregularities in the data and interpretation of boundaries. In areas where extreme variability occurred, boundary position was approximated to fit directional trends.

The presence of horizontally and vertically continuous sand units in the subsurface is of major importance to groundwater movement beneath APG. The cross sections in Figures 8 and 9 show the limits of various geologic units, where the data allow correlation. In the Edgewood area, a sand body of some significance is present near the surface and outcrops along the APG boundary. This upper sand has been identified locally as the Canal Creek Aquifer by the U.S. Geological Survey (Oliveros and Vroblesky, 1989a, 1989b). Geologic cross sections across the Edgewood area indicate this sand generally extends not only downdip (i.e., southeast), but also continues southwest along the regional axis of Chesapeake Bay to the Gunpowder River. The Canal Creek sand is not present in the Aberdeen area.

Another sand sequence is present beneath APG above the crystalline basement rock. The horizontal and vertical limits of this sand unit, which may consist in part of saprolite, are unknown; its presence is documented only at those few locations where this sand has been penetrated by borings.

Pleistocene geomorphic processes and geologic units

Pleistocene deposits cover the majority of the land area at APG and correspond to sediments previously mapped as the Talbot Formation (Owens, 1969; Southwick and Owens, 1968; Miller et al., 1917). Topographic and boring data identify the Talbot Formation as having a complex lithology, controlled by the underlying Cretaceous sediments and directly related to former courses of the Susquehanna River. At least three (and possibly four) different Quaternary terrace (QT) levels (depicted in Figs. 7B, 8, and 9) are present at APG. Each terrace level represents the remains of a flood plain that corresponds to a former Susquehanna River course. The youngest terrace deposits identified on the cross sections and maps of this study are labeled as QT1, and the oldest are identified as QT3. The QT1 is the lowest terrace and is mapped only in the Aberdeen area. An intermediate level terrace, QT2, is present at both the Aberdeen and Edgewood areas; this unit represents the majority of the land area at APG. The third or oldest terrace identified at APG, QT3, is situated along the western and northern boundaries of APG. Collectively, the alluvial fill beneath these three different terraces at APG comprises the Talbot Formation.

Throughout the Pleistocene, the Susquehanna River has progressively downcut into the crystalline basement rock above the Fall Line and carved a well-defined river valley. This valley extends seaward, beneath Chesapeake Bay and beyond the limits of the Delmarva Peninsula. A complex drainage network of abandoned Pleistocene river courses exists because of erosion by the Susquehanna River into the Cretaceous and younger sediments. Three generations of the ancestral Susquehanna River system have been mapped beneath Chesapeake Bay and the southern Delmarva Peninsula (Colman et al., 1990). Pleistocene sediments present at APG are directly related to these previous Susquehanna River courses.

The gradual increase in sediment grain size with decreasing depth in an estuarine unit underlying QT2 represents the progressive filling, and corresponding movement down the Susquehanna River valley, of the sediment source closer to the point of deposition. Eventually, the river progrades down the valley, beyond the limits of the filled area. The gravels that are present at the base of the upper fluvial deposits (unit C) correspond to the point at which the river's mouth begins forming a series of short-lived distributary mouth bar channels in a freshwater deltaic setting. These transitory channels are rapidly abandoned, in favor of a single trunk channel, as the head of the delta system progresses down the bay. Subsequently, the main channel of the river may begin to meander laterally and the flood plain to aggrade vertically; the deposition of overbank or vertical accretion deposits of fine-grained sediments become the dominant depositional process. This filling process is evident today in tributaries in the headwaters of the Gunpowder River (west of Edgewood Peninsula).

Because of the age and coarse nature of the terrace sediments, it is difficult to obtain pollen or other organic materials to accurately date these deposits. Weathering and oxidation have destroyed the organic materials that may have been present in these sediments. Carbon-14 dating of organic sediments from the estuarine unit at the UNDEX site has defined the age of the QT2 as being older than 45 000 years. Owens (1969) reported similar results from dating woody sediments from the base of the Talbot Formation. This age is generally considered the upper limit of the conventional radiocarbon method.

Another dating technique that has been successfully used at APG is amino acid dating of shells from the estuarine unit below the QT2 surface. Detailed information on this dating technique is described by Wehmiller (1993). In summary, this dating technique measures the ratio of one form of an amino acid in certain species of mollusks to an altered form of the amino acid following the death of the host mollusk. This ratio has been calibrated to other dating methods and geologic formations where time boundaries are more precisely known. Amino acid dating of shell samples from the UNDEX site defines the age of the estuarine unit beneath the QT2 as being approximately between 80 000 and 120 000 yr (i.e., Sangamon age or Oxygen-Isotope stage 5). The estuarine unit below the QT2 occurs beneath much of the APG area.

Amino acid racemization ages were obtained on shell samples from deposits under the Edgewood Peninsula. These dates suggest the possibility of an older Susquehanna River sequence at APG. The ages for these shells imply deposition of the estuarine sediments sometime before 300 000 yr B.P. (Oxygen-Isotope stage 9 or older), perhaps during the interglacial period, which is between the classical Kansan and Illinoian glacial periods.

The age of the uppermost terrace or QT3 is unknown without pollen or fossils to accurately date this fluvial unit. Based on its elevation and position compared to other terraces at APG, the QT3 is the oldest terrace. Boring data support the older age for this terrace as the sediments beneath this surface are generally

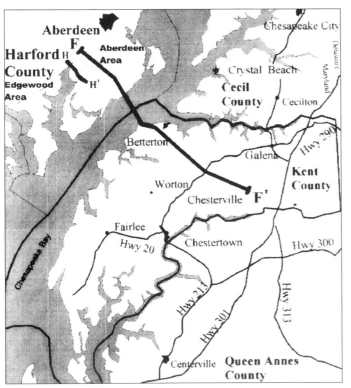

Figure 7A. Locations of cross sections depicted in Figures 7B (on following page) and 8.

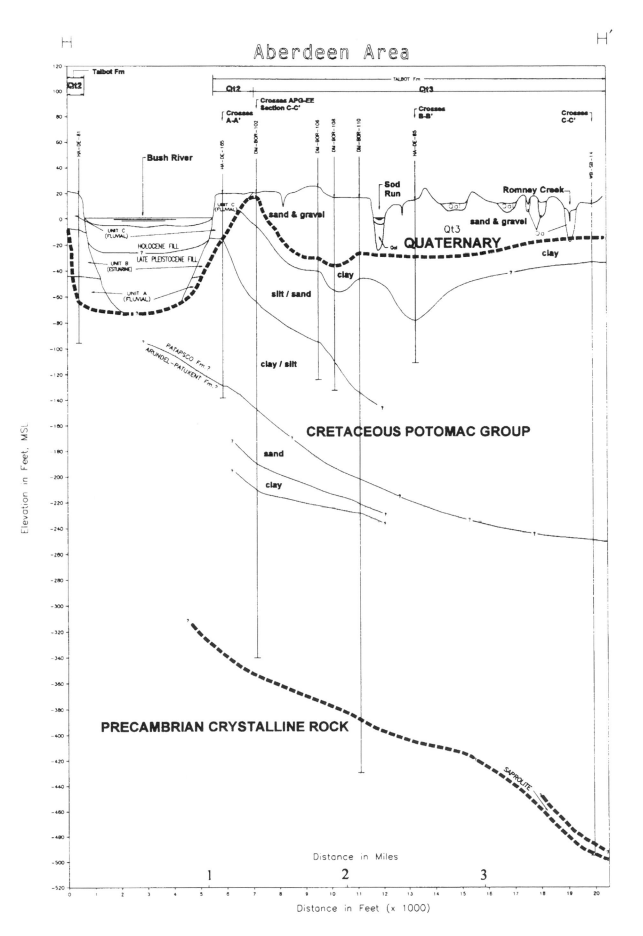

Figure 7B. Cross section H–H′ from Bush River onto Aberdeen area (from Dunbar et al., 1997).

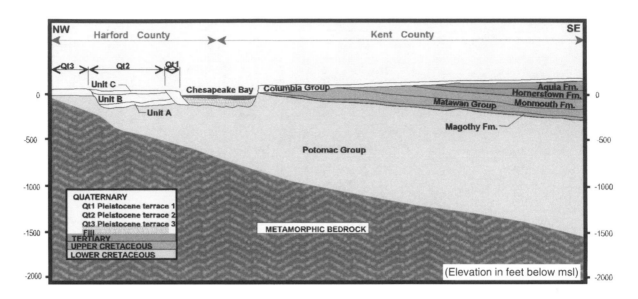

Figure 8. Generalized regional correlation from Aberdeen area across Chesapeake Bay into Kent County, Maryland (cross section F–F′ from Fig. 7A), approximately 18 miles long. MSL is mean sea level.

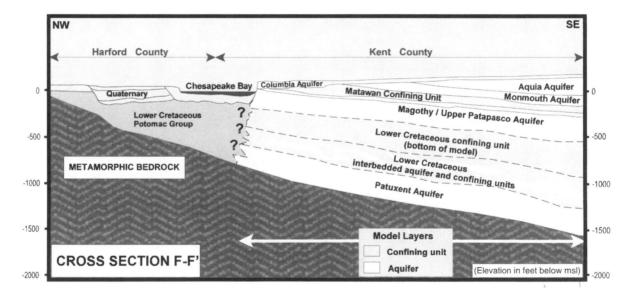

Figure 9. Details of aquifers dipping southeastward from APG (cross section F–F′ from Fig. 7A).

more oxidized. Additionally, boring data often identify the presence of ironstone lenses within this upper terrace, further indicating prolonged exposure and higher degree of weathering. The age of the QT3 thus is assumed to be early or middle Pleistocene.

SIGNIFICANCE OF THE GEOLOGIC CONCEPTUAL MODEL

This extensive regional study revealed three main aquifers, which are not continuous between the two peninsulas. The coarse-grained QT3 sediments form a major aquifer from 14 to 25 m thick along the western edge of the Aberdeen area. An aquifer of QT2, confined in the central part of the Aberdeen Peninsula, varies from lenses of permeable silty sands to impermeable clay lenses. One unit of QT2 acts as an aquitard. Permeable sandy aquifers in the Cretaceous can be correlated along strike, but are poorly connected laterally or vertically. Figure 9 shows the general relationship of APG strata with regional aquifers. Whitten et al. (1997) and Dunbar et al. (1997) give details on the distribution of these aquifers.

Members of the public may believe that geologic research at DoD facilities is based on systematic site study performed to progress toward a full understanding of regional trends and resulting risks to the biosphere. However, geologic research that addresses critical environmental issues at APG and other DoD military facilities is tied to SWMUs and their changing importance and significance. Large bodies of data may accumulate at DoD facilities about many sites, but seldom come to rest in the hands of a geology team for a systematic regional analysis and interpretation. Much of military geology is site specific and occurs at the intersection between what the facilities' managers must do to respond to evolving regulations or changing orders, and what the geologists require to answer the questions about the subsurface geologic controls on the movement of water.

This study is an example of military geology and development of a geologic conceptual model with defensible data that had not previously been considered in a unified manner. The refined model resulting from this study provides a basis for defining Cretaceous and Quaternary aquifers beneath the installation and determining the extent to which aquifers might be isolated or hydrologically connected. Understanding the depositional environments allowed development of an explanation in the conceptual model for the discontinuous nature of major water-bearing units. The model became a tool, used by facility managers to provide rational, scientific explanations to area residents about their environmental security. The model provides a stronger basis for remediation decisions and long-term monitoring, as well as a technical foundation for allaying the concerns of residents across the bay and in surrounding counties. The model, in the hands of competent managers and scientists, makes Pleistocene sea-level changes relevant to people who must select among remediation alternatives in an area where past and present military use may impact daily human use of the land beyond the installation boundaries.

APPENDIX: ADDITIONAL DATA SOURCES

Additional sources of data for Aberdeen area

Derryberry, N.A., Miller, S.P., and Breland, P.L., 1990, Resource Conservation Recovery Act facility assessment, other areas: Vicksburg, Mississippi, U.S. Army Engineer Waterways Experiment Station, draft report, 1000 p.

McMaster, B.N., Bonds, J.D., Hendry, C.D., Williamson, D.F., Holly, J.B., Wiese, J.H., Marsh, J.D., Jones, C.F., Denahan, S.A., Govre, K.C., and Regenatraif, A.A., 1981, Installation assessment of Aberdeen Proving Ground–Aberdeen area: Gainesville, Florida, Environmental Science and Engineering, Inc., Report No. 301, 188 p. (prepared for U.S. Army Toxic and Hazardous Materials Agency, Environmental and Safety Division, Aberdeen Proving Ground, Maryland).

Miller, S.P., Derryberry, N.A., Breland, P.L., and Wade, R., 1990, Michaelsville landfill hydrogeologic assessment: Vicksburg, Mississippi, U.S. Army Engineer Waterways Experiment Station, draft report, 142 p.

U.S. Army Corps of Engineers, 1980, Hydrogeology of Michaelsville and Phillips Army Airfield landfills, Aberdeen Proving Ground, Maryland: Baltimore, Maryland, U.S. Army Corps of Engineers District, Baltimore, 6 p.

U.S. Army Corps of Engineers, 1983, An evaluation of existing wells and water supply potential for Aberdeen Proving Ground, Maryland: Baltimore, Maryland, U.S. Army Corps of Engineers District, Baltimore, 69 p.

Whitten, C.B., Miller, S.P., and Derryberry, N.A., 1992, Aberdeen area fire training area, hydrologic assessment, Aberdeen Proving Ground: Vicksburg, Mississippi, U.S. Army Engineer Waterways Experiment Station, Technical Report GL-92-20, 325 p.

Woodward-Clyde Federal Services, 1996, Conceptual geologic interpretation for Aberdeen area, Aberdeen Proving Ground: Gaithersburg, Maryland, Woodward-Clyde Federal Services, draft report, 29 p.

Additional sources of data for Edgewood area

General Physics Corporation, 1993, Final report, Shallow and deep groundwater monitoring wells, Nike site, Aberdeen Proving Ground: Columbia, Maryland, Environmental Engineering Division, Contract No. DAAD05-89-D-0060, GP-R-71193048, APG-ER-013, 69 p.

General Physics Corporation, 1995, Shallow groundwater monitoring well installation report for Cluster 18, 35, and 36 of the Bush River study area, Aberdeen Proving Ground: Edgewood, Maryland, Environmental Engineering Division, Contract No. DAAD05-93-D-7053, GP-R-71195031, APG-ER-011, 217 p.

Ham, L.K., Sears, L.N., Philips, S.C., and Tenbus, F.J., 1991a, Hydrogeologic data for Carroll Island, Aberdeen Proving Ground, Maryland: Towson, Maryland, U.S. Geological Survey, Open-File Report 89-388, 105 p.

Ham, L.K., Tenbus, F.J., Sears, L.N., and Philips, S.C., 1991b, Hydrogeologic data for Graces Quarters, Aberdeen Proving Ground, Maryland: Towson, Maryland, U.S. Geological Survey, Open-File Report 91-71, 68 p.

Hughes, W.B., 1991, Application of marine seismic profiling to a ground water contamination study, Aberdeen Proving Ground, Maryland: Ground Water Monitoring Review, Winter, p. 97–102.

Lorah, M.M., and Vroblesky, D.A., 1989, Inorganic and organic ground-water chemistry in the Canal Creek area of Aberdeen Proving Ground, Maryland: Towson, Maryland, U.S. Geological Survey Water Resources Investigations Report 89-4022, 97 p.

U.S. Army Environmental Hygiene Agency, 1996, Geohydrogeologic Study No. 38-26-1253-90, Resource Conservation Recovery Act facility investigation, Nike missile battery site, Aberdeen Proving Ground, Maryland: Aberdeen Proving Ground, Maryland, U.S. Army Environmental Hygiene Agency, 50 p.

REFERENCES CITED

Bandoian, C.A., and Waldrop, R.T., 1985, Hydrogeology of the proposed Perryman power plant: Environmental Resources Management, Inc., for the Power Plant Siting Program, State of Maryland Deprtment of Natural Resources, p. 1–87.

Cleaves, E.T., 1968, Piedmont and coastal plain geology along the Susquehanna Aqueduct, Baltimore to Aberdeen, Maryland: Baltimore, Maryland Geologic Survey, Report of Investigation, n. 8, 45 p.

Colman, S.M., Halka, J.P., Hobbs, C.H., III, Mixon, R.B., and Foster, D.S., 1990, Ancient channels of the Susquehanna River beneath Chesapeake Bay and the Delmarva Peninsula: Geological Society of America Bulletin, v. 102, p. 1268–1279.

Drummond, D.D., and Blomquist, J.D., 1993, Hydrogeology, water-supply potential, and water quality of the coastal plain aquifers of Harford County, Maryland: Baltimore, Maryland Geological Survey, Report of Investigations, n. 58, 160 p.

Dunbar, J.B., Blaes, M., Snartzel, S.M., Whitten, C.B., and Miller, S.P., 1997, Geology and geomorphology of Aberdeen Proving Ground, Aberdeen, Maryland: Vicksburg, Mississippi, U.S. Army Engineer Waterways Experiment Station, Open-File Report CEWES-GGY-97-1, 55 p.

Miller, B.L., Mathews, E.B., Bibbins, A.B., and Little, H.P., 1917, Geologic atlas of the United States, Tolchester folio, Maryland: Washington, D.C., U.S. Geological Survey, n. 204, scale 1:62 500.

Oliveros, J.P., and Vroblesky, D.A., 1989a, Hydrogeology of the Canal Creek area, Aberdeen Proving Ground, Maryland: Towson, Maryland, U.S. Geological Survey, Water Resources Investigations Report 89-4021, 50 p.

Oliveros, J.P., and Vroblesky, D.A., 1989b, Hydrogeologic data for the Canal Creek area, Aberdeen Proving Ground, Maryland, April 1986–March 1988: Towson, Maryland, U.S. Geological Survey, Open-File Report 89-387, 71 p.

Owens, J.P., 1969, Coastal plain rocks of Harford County, *in* The geology of Harford County, Maryland: Baltimore, Maryland, Department of Natural Resources, p. 77–103.

Owens, J.P., and Denny, C.S., 1979, Upper Cenozoic deposits of the central Delmarva Peninsula, Delaware and Maryland: Washington, D.C., U.S. Geological Survey Professional Paper 1067-A, 28 p.

Richards, H.G., 1948, Studies on the subsurface geology and paleontology of the Atlantic Coastal Plain: Philadelphia Academy of Natural Sciences Proceedings, v. 100, p. 39–76.

Rosholt, J.M., Colman, S.M., Stuiver, M., Damson, P.E., Naeser, C.W., Liddicoat, J.C., Machette, M.N., and Pierce, K.L., 1991, Dating methods applicable to the Quaternary, *in* Morrison, R.B., ed., Quaternary nonglacial geology: Conterminous U.S., Boulder, Colorado, Geological Society of America, Geology of North America: K-2, p. 45–74.

Southwick, D.L., and Owens, J.P., 1968, Geologic map of Harford County: Baltimore, Maryland Geological Survey, scale 1:62 500.

U.S. Geological Survey (USGS), 1967, Engineering geology of the northeast corridor, Washington, D.C., to Boston, Massachusetts, coastal plain and surficial deposits: U.S. Geological Survey Miscellaneous Investigations Map I-514-B.

Vroblesky, D.A., and Fleck, W.B., 1991, Hydrogeologic framework of the coastal plain of Maryland, Delaware, and the District of Columbia: U.S. Geological Survey Professional Paper 1404-E, 45 p.

Wehmiller, J.F., 1993, Applications of organic geochemistry for Quaternary research, chapter 36, *in* England, M.H., and Macko, S.A., eds., Organic geochemistry: New York, Plenum Press, p. 755–783.

Whitten, C.B., Swartzel, S.M., Miller, S.P., and Blough K., 1997, Conceptual hydrogeologic model of Aberdeen Proving Ground–Aberdeen area: Vicksburg, Mississippi, USAE Waterways Experiment Station, Technical Report GL-97-16, 131 p.

MANUSCRIPT ACCEPTED BY THE SOCIETY OCTOBER 27, 2000

Geological Society of America
Reviews in Engineering Geology, Volume XIV
2001

Geoenvironmental factors in the regeneration of military airfields in Great Britain

Ronald N.E. Blake

Faculty of Construction and the Environment, The Nottingham Trent University,
Burton Street, Nottingham NG1 4BU, United Kingdom

ABSTRACT

Britain is littered with active and disused military airfields, arguably the most distinctive feature of its twentieth-century defenses. More than 850 airfields were active during World War II, covering about 162 000 hectares or 0.7% of the national land area. Today, fewer than 50 remain active, the majority having been transferred to ground defense roles, civil flying, agriculture, and other land uses.

There is a strong spatial association between the leading air bases and well-drained Middle Jurassic limestone, Upper Cretaceous chalk, and Quaternary fluvioglacial sands and gravels. Peacetime consolidation at a dwindling number of key bases has intensified impacts on these permeable lithologies, which are vulnerable to groundwater contamination, soil degradation, and erosion of landscapes rich in ecological and archaeological heritage.

Demolition for agriculture has been uncoordinated and incomplete. Alternative uses include laboratories, prisons, and motor racing, many introduced without environmental controls. Asset stripping of valuable infrastructure has become a public issue since the ending of the Cold War.

Disused airfields are now the foci of comprehensive regeneration schemes. Options include mineral extraction, afforestation, new towns, and runway conversion to airports. Decision making involves careful assessment of geological resources, geologic hazards, and available remediation technologies within the framework of a systematic environmental audit.

Britain's "airfield problem" is the unique product of a densely settled countryside, a rich aeronautical history, and an imperfect planning system. Experience gained trying to solve this problem has many international applications.

INTRODUCTION

The impact of military airfields on the environment is a characteristically British problem, yet one of increasing international significance (Childs, 1998). For historical and strategic reasons, Great Britain has an exceptional concentration of airfield infrastructure, much of which is no longer needed for defense and has now been switched to civil aviation or redeveloped for non-aeronautical purposes.

While few countries can match Britain's airfields in density, there are many regions on both sides of the former Iron Curtain where the localized impact of large airbases is acute and where British planning practice could be applied (Jauhiainen, 1997). By virtue of their large numbers and diverse environmental settings, the airfields of Britain provide a wealth of land-use experience in the form of individual case studies and thematic reviews.

Britain's "airfield problem" is rooted in the massive expansion of air capability during the 1930s and World War II

Blake, R.N.E., 2001, Geoenvironmental factors in the regeneration of military airfields in Great Britain, *in* Ehlen, J., and Harmon, R.S., eds., The Environmental Legacy of Military Operations: Boulder, Colorado, Geological Society of America Reviews in Engineering Geology, v. XIV, p. 203–219.

(1939–1945). Their substantial engineering legacy was responsible for the disproportionate contribution by the Royal Air Force (RAF) to the defense of Western Europe under the auspices of the North Atlantic Treaty Organization (NATO) from the late 1940s onward. Successive waves of air base decommissioning consequent upon new weapons, efficiencies in training, and détente between the Superpowers have created the phenomenon of the ubiquitous disused airfield. Public awareness of the environmental and socioeconomic implications of air base closure has been heightened by the recent departure of the majority of United States Air Force (USAF) units from British soil.

An impression of Britain's wartime airfield distribution is embodied in Figure 1, which juxtaposes the high density achieved at the historic peak with the vastness of the western United States. The process of expansion, contraction, and transformation has been played out within the confines of a long-industrialized and intensively farmed island nation founded on a famously diverse geology (Stamp, 1960). In Britain neither active nor disused air bases can be regarded as of marginal public concern, for they are locked into a fundamental competition for some of the world's most productive land (Best, 1981; Stamp, 1962) and are perfect examples of "contested places" as recognized in current planning debates (Gallent et al., 1999a, 1999b).

Despite an expanding literature on the architecture, engineering, and construction of British airfields (Francis, 1996; Higham, 1998), there is still no comprehensive reference on the all-important relationship between reuse and terrestrial resources.

AIMS AND DEFINITIONS

The central aim of this chapter is to describe the physical impacts of military airfields on the environment, with a focus on geological resources and geologic hazards. To complement the technical analysis, an appreciation is made of the many statutory, commercial, and voluntary bodies involved in managing functional change during the life cycle of airfields.

"Geoenvironmental factors" refer in this context to all considerations in the planning process that relate to: (1) the influence of lithology on site selection and construction, (2) rock-dependent land-use controls (e.g., soils, minerals, hydrology, landscape character), and (3) geotechnical constraints on redevelopment and reuse, whether natural or induced.

"Regeneration" covers the whole spectrum of environmental improvements including reclamation, restoration, redevelopment, restructuring, rehabilitation, renewal, and conservation. These overlapping terms are used selectively throughout the chapter to suit particular contexts and to avoid repetition. While the chapter is essentially about disused airfields, references are necessarily made to the active phase in their history when infrastructure was being developed and landscape disturbance taking place. Currently active airfields are also closely observed because they are the regeneration sites of tomorrow.

The terms "airfield," "aerodrome," "air base," and "(air) station" are used interchangeably, and the subtle distinctions between them are not rehearsed (Blake et al., 1984). "Abandoned," "decommissioned," "defunct," "disused," "idle," "redundant," and "vacant" provide descriptive alternatives that are largely self-explanatory.

For the purpose of discussion, "Britain," "Great Britain," and "United Kingdom" (UK) are regarded as the same geographical area (although Northern Ireland is strictly not part of Britain and the Isle of Man is not constitutionally part of the UK). Figures 1 and 2 depict the fullest interpretation of British home territory, minus the Channel Islands (off France), which have no air defense significance. "The war" (and "wartime"), unqualified, refer to World War II.

To assist the reader wishing to visit particular airfields, or to trace them on medium-scale topographical maps, an Ordnance Survey (OS) National Grid Reference (NGR) is supplied for all sites described in the chapter to a resolution of 500 m. Airfields mentioned in passing and which are not included in Table 1 are pinpointed by the appropriate grid reference in squared brackets.

AIRFIELD DEVELOPMENT AND IMPACT

The scale and chronology of airfield development hold the key to an understanding of their environmental impact and regeneration potential. World War II expansion and post-war contraction represent the two critical phases in airfield evolution, which need outlining as a preamble to geoenvironmental appreciation.

Wartime expansion

In 1945 the UK contained an estimated 856 military airfields in active use, on standby, or nearing completion (Blake, 1989). Of these, about 250 were inherited from the pre-war period, comprising about 120 RAF and Royal Navy (RN) air stations and about 130 requisitioned civil airports and smaller aerodromes. Both sectors included airfields dating from World War I (1914-1918), e.g., Biggin Hill, Kent [TQ415605] and Croydon, Surrey [TQ302632], plus a few, e.g., Farnborough, Hampshire [SU860540], which had originated in the pioneer period before 1914.

It has been calculated that Britain's wartime airfields contained enough concrete for a motorway from London to Peking (Smith, 1989). By 1945 there were 475 aerodromes (55%) equipped with hard runways, while 275 had all-grass landing areas, 63 had steel-clad strips, and 43 were flying-boat bases, factories, or moorings. The 813 land-based airfields (the sum of the first three categories) obviously had the greatest direct impact on geology, although "marine" airfields undoubtedly did some damage to the littoral environment.

A total of 162 000 hectares (ha) were taken for airfields, overwhelmingly at the expense of agricultural land, which a nation under blockade could ill afford. This represented 0.7% of the UK's land, equivalent to the County of Hertfordshire to the north of London. In several counties, e.g., Oxfordshire and Suffolk, coverage by airfields exceeded 2%, and in hundreds of market towns and villages the social and economic impact of the air force presence was considerable (Smith, 1989). Over one hundred stations were assigned to U.S., Canadian, other British Commonwealth, and anti-Axis European air forces during the campaign (Freeman, 1984).

The average size of a "paved" aerodrome (typically designed with three intersecting runways; see Fig. 3) was 262 ha, while the combined average for the grass and steel types was 108 ha. Class "A" bomber airfields, e.g., Marham, Norfolk [TF725085], invariably exceeded the larger figure and these were the preferred locations for post-war RAF (and USAF) development.

Post-war contraction

Within ten years of Victory in Europe (VE-day, 8 May 1945) the number of active air bases had fallen to about 180, the pre-war stations generally being retained because of their robust infrastructure and good road communications (Appleton, 1962). Following deployment of the jet V-force (to deliver nuclear weapons), numbers were reduced to about 100 by the mid-1960s, but thereafter the closure rate slowed (Wynn, 1994). By 1975 there were 85 still active and by 1985, 75 (Table 2). Today, the 49 active military flying establishments represent a mere 6% of the wartime list. Understandably, no virgin site has needed to be acquired since 1945 or, put another way, every current air base has a wartime history.

The latest phase in the rundown was heralded by the "Options for Change" government statement of 1990 (House of Commons, 1991) which outlined Britain's response to the ending of the Cold War (the "peace dividend"). Reductions in frontline ("strike") bases took place first, followed by rationalizations in training and aircraft servicing ("support") (Ministry of Defence, 1994). One exceptional reopening—Colerne, Wiltshire [ST805715]—accounts for the presence in Figure 2 of 76 airfield symbols.

In 1998, a total of 16 575 ha were held by the Ministry of Defence (MoD) for active flying. This figure is closer to 10% of the wartime holding as postwar airfields are large by UK historical standards (average size, 340 ha). The areas transferred to "civil aerodromes" (Civil Aviation Authority, 1996) and to "other military uses" (e.g., radar, storage, ground training, and logistics) are more difficult to estimate because of partial disposals and agricultural tenancies. A considered guess puts the share of all 1945 airfield land still used for aeronautical and ancillary defense purposes at about 25%.

Figure 1. Pattern of World War II airfields in the United Kingdom compared with the landmass of the western part of the United States of America. Source: Blake, 1989.

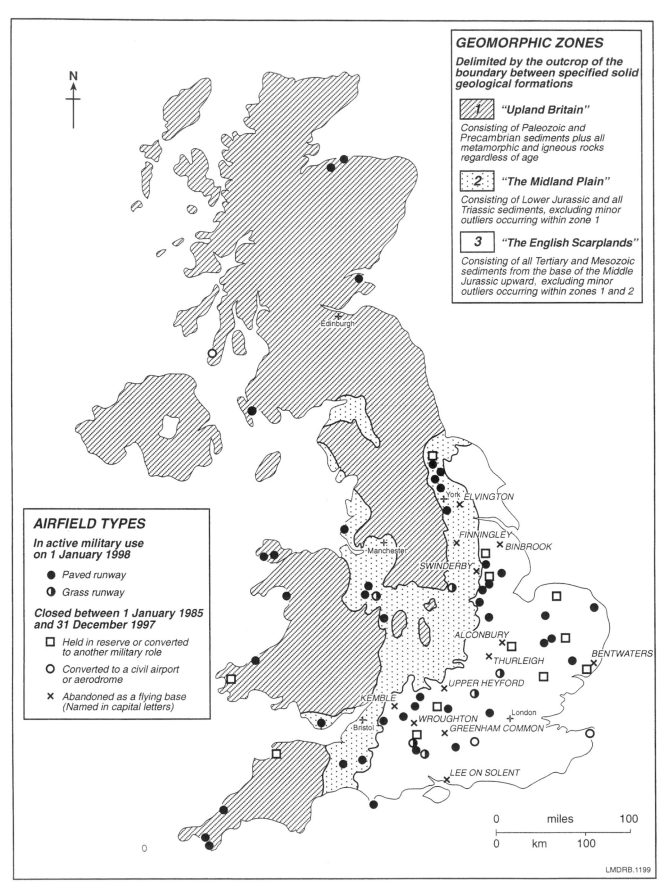

GEOMORPHIC ZONES

Delimited by the outcrop of the boundary between specified solid geological formations

| 1 | "Upland Britain" |

Consisting of Paleozoic and Precambrian sediments plus all metamorphic and igneous rocks regardless of age

| 2 | "The Midland Plain" |

Consisting of Lower Jurassic and all Triassic sediments, excluding minor outliers occurring within zone 1

| 3 | "The English Scarplands" |

Consisting of all Tertiary and Mesozoic sediments from the base of the Middle Jurassic upward, excluding minor outliers occurring within zones 1 and 2

AIRFIELD TYPES

In active military use on 1 January 1998

● Paved runway

◑ Grass runway

Closed between 1 January 1985 and 31 December 1997

☐ Held in reserve or converted to another military role

○ Converted to a civil airport or aerodrome

✕ Abandoned as a flying base (Named in capital letters)

Edinburgh

York ELVINGTON

FINNINGLEY
BINBROOK

Manchester

SWINDERBY

ALCONBURY

THURLEIGH
BENTWATERS

UPPER HEYFORD

KEMBLE

London

WROUGHTON
GREENHAM COMMON

Bristol

LEE ON SOLENT

| 0 | miles | 100 |

| 0 | km | 100 |

LMDRB.1199

Figure 2. Distribution of currently active and recently deactivated military airfields in the United Kingdom in relation to broad "geomorphic zones." Source: Stamp, 1960; Airfield Research Group.

TABLE 1. GEOENVIRONMENTAL DATA FOR 12 UNITED KINGDOM MILITARY AIRFIELDS DISPOSED OF OR AWAITING DISPOSAL SINCE THE "OPTIONS OF CHANGE" DEFENSE REVIEW (1990)

Name of airfield	Administrative county	Location (OS/NGR)	Elevation (meters above sea level)	Surface geology [†]	Agricultural land quality grade [§]
Alconbury*	Cambridgeshire	TL210765	49	Quaternary till [Upper Jurassic clay]	3
Bentwaters*	Suffolk	TM355535	26	Quaternary sand and gravel [Pliocene Crag]	2
Binbrook	Lincolnshire	TF190960	115	Upper Cretaceous chalk	2
Greenham Common*	Berkshire	SU500645	122	Quaternary sand and gravel [Eocene sand]	4
Elvington	North Yorkshire	SE670480	15	Quaternary lacustrine sand [Triassic sandstone]	3
Finningley	South Yorkshire	SK660990	17	Quaternary sand and gravel [Triassic sandstone]	3
Kemble*	Wiltshire	ST960965	132	Middle Jurassic limestone	3
Lee on Solent	Hampshire	SU560020	9	Quaternary sand and gravel [Eocene sand]	3
Swinderby	Lincolnshire	SK885620	17	Quaternary sand and gravel [Lower Jurassic clay]	3
Thurleigh	Bedfordshire	TL040600	90	Quaternary till [Upper Jurassic clay]	2
Upper Heyford*	Oxfordshire	SP515265	134	Middle Jurassic limestone	3
Wroughton	Wiltshire	SU140790	207	Upper Cretaceous chalk	2

* Former United States Air Force bases.
[†] Solid rock lying beneath drift deposits is indicated in squared brackets.
[§] Source: Ministry of Agriculture, Fisheries and Food, 1966-74, Agricultural land classification maps, scale 1:63 360. Agricultural land in England and Wales is graded on a scale from 1 (the best) to 5 (the worst). Grade 2 represents "good general-purpose arable land," grade 3 represents "average quality mixed arable and pasture land", and grade 4 represents "below average quality grazing land." Grades 1 (horticulture) and 5 (rough grazing) are not represented in this survey.

Transatlantic perspective

By international standards Britain has a small land area of only 243 775 km², being less than half the size of France and one-fortieth the size of either Canada or the United States. The United Kingdom has approximately the same surface area as the state of Colorado and its latitudinal span could be accommodated within several pairs of states (Fig. 1). Britain possesses no flat, arid wilderness such as are available in the United States (Neal, 1998), and all airfield development has therefore taken place within mature countryside (Hoskins, 1955). According to federal statistics (U.S. General Accounting Office, 1995), the average size of a recently decommissioned air base in the United States is about 3350 acres, roughly four times the British figure.

Britain's current population density of 237 persons per km² (1991 Census) is nine times that of the United States and most of its active and recently decommissioned airfields are located in the administrative counties of "Middle England" where relatively fast rates of economic development and household formation are being recorded. It is against the backdrop of a crowded, fertile, and cherished landscape that the evolving impact of airfields is elucidated below.

GEOMORPHIC ZONES AND AIRFIELD LOCATION

The location of military airfields in Britain is strongly influenced by the nation's geomorphology, which itself is derived from a distinctive sequence of geological formations. This rela-

tionship is crucial to the discussion, for it assists an understanding of how the pattern of alternative land uses on airfields has evolved in relation to the different opportunities and constraints afforded by contrasting geoenvironments.

Broadly, the main physical components of Britain's landscape are aligned on a northeast-southwest trending axis, with the oldest geological material facing the Atlantic Ocean and the youngest material facing the mainland of Europe. Three "geomorphic zones" may be recognized at a first level of subdivision (Fig. 2), differentiated by shadings chosen to emphasise the older formations. Against this backdrop the 76 military airfields are plotted, comprising 49 still active at the time of writing and 27 closed to regular flying since the end of 1984 (the approximate beginning of NATO-Soviet demilitarization).

Active airfields are subdivided into "paved" and "all-grass," the latter generally imposing fewer regeneration problems. Recently disused airfields (those closed between 1 January 1985 and 31 December 1997) are also subdivided, into those now performing other military roles (twelve), those adapted for civil flying (three), and those that have become the foci of major regeneration initiatives (twelve). The geomorphic character of each zone, together with its current airfield content, merits closer examination.

Upland Britain

Defined here as the solid outcrop of Britain's Precambrian and Paleozoic sediments, together with all metamorphic and igneous

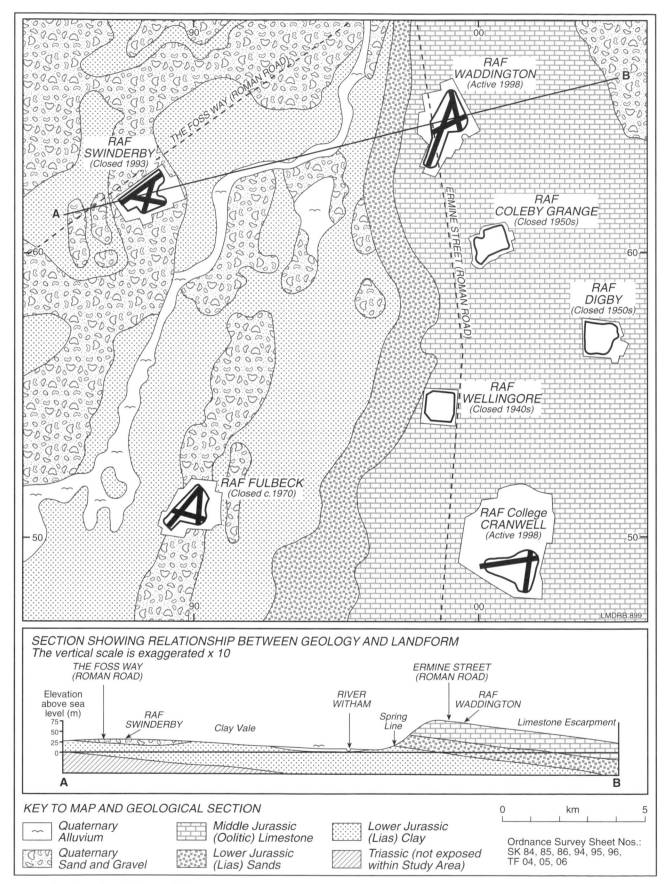

KEY TO MAP AND GEOLOGICAL SECTION

Quaternary Alluvium	Middle Jurassic (Oolitic) Limestone	Lower Jurassic (Lias) Clay
Quaternary Sand and Gravel	Lower Jurassic (Lias) Sands	Triassic (not exposed within Study Area)

Ordnance Survey Sheet Nos.:
SK 84, 85, 86, 94, 95, 96,
TF 04, 05, 06

Figure 3. Siting of World War II airfields in relation to the surface geology of a part of south Lincolnshire, England. Source: British Geological Survey, 1:50 000 scale geological maps, sheets 114, Lincoln (1973) and 127 Grantham (1996); Blake et al., 1984.

TABLE 2. GEOLOGICAL SITING OF SECOND WORLD WAR, RECENTLY ACTIVE, AND CURRENTLY ACTIVE MILITARY AIRFIELDS IN THE UNITED KINGDOM

Geological outcrop type	Land area (%)	Airfields								
		World War II, 1939–45			1985			1998		
		No	%	LQ	No	%	LQ	No	%	LQ
Quaternary sands and gravels	6.9	147	18.1	2.6	16	21.3	3.1	10	20.4	3.0
Quaternary till	30.6	267	32.8	1.1	12	16.0	0.5	6	12.2	0.4
All other drift deposits	16.9	141	17.3	1.0	13	17.3	1.0	9	18.4	1.1
Upper Cretaceous chalk	3.8	62	7.6	2.0	11	14.7	3.9	7	14.3	3.8
Middle Jurassic limestone	2.2	62	7.6	3.5	10	13.3	6.0	7	14.3	6.5
All other solid rocks	39.5	134	16.5	0.4	13	17.3	0.4	10	20.4	0.5
	100.0	813	100.0	—	75	100.0	—	49	100.0	—

outcrops regardless of age, this zone accounts for more than two-thirds (68%) of the UK land area. It represents the nation's hardest and most tectonically distorted rocks and is broadly coextensive with the highest, most rugged, and least hospitable terrain. Except for Triassic outliers of limited extent, chiefly attributable to downfaulting, the "uplands" comprise all of Wales, Scotland, Northern Ireland, the Isle of Man, the Pennines of northern England, and the Devon-Cornwall peninsula of England's southwest region. Three upstanding inliers pierce the Triassic of the English central midlands. The mantle of Quaternary "drift" (the British term for glacial, periglacial, and postglacial material) is 52%, somewhat less than in either of the other two zones. Drift deposits consist predominantly of hill peat and glacial till (Boulder Clay), the latter mantling the lower landscapes.

Eleven military airfields (22%) survive in the upland zone, seven of which are sited on drift deposits in low-lying coastal pockets. Figure 2 confirms the overwhelming coastal orientation, with small clusters on Anglesey in north Wales, on the Lizard peninsula of west Cornwall, and flanking the Moray Firth in northeast Scotland. Those sited directly on solid rock fall mainly in Cornwall, which is virtually drift-free, having escaped Quaternary glaciation. Only three airfields within the zone have been closed since the mid-1980s: Chivenor, north Devon [SS495345], the last operational station to occupy Holocene alluvium; Machrihanish, Strathclyde [NR665225], sited on raised beach deposits; and Brawdy, Dyfed, in southwest Wales [SM850250], sited on Paleozoic rock.

There is no comprehensive airfield regeneration scheme within the upland zone because all three of the last-mentioned bases have been switched to other defense roles or civil flying. All currently active and recently closed airfields are of the paved runway type because natural smooth landing surfaces are rare. Due to relative remoteness, adaptation for public-sector purposes has prevailed over commercial redevelopment.

The Midland Plain

This zone separates the nation's oldest and youngest lithostratigraphic formations. It is defined here as the "sub-drift" surface of all Triassic and Lower Jurassic sediments, running northeast-southwest through central England and forming an almost continuous landscape of moderate attractiveness to airfields. Only 9% of the national land surface falls within this zone which is characterized by: (1) the landlocked conurbation of Birmingham; (2) the heavily industrialized estuarine lowlands around Bristol, Cardiff, Liverpool, and Teeside; and (3) the extensive coalfields of South Yorkshire and Nottinghamshire. Almost two-thirds (63%) of the zone is covered by drift, primarily glacial till.

Currently, 14 military airfields (29%) are active in the zone, overwhelmingly assigned to training and technical support roles, which reflects their proximity to the motor engineering services and universities of central England. The principal airfield cluster occupies the drift-strewn Vale of York, e.g., Linton-on-Ouse [SE490615], where airplane training is concentrated. A secondary cluster is located in Shropshire (between Manchester and the Welsh massif) where the emphasis is on helicopter training, e.g., Shawbury [SJ550225]. The UK's premier aircraft engineering center is located at St. Athan, near Cardiff in South Wales [ST005685]. Only two "combat-ready" bases occupy the Midland Plain today, namely RAF Leeming, Yorkshire [SE305890], and Royal Naval Air Station Yeovilton, Somerset [ST550235], which command the north and south extremities, respectively.

The zone encompasses three (of the 12) "regeneration" airfields resulting from post-Cold-War decommissioning, all located in the Humber region within easy reach of the Great North Road (highway A1), e.g., Swinderby, Lincolnshire (Fig. 3).

The English Scarplands

The bulk of Britain's non-upland terrain comprises the outcrops of the Middle Jurassic, Upper Jurassic, Cretaceous, and Tertiary systems, which together form a coherent peneplain falling entirely within England (Fig. 2). Almost a quarter (23%) of Britain's landscape falls within this zone, which is characterized by an alternation of calcareous escarpments and clay vales, locally diversified by sandstone ridges and river gaps. A drift cover of 56% is slightly less than in the Midland Plain and consists largely of till north of the Thames and fluvioglacial sands and gravels and plateau gravels more widely.

Arable farming predominates, with closely spaced market towns and villages completing the landscape beyond the tentacles of Greater London. Twenty-four (49%) of the UK's currently active military airfields lie within the zone, with strong clusters of fighter-bomber bases in Lincolnshire and East Anglia and air transport bases in the Cotswolds and Wessex. More pertinently, nine (75%) of the current "regeneration" airfields are located on scarpland sites, testifying to the extent of post–Cold War defense cuts. Most of these stand on permeable lithologies, which are generally attractive to the redeveloper, but are also potential conduits for pollution. Among them are five defunct USAF bases (details in Table 1).

The majority (75%) of conversions to "other military uses" and civil flying are also in scarpland locations where further geoenvironmental problems can be anticipated in the longer term.

GEOLOGY AND AIRFIELD SITING

The image of wartime Britain as "a giant aircraft carrier anchored off northwest Europe" (Smith, 1989) has given rise to the myth that airfields could be located anywhere that was flat and sparsely inhabited. Over much of eastern and southern England there was an undeniable regularity in airfield spacing by 1945, but within many counties the subtle constraints of geology produced discernible clusters and lacunae. Lincolnshire is representative of this tendency and has notable gaps in its airfield distribution due to high water table in some areas and hilliness in others (Blake, 1981; Blake et al., 1984). The relatively high airfield density on the "Lincoln Edge" (limestone plateau) compared with the Vale of Belvoir (clay lowland) immediately to its west is illustrated in Figure 3.

General principles

Surface geology is a logical starting point for the environmental assessment of airfields, as this had a direct influence on construction. Geological conditions at greater depth and in the surrounding area also need to be borne in mind, particularly when formulating regeneration plans within a wider land-use framework. For practical reasons this review is confined to surface geological characteristics, but it is acknowledged that every site has geoenvironmental peculiarities not evident from published geological maps (Table 1).

The primary desiderata for constructing a competent aircraft operating surface can be summarized as: (1) high load-bearing capacity; (2) ease of excavation ("diggability"); (3) permeability; (4) low diurnal and seasonal temperature changes; (5) freedom from faulting, sinkholes, and voids; and (6) rapid grass growth (Blake, 2000). Standard tests include the "Modulus of Subgrade Reaction" (*k*) and the "California Bearing Ratio" (CBR), which measure the degree of soil compaction and possible pavement failure on different prepared surfaces under different aircraft loadings (Ministry of Defence, Defence Works Services, 1994). In essence, the ideal ground conditions for both an operational

airfield and a regeneration plan are diggable-but-firm rocks, freedom from loose material, an absence of freeze-thaw effects, and consistently good drainage.

On a spectrum of rock types, the best airfield subgrades are coarse gravels followed by fine gravels, sands, limestones, sandstones, silts, clays, organic clays, and peat (the worst). To ascertain whether Britain's military airfields are positively correlated with hypothetically compliant lithologies, a comparison was made between geological maps and the distribution of airfields on key dates. Table 2 shows the geological distribution of active airfields during World War II, in 1985, and in 1998 across six pertinent lithologies and lithological groupings (lithotypes). Numbers and percentages are given for each date, together with a "location quotient" (LQ) to highlight the relative importance of each lithotype in geographical space and over time.

LQ is an index of attractiveness calculated in this exercise by dividing the percentage of airfields sited on a lithology by the percentage area occupied by that lithology. LQ has a neutral value of 1, higher values indicating that a particular lithotype has more airfields than might be expected from its surface area. To illustrate the principle, an LQ of 2 indicates an airfield density twice the national average while 0.5 indicates a density one-half the national average.

In reality most airfields occupy a single lithology, so for every case surveyed the central point of the main runway or grass landing area was taken as the geological signature. In the absence of published outcrop statistics for the UK, a 5-km grid containing 9751 sample points was used to establish the percentage area for each lithotype.

Favorable and unfavorable outcrops

On a national scale airfield siting has undergone noticeable changes since military aviation began before World War I. To defend London against German airships a number of early aerodromes were sited on Tertiary clays and Quaternary alluvium, which ultimately proved unsatisfactory. By contrast, airfields sited on Upper Cretaceous chalk, e.g., Manston, Kent [TR335665], survived beyond World War II and evolved into airports. Large chalk-based airfields are now grouped on Salisbury Plain, e.g., Boscombe Down, Wiltshire [SU180405], and around the Breckland subregion of East Anglia, e.g., Lakenheath, Suffolk [TL740820]. Chalk's LQ has almost doubled since 1945, rising from 2.0 to 3.8.

The other calcareous Mesozoic formation of significance to airfields is the Middle Jurassic (oolitic) limestone, which accounts for the enduring presence of large air bases in south Lincolnshire (see Fig. 3) and in the Cotswolds, e.g., Brize Norton, Oxfordshire [SP295060]. This outcrop, which represents slightly over 2% of the UK land surface, supported almost 8% of all wartime airfields (LQ of 3.5). Today, seven air bases are active on the Middle Jurassic, which bears the enhanced LQ of 6.5.

Approximately half (51%) of currently active military airfields are sited on Quaternary deposits. In wartime the proportion was 68%, but this slipped due to a progressive retreat from glacial till, which has inconsistent geotechnical properties (Gray, 1993). Quaternary sands and gravels of all kinds (fluvioglacial and plateau) have maintained a consistently high airfield quotient (of about 3.0) since 1945, whereas till has declined in attractiveness from 1.1 to 0.4. "Sand-and-gravel" airfields are now the largest geological group (ten) but "other drift deposits" collectively support almost as many airfields (nine). The latter include raised beach deposits and blown sand, both having very high concealed quotients, which reflects the paucity of level ground in the west and north of Britain (Institute of Geological Sciences, 1977).

Geological dividend

The 16 575 ha still held for active military airfields represents <0.1% of the UK land area. In addition, approximately 10 100 ha have been transferred to civil flying, other military uses, or redeveloped since the mid-1980s and are the "geological dividend" available for development, exploitation, or conservation. While by North American standards the 4425 ha covered by "regeneration" airfields (included within the 10 100 ha) looks insignificant in real estate terms, in relation to Britain's precious terrestrial resources and tightly regulated landscape, this "dividend" is of some political consequence.

Implicit in Table 2 is a decline in active airfields since 1985 of roughly a third (35%), more than half going to civil flying or other military uses. Examination of the six lithotypes reveals above-average closure rates on Quaternary sands and gravels and till, and below-average closures on the Middle Jurassic limestone and Upper Cretaceous chalk outcrops. Of the 12 "regeneration" airfields (Table 1), five (42%) have a sand and gravel "dividend," whereas the calcareous plateau sites have been released roughly in proportion to 1985 airfield stock.

GEOLOGY-RELATED PLANNING ISSUES

Runway protection

Civil aviation in post-war Britain has expanded almost exclusively from wartime sites. A number of regional airports, e.g., Glasgow Abbotsinch [NS480670], were established as conversions in the 1960s, but the main requirement today is for smaller "general aviation" centers (Pooley and Patel, 1998). The supply of jet-length runways now exceeds demand and when left idle for long periods this future transportation resource degrades. At Elvington (Fig. 4), a 1950s extension to the runway over made ground has started to warp, causing cracks and incipient damage to the concrete by weeds (author's fieldwork).

At Burtonwood, Cheshire [SJ570910], concrete areas became so badly affected by fault reactivation from coal mining subsidence that plans for an airport were abandoned (Ferguson, 1986). Alconbury's runway has been safeguarded until 2006 for a possible railside freight airport, but maintenance is already proving costly (Huntingdonshire District Council, 1995).

Hydrology and aquifer protection

Concentration of post-war air bases on high-permeability lithologies renders the ground vulnerable to contamination. This is an important consideration in the English scarplands where drinking water is abstracted principally from artesian sources rather than from upland reservoirs (National Rivers Authority, 1993). At Hardwick airfield in Norfolk [TM250905], a proposal to dump domestic waste on glacial till was withdrawn after geotechnical evidence demonstrated that the till contained sand lenses capable of transmitting toxic leachate into watercourses and the chalk aquifer below (Gray, 1993, 1997b).

At Fulbeck airfield (Fig. 3), a proposal by the Nuclear Industry Reprocessing Executive to bury radioactive waste was ultimately withdrawn after similar misgivings about the geological security of the clay, shale, and mudstone site (Sir Alexander Gibb and Partners et al., 1988). Table 3 conveys the range of airfield contaminants, which can in principle affect public water supplies.

Soils and agriculture

The ideal terrain for airfield development in Britain is essentially the same as for arable farming. Consequently, there is a strong spatial association between major air bases and the higher grades of farmland (Ministry of Agriculture, Fisheries and Food, 1966). Scope for deflecting airfields onto less productive soils has been limited by steep gradients, harsh climate, and poor surface communications.

Except in the low-lying fens of Cambridgeshire, top-grade arable land was taken for airfields at a rate disproportionate to reserves (Blake, 1989). Strenuous efforts were therefore made to avoid demolition of farmsteads and splitting up of farm units. Zigzag boundaries testify to a policy by wartime agricultural executives to maintain cultivation as close to runways as safety and security allowed (McHardy and Holmes, 1950).

Although approximately half of all wartime airfield land is now back in farmers' hands, its fertility is permanently impaired by discordant and uncharted runway drainage systems. Protection of the best soils should be integral to any geoenvironmental assessment carried out prior to regeneration. Where soils happen to be of inherently low productivity, extensive afforestation is a feasible option.

Quarrying and landfill

There is a long-standing relationship between airfields and quarrying in Britain. During World War II, riverside gravel pits in "bomber" counties such as Lincolnshire, Norfolk, and Suffolk were greatly expanded to meet contractors' demands (Blake, 2000). Since 1945, disused runways have themselves become a supplementary source of construction aggregate and in certain cases whole, or substantial parts of, airfields have been dug up for the minerals beneath runways.

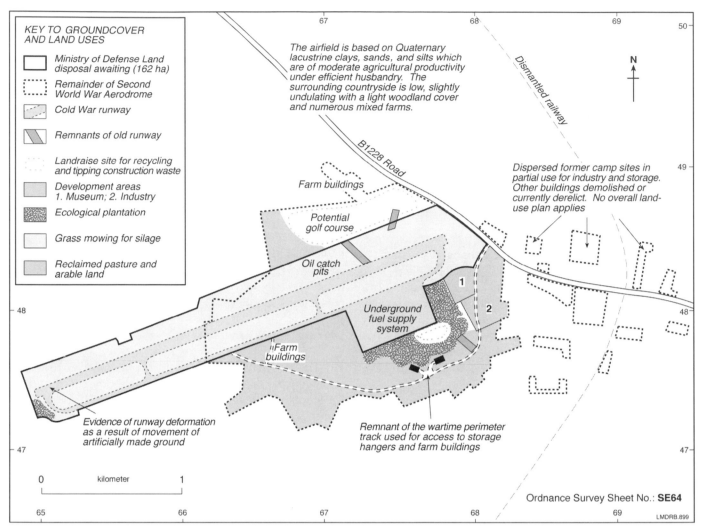

Figure 4. Geoenvironmental consideration in the regeneration of the decommissioned Elvington RAF airfield, Yorkshire, England. Source: City of York planning department records; author's fieldwork.

Lee-on-Solent, in Hampshire, and Swinderby (Fig. 3) are the latest examples of sand and gravel becoming available as a dividend of airfield closure. An added reason for encouraging this industry is the fact that lowland England has few natural expanses of inland water. Worked-out gravel pits, e.g., at Fairlop airfield, Greater London [TQ455905], have been effectively transformed into country parks.

Apart from being a hazard to aquifers, landfill is difficult to control aesthetically. Derelict airfields are a soft target for "fly-tipping" (unauthorized waste disposal), partly because they tend to lie beyond the range of neighborhood watch.

Ecology and wildlife protection

Flora and fauna quickly regenerate when airfields are abandoned, and numerous wildlife protection sites are now established within airfield perimeters. Geological exposures are also of scientific and educational interest; for example, Jurassic fossils

are a feature of Cotswold airfields. Because of flatness, the full geological character of airfields does not usually become apparent until destructive excavations are carried out.

The former USAF cruise missile base at Greenham Common, famous for its 1980s women's peace camp, has since been comprehensively restored to its original heathland state. The lifting of the 3050 m runway is the only recent demolition on this scale in the UK, and was done for nature conservation and public access reasons under ancient "common land" legislation (Newbury District Council, 1994).

Landscape protection and archaeology

Several of the "regeneration" airfields fall within "Areas of Outstanding Natural Beauty" (AONB) where there is a presumption against urban development. Much of England's rolling chalkland is so designated, including Binbrook airfield in Lincolnshire and Wroughton airfield in Wiltshire (Table 1). Kemble

TABLE 3. CONTAMINANTS, GEOHAZARDS, AND ENVIRONMENTAL STRESSES ENCOUNTERED ON DISUSED AIRFIELDS IN THE UNITED KINGDOM

From the construction phase
- Scraping and filling
- Subterranean bunkers
- Subterranean cable ducts
- Subterranean fuel tanks and pipes
- Buried rubble
- Buried tree trunks
- Catch pits
- Enemy bomb craters

From the operational phase
- Aircraft crash sites
- Buried engines and aircraft parts
- Unexploded ordnance
- Metal tracking and barbed wire
- Mustard gas
- Radioactive paints
- Petrol, oils, and lubricants
- Asbestos
- De-icers
- Cleaning solvents
- Batteries and transformers
- Bird scarers
- Herbicides and pesticides

From typical after-uses
- Silage bags incineration
- Intensive livestock farming
- Animal reprocessing
- Timber preserving
- Road haulage vehicle maintenance
- Refrigeration
- Vehicle dismantling and scrap yards
- Domestic waste recycling
- Construction waste recycling
- Ceramics, cement, and asphalt

From long-term neglect and decay
- Mining subsidence and fault reactivation
- Ground collapse into voids
- Runway cracking
- Dilapidation of built infrastructure
- Burrowing mammals

Sources: Geotechnical reports, planning briefs, airfield histories, Department of the Environment industry profiles.

airfield, sited on the Jurassic limestone plateau of the Cotswolds AONB, straddles a section of the Fosse Way where Roman soldiers marched nearly 2000 years ago and may have left pottery and coins in the ground. Roman roads across Britain later provided a rudimentary navigational aid for RAF pilots in the days before radar, and accordingly attracted a number of riparian aerodromes (see Fig. 3).

Elvington airfield (Fig. 4) lies within a "greenbelt" designated to resist the spread of York into open countryside regardless of the latter's low scenic quality (City of York, 1995). The prevailing local policy in this peri-urban community is to encourage the airfield's economic redevelopment within a landscaped envelope. Plans elsewhere for golf courses on "landraise" sites, e.g.,

Rivenhall airfield, Essex [TL820205], have provoked concern about the loss of "landscape authenticity" and the degree of landform modification that should be allowed under the guise of airfield reclamation (Gray, 1997a).

Built heritage

A number of airfield installations have been "listed" for their architectural merit. English Heritage, the body responsible for advising central government on listings, takes cues from amateur experts such as the Airfield Research Group (ARG). Certain RAF stations commissioned in the 1930s were designed to harmonize with local building traditions, e.g., the headquarters block at Hullavington, Wiltshire [ST905810] was faced with Cotswold stone (Air Ministry, 1956). RAF Finningley has been the subject of a meticulous photographic survey in anticipation of the station's disposal (Royal Commission on the Historic Monuments of England, 1998). To coordinate these various initiatives, a "Defence of Britain" project funded by the National Lottery has been running for several years (Lowry, 1995).

TOWARD A LAND-USE POLICY

Thus far the discussion has focused on 12 large and complex "regeneration" airfields, with a sideways glance at active air bases that could unleash problems of a similar magnitude if they were to close. With geological factors in mind, it is now appropriate to examine the evolution of land-use policy in relation to disused airfields more generally, to see what can be learned from over five decades of central and local government experience.

Uncoordinated reclamation and reuse

On VE-day in 1945 most UK airfields were already inactive, and peripheral reclamation had begun (McHardy and Holmes, 1950). Vacant runways typically became dumps for surplus war equipment and many camps were occupied by homeless people, including refugees. To ease food shortages farmers were encouraged to recultivate land between runways and utilize empty buildings for livestock, feedstuffs, and machinery. In this way the concrete, hangars, and huts could be quickly reactivated in any military emergency (Treadgold, 1945).

By the late 1950s a number of unforeseen problems were becoming apparent: (1) the random dismantling of hangars, stripping of copper, and uncontrolled leasings to third parties, much of it outside normal planning and public health controls, turned the fringes of many towns and villages into rural slums (Nairn, 1955; Brett, 1965); (2) Crown immunity aggravated this mess, because the Air Ministry (the responsible government department at that time) was not obliged to carry out comprehensive demolition prior to disposal (Griffith, 1987); (3) sites were frequently sold off at reduced valuations to take degradation into account and few of the new owners were prepared to undertake clearance work for no gain; (4) tenancies agreed before disposal presented local authorities with expensive legal wrangles concerning "existing use rights;" and (5) landowners exploited loopholes in the planning rules by leasing premises to quasi-agricultural firms, thereby compounding the untidy appearance.

The increasing pace of urban construction in the late 1950s encouraged a piecemeal breaking up of runways to win hardcore for motorways, new towns, and other capital projects (Newton, 1960). Reclamation works in scenic coastal areas involved untrained civilian volunteers, an arrangement that led to concerns regarding insurance and objections from trade unions (Dower, 1959). To this day there is no effective control over hardcore removal because under planning law it is classed as demolition and not a statutory "change of use."

Deals struck between farmers and demolition contractors were an inevitable twist in the rural economy caused by the absence of a land-use policy. Whatever conclusions historians may ultimately reach, this piecemeal reclamation was a significant undercurrent of airfield reuse during the early post-war years.

Purposeful occupancies

While the government's primary rural policy was to maximize home-grown food supplies, a range of institutional "colonizations" also took place on airfields, predominantly by public sector agencies requiring large out-of-town premises (Blake, 1986). Statutory arrangements whereby surplus airfields are offered sequentially to other government departments, public utilities, local authorities, the previous owners, and finally new owners, resulted in a number of large establishments redeploying to vacant airfield sites (Griffith, 1987).

Beneficiaries of this unexpected land availability were: atomic research laboratories, e.g., Harwell, Oxfordshire [SU480865]; HM prisons, e.g., Ford, Sussex [SU990030]; construction industry training, e.g., Bircham Newton, Norfolk [TF785345]; fire services training, e.g., Moreton-in-Marsh, Gloucestershire [SP220330]; district council offices, e.g., West Malling, Kent [TQ680555]; and university halls of residence, e.g., Horsham St Faith, Norfolk [TG220135]. Motor-racing circuits, e.g., Silverstone, Northamptonshire [SP675420], and county show grounds, e.g., at Winthorpe, Nottinghamshire [SK825565], demonstrate how mass spectator events were also catered for.

Apart from automobile development, e.g., Rover at Gaydon, Warwickshire [SP355545], the manufacturing industry on former airfields is generally located within trading estates and consists of low-employment processes such as saw-milling. The majority of reoccupied premises are therefore warehouses, depots, dealerships, and repair shops. Other typical occupancies include mushroom growing, touring caravans, astronomy apparatus, radio transmitters, wind-powered turbines, go-carting, and land-yachting (Fig. 5).

Airfield attributes

From the above examples gleaned from questionnaires and land-use surveys (Blake, 1969, 1995; Blake et al., 1984), it is

Figure 5. Land-yachting at Strubby airfield [TF450810] Lincolnshire, England, in the late 1970s. This typical reuse exploits the strong winds that blow along and across the unencumbered surfaces of vacant runways. Source: W.J. Taylor.

apparent that airfields have a range of positive attributes that helped counterbalance the environmental stresses identified earlier. An appreciation of why airfields have attracted such a diversity of purposeful occupancies is gained when those attributes are expressed in terms of the structural elements of airfield design.

There are 12 recognizable attributes as follows: (1) remoteness from habitation (noisy and malodorous activities are tolerated); (2) flatness (reduces construction costs and the drone of vehicles); (3) openness (affords room for error, e.g., fireworks testing, student driving); (4) hard surfaces (for storage, parking, fire-breaks); (5) free circulation (wide strips and radius curves); (6) unified ownership (transfer to institutions, new settlements); (7) capacious hangars (dry and secure conditions); (8) cheap huts (for under-capitalized trades); (9) salubrious accommodation (office quarters, affordable housing); (10) earthworks (visual and acoustic screening); (11) natural camouflage (war games, wildlife); and (12) historic atmosphere (authentic background for films, TV documentary, and advertising).

This compilation provides a tentative guidance for planners searching to rationalize development control decisions.

Regeneration

By the 1970s (Blake, 1969) local authorities (but not central government) began to reappraise the airfield problem (Miller, 1973). The chief triggers were: (1) realization that the traditional landscape was not recovering; (2) the increasing scale and complexity of each successive closure; (3) changing patterns of industrial location (manifest particularly in the expanding motorway network); and (4) questions regarding the future role of the countryside, especially the primacy of agriculture.

The 1980s saw a right-wing Treasury put pressure on the MoD to release surplus land as swiftly as possible to stimulate the property market. Relaxation of planning controls encouraged "asset stripping" and by the end of the decade even conservative politicians were fearful of a backlash from voters. A cross-party consensus accordingly emerged, involving public-private sector partnerships, to regenerate the many idle factories, gas works, rail yards, hospitals, and defense installations that were being made redundant by technological and organizational change.

Redundant airfields have subsequently become an integral part of a general government strategy of regenerating "brownfield" sites in preference to building on "greenfield" sites. The opportunity to solve a major dereliction problem by steering development into airfield "footprints" has not been missed, e.g., at Upper Heyford, near Oxford (Wills, 1994). Air bases of this size have sufficient land in principle for a new town of about 30,000 inhabitants (Best, 1981).

In more remote rural areas, European Union funds under "Objective 2b" (depressed rural areas) and KONVER (areas affected by military base closures) programs have been made available for job creation. The reason central government has been slow to issue physical planning guidance for regenerating defense sites is probably a fear of committing public funds to ambitious projects with uncertain prospects of success.

Environmental geology

Until recently the geotechnical history of aerodrome construction (Betts, 1995) and the present-day technique of environmental impact analysis were unconnected research areas. A recent proliferation of consultants' reports on land disposal (e.g., Segal Quince Wicksteed, 1994; Barton Willmore, 1996) has for the first time brought both historical and geological considerations into the mainstream of land-use planning and regeneration practice.

In 1997 the Department of the Environment, Transport and the Regions (DETR) commissioned a set of guidance leaflets aimed at local government officers on the physical capability of land for different kinds of development. Introducing the term "environmental geology," these leaflets represented a turning point in public policy toward land-use questions (DETR/Symons Travers Morgan, 1997a, 1997b). Key matters identified in the publications are: (1) the natural characteristics of the ground, (2) the legacy of previous land uses, and (3) the physical processes that influence the sustainability of proposed developments. Their common purpose is to explain the importance of geology for land-use planning and especially the role of geology in strategic regeneration.

Through this medium DETR urges professional geologists and geotechnical engineers to become acquainted with national and regional planning guidance, local authority plan-making methods, and the processes by which control decisions are developed. A number of "emerging policy issues" are identified, those most applicable to airfield regeneration being waste disposal, tourism promotion, and integrated river basin management. In relation to each issue the involved parties are advised to approach regeneration from four main angles: assets, constraints, liabilities, and responsibilities.

To ensure "best practice," DETR advocates that local planning authorities routinely take environmental geology into account when considering proposals for new construction or changes of land use, and to make appropriate and effective use of earth science information. It is recommended that all critical data are made available evenhandedly to all other statutory bodies, commercial developers, insurers, conservation agencies, pressure groups, and independent consultants. Much relevant geoenvironmental information is at present expensive to obtain in the short time allowed for processing development applications (British Geological Survey/Roger Tym and Partners, 1997).

GEOENVIRONMENTAL AUDIT

Although routine fieldwork by UK land-use planners fell temporarily out of fashion in the 1970s, the ending of the Cold War saw a return of environmental assessment, master planning, and design guidance to the mainstream of planning practice at the local level. A particularly useful model for the physical regeneration of disused airfields is the "Commercial Audit Methodology," devised by an international consortium of European local authorities to hasten the economic regeneration of redundant defense installations of all kinds (Network Demilitarized, 1994). The "Strengths-Opportunities-Constraints" method of analysis is also eminently applicable to former airfields.

"Geoenvironmental audit" describes a systematic approach to regeneration in which all the physical dimensions are cross-referenced, so as to prevent overall resources being jeopardized by hasty decisions based on single issues. While there is no official publication explaining how auditing should be done, and each site investigation case tends to involve a costly "starting-from-scratch" approach, a methodology is now in place comprising five broad stages that cascade down from site identification to environmental management.

Site identification

This stage entails a determination of where airfields actually exist within a given area of search (economic planning region, administrative county, or district). Site identification is fundamental to the compilation of a definitive record of all potential airfield problems and assumes a financial commitment by central government to promote regeneration in a systematic way.

The identities of all UK wartime airfields, including postwar extensions to runways and residential areas, have been in the public domain for much of the postwar period through Ordnance Survey maps, aeronautical charts, and historical compilations (e.g., Willis and Holliss, 1987). Scope for concealment in a crowded island is limited, although from time to time obscure dispersal and decoy airfields are brought to light as a result of investigations by ARG and kindred enthusiasts. Searches at the Public Record Office, together with collation of local reminiscences, have led in some instances to the discovery of historically significant artifacts and potential geologic hazards.

Destruction of relevant archives during departmental moves and reorganizations has hampered the compilation of a 100%-complete list of airfield sites. A master list of all existing and former bases is an indispensable tool, which must be kept under constant review.

Site characterization

This second stage in the "cascade of audits" is the point of entry for planners, surveyors, and geotechnical engineers. In the first instance a wide range of airfield data can be acquired from secondary sources through a "desk study," which classically includes geological, topographical, soil, hydrological, and archaeological maps.

Images transmitted from satellites are of special assistance in identifying mineral reserves and diagnosing such problems as water deficit and waterlogging, while air photographs provide evidence of archaeological remains, illicit occupancies, and the extent of concrete. Records of former land uses held by local authorities and academic libraries provide a useful supplement to the graphic images. Archival maps and unpublished government records are essential to building an accurate impression of a site's unique character.

Site investigation can be enhanced further by an intimate knowledge of the operational history of an airfield. The type of aircraft and the intensity of their missions have an important bearing on the position of installations and the pattern of environmental stresses they cause. Fully integrated data sets for airfields do not at present exist in a readily accessible form, although the Royal Air Force has recently commenced internal studies of its bases in anticipation of possible additional closures (Richmond and James, 1995).

Site investigation

The third stage in the regeneration process normally follows a decision to carry out a major redevelopment or promote a significant change of land use within a planned framework (Department of the Environment, Contaminated Land and Liabilities Division, 1995). It is customary here for independent consultants to be engaged, either on behalf of the MoD as vendor, the purchaser, or the local planning authority. Consultants provide geotechnical expertise not available within most authority offices as well as lending scientific objectivity to the decision-making process. Selective drillings to confirm natural processes, disturbances, and contamination are essential not only for the reconstruction work but also for commercial site valuation and legal indemnity purposes. In addition to boreholes, test pits, and other probes, it is advantageous to have original airfield plans at the ready as these show the precise disposition of every building, earthwork, runway drain, and fuel pipe.

The enlisting of eyewitnesses, many of whom are now elderly, is a useful adjunct to geotechnical knowledge. Given the shortcomings of public land-use records, the oral evidence that local people can supply about crashes, waste burying, and undocumented tenancies greatly assists in building a profile of remembered and suspected geologic hazards (Table 3). Risk assessment methodologies provide a basis for reducing the cost of invasive work, for example by designing ground survey grids with an appropriate spacing between probes. Sadly, it is unlikely that public funds will ever be made available for a full retrospective investigation of the hundreds of airfields abandoned during the early postwar years.

Site remediation

At this stage the ground and buildings are actually treated to remove or neutralize contaminants. In addition to chemical and radioactive substances, there are inert "contaminants" such as dangerous ruins (e.g., crumbling control towers with rusty external staircases) and subterranean impediments to site clearance. The safety of persons entering the site on business, for historical interest, or simply out of curiosity, is an important consideration as vacant airfields in Britain attract a lot of casual visitors and are difficult to patrol (Fig. 6).

Contamination is most acute on airfields decommissioned following the end of the Cold War, for these have had the longest time to accumulate toxins from jet aircraft, weapons, ground equipment, and personnel support services. Top contaminants on large redundant air bases are radioactive wastes, fuels, lubricants, paints, and asbestos (Table 3). Airfields closed between the mid-1960s and mid-1980s contain these hazards to a lesser degree, but they may be present on former V-bomber bases and centers of intensive jet training.

Airfields closed immediately after the war and during the 1950s do not generally have contaminating substances in alarming quantities, although there may be hidden spills of oil, gas canisters, and dead ground caused by burning fog dispersants (Williams, 1995). Sites with little or no post-war record of military flying may nevertheless have contaminants from successor land uses. Temporary missile pads located on disused wartime bomber bases (Fig. 7) fall into this category and have been the subject of recent expert studies (Royal Commission on the Historic Monuments of England, 1998). Laboratories, firework factories, and scrap yards exemplify the many airfield after-uses for which MoD no longer has any responsibility.

In all these cases the preferable method of remediation is in situ cleaning rather than expensive transfer of contaminated soil to distant treatment locations by truck along tortuous lanes. By virtue of their ample size, airfields have considerable scope for "self-cleaning" operations and therefore meet some of the performance criteria for sustainable development (Borch, 1995). While sprawling installations and interstitial rough land explain the proliferation of many environmentally unsound occupancies, these characteristics do conveniently provide the space needed for clean-up machinery.

The most common remediation activities encountered on airfields are the removal of buried concrete and metalwork where

Figure 6. The derelict World War II control tower at Husband Bosworth airfield, Leicestershire, England [SK655825] in the late 1970s. Since the photograph was taken, the tower has further deteriorated. Source: Roy Bonser.

Figure 7. "Bloodhound Mk1" surface-to-air guided missile launch pad at Woodfox Lodge airfield, Rutland, England [SK960130]. This now derelict installation, operational from 1960 until 1964, is both of heritage interest and a possible geohazard. Source: Roger J.C. Thomas, Royal Commission on the Historic Monuments of England, 1998.

this hazard is damaging to agricultural implements, impedes drainage, or is likely to induce collapse into voids. The use of clay barriers to arrest the lateral and downward movement of contaminants is apposite for industrializing airfields sited on permeable lithologies (Gray, 1996).

Site management

Systematic management of disused airfields is fundamental to their holistic and sustainable regeneration, yet this aspect was overlooked for decades. Before the recent wave of post Cold War disposals, airfields were effectively exempt from normal planning controls while still in MoD ownership and fell outside the framework of wider environmental policy (Department of the Environment, 1984). Under pressure from the Treasury, many sites were sold off in bits and could only have been described as "managed" in the purely financial sense. Within the last half-decade, MoD has become noticeably more responsive to public and professional concerns about the mess caused by "cherry picking" of assets and the unsatisfactory practice of leaving the rest to decay pending interest from developers.

Despite the basic difficulty in securing a coherent land-use transformation, airfields have the inherent advantage of being in single ownership up to the time of disposal. Through the planned regeneration process, which is now widely and increasingly accepted as publicly desirable, there are rising prospects of former air bases being continuously managed from the rundown of flying operations, through the disposal phase, to restructuring, reuse, and after-care. This management process is normally led by the local planning authority in partnership with one or more central government departments, development companies, or relevant specialist agencies.

Crucial in this regard is the principle that all proposed changes, including demolitions and minor intensifications of use,

should be closely monitored for their cumulative impact on the geological environment, even where planning permission is not strictly required. Although such regulation runs counter to the laissez-faire regime for which disused airfields are celebrated in some quarters, careful controls are justified by the vulnerability of the various environmental and regeneration subsystems that exist within such sites.

To summarize, there are three regeneration systems present on most disused airfields where expert management is necessary. In the economic field there is the maintenance and servicing of buildings for reoccupation by businesses and community service providers as local demand picks up. In the cultural field there is the preservation of historically important buildings as part of industrial, military, and aviation archaeology (Innes, 1995). And in the ecological field there is the "greening" of all developments by landscaping, having due regard to both the texture of the prewar landscape and the integrity of the airfield layout itself.

CONCLUSIONS

Despite their wide geographical distribution, Britain's military airfields remain geologically selective. Recognition of broad geomorphic zones has highlighted their clustering on younger geological formations. The early adherence to calcareous Mesozoic escarpments has been maintained, but Quaternary sands and gravels have emerged as the predominant lithotype of the post-war period. Since the latest round of airfield disposals has disproportionately released Quaternary sands and gravels, expert knowledge of fluvioglacial and periglacial processes needs to be reflected in regeneration management teams.

The impact of airfields on the environment has varied according to the stage reached in their life cycle. Active airfields are characterized by extensive land-take, operational hazard, noise, high employment, traffic, spending power, and demand for housing and schools. Disused airfields are characterized by multiple use, fragmented redevelopment, low employment, landscape decay, and incoherent planning policy. Geoenvironmental considerations transcend this divide and are relevant to most facets of the airfield problem.

In reviewing the spectrum of geologic hazards and environmental stresses a broad distinction emerges between the "acute" effects of a relatively small number of major air bases decommissioned during the past decade and the "chronic" effects of hundreds of disused airfields abandoned and reused during Cold War defense reorientation. It has been instructive to cross-reference the two groups of effects and arrive at a more complete understanding of one of Britain's long-standing and continuing derelict land problems.

The capacity of airfields to attract alternative uses that are generally impractical or unpopular in urban areas has undoubtedly been prejudicial to the conservation of traditional countryside, yet Britain has previously absorbed disused canals, railways, and quarries that are now useful and admired features of the landscape. In a "stress-and-recovery" model of environmental management, an associated reason for regenerating airfields is to provide centers of enterprise and innovation for rural areas that have been denuded of biodiversity, jobs, and cultural identity by modern agribusiness.

As feats of engineering and building construction, Britain's wartime airfields caused widespread superficial disturbance to the ground environment. While their installations were characteristically dispersed, low-profile, and subterranean only to a limited extent, a wide range or geologic hazards were nevertheless left in the ground. Due to secrecy and the peculiarities of land acquisition, tenure, disposal, and control, an inclusive and transparent approach to environmental monitoring has been difficult to achieve. Geological, geotechnical, and land-use assessments are relative newcomers to the planning agenda for disused airfields.

The regeneration of airfields is inescapably a multi-disciplinary area, involving everyone from local historians to geochemists and the proponents of sustainable development. In compiling technical guidance for future management, the land-use planner cannot rationally ignore the geological environment in which airfields are located.

REFERENCES CITED

Air Ministry (Air Historical Branch), 1956, The Second World War 1939–45: RAF works: London, Air Ministry, Publication 3236. Reprinted for the Ministry of Defence, 1997, The Royal Air Force builds for war: A history of design and construction in the RAF 1935–1945: London, The Stationery Office, 764 p.

Appleton, J.H., 1962, The geography of communications in Great Britain: Oxford, Oxford University Press, 251 p.

Barton Willmore Planning Partnership, 1996, Thurleigh airfield master plan statement: Reading, Barton Willmore Planning Partnership, 24 p.

Best, R.H., 1981, Land use and living space: London, Methuen, 197 p.

Betts, A., 1995, Royal Air Force airfield construction service 1939–46: Ware, Airfield Research Publishing, 151 p.

Blake, R.N.E., 1969, The impact of airfields on the British landscape: Geographical Journal, v. 135, p. 508–528.

Blake, R.N.E., 1981, The changing distribution of military airfields in the East Midlands, 1914–1980: East Midlands Geographer, v. 7, p. 286–302.

Blake, R.N.E., 1986, Old airfields take off: New uses for aerodromes: Geographical Magazine, v. 58, p. 272–274.

Blake, R.N.E., 1989, The development of military and civil airfields in the United Kingdom since 1909, with special reference to land use [Ph.D. thesis]: London, University of London, 655 p.

Blake, R.N.E., 1995, Alternative strategies for the restoration and re-use of abandoned airfields, *in* Coulson, M., and Baldwin, H., eds., Proceedings, International Symposium on the Environment and Defence, NATO Committee on the Challenges of Modern Society Report No. 211: Swansea, University of Wales, p. 321–332.

Blake, R.N.E., 2000, Geological influences on the siting of military airfields in the United Kingdom, *in* Rose, E.P.F., and Nathanail, C.P., eds., Geology and warfare: Examples of the influence of terrain and geologists on military operations: Geological Society [London], p. 275–312.

Blake, R.N.E., Hodgson, M., and Taylor, W.J., 1984, The airfields of Lincolnshire since 1912: Leicester, Midland Counties Publications, 296 p.

Borch, H.J.W., 1995, Canadian Department of National Defence contaminated sites remediation framework, *in* Coulson, M., and Baldwin, H., Proceedings, International Symposium on the Environment and Defence: Swansea, University of Wales, NATO Committee on the Challenges of Modern Society Report No. 211, p. 45–52.

Brett, L., 1965, Landscape in distress: London, Architectural Press, 159 p.

British Geological Survey/Roger Tym and Partners, 1997, Earth science information in support of major development initiatives 1995–97: Keyworth, British Geological Survey, Technical Report WA/97/84, 56 p.

Childs, J., 1998, The military use of land: A history of the defence estate: Bern, Peter Lang, 302 p.

City of York, Directorate of Environment and Development Services, 1995, Elvington airfield development plan: York, City of York Council, 11 p.

Civil Aviation Authority, 1996, UK Aerodrome Index (CAP481): Hounslow, Aeronautical Information Service, 43 p.

Department of the Environment, 1984, Circular 18/84: Crown Land and Crown Development: London, Her Majesty's Stationery Office, 14 p.

Department of the Environment, Contaminated Land and Liabilities Division, 1995, Industry profile: Airports: Ruislip, Department of the Environment Publications, 11 p.

Department of the Environment, Transport and the Regions/Symons Travers Morgan, 1997a, Environmental geology in land use planning: Emerging issues: East Grinstead, Symons Travers Morgan, 40 p.

Department of the Environment, Transport and the Regions/Symons Travers Morgan, 1997b, Environmental geology in land use planning: Advice for planners and developers: East Grinstead, Symons Travers Morgan, 12 p.

Dower, M., 1959, Clearance of derelict military buildings: Journal of the Town Planning Institute, v. 45, p. 272–274.

Ferguson, A.P., 1986, Burtonwood: Eighth Air Force base air depot: Reading, Airfield Publications, 136 p.

Francis, P., 1996, British military airfield architecture: From airships to the jet age: Cambridge, Patrick Stephens, 224 p.

Freeman, R.A., 1984, Mighty Eighth war manual: London, Jane's Publishing, 320 p.

Gallent, N., Howe, J., and Bell, P., 1999a, Alternative land uses on small rural airfields: Manchester, University of Manchester, Department of Planning and Landscape–Economic and Social Research Council, Project R000222539, 31 p.

Gallent, N., Howe, J., and Bell, P., 1999b, Happy landings? Reuse of redundant airfields: Town and Country Planning, v. 67, p. 32–33.

Gray, J.M., 1993, Quaternary geology and waste disposal in south Norfolk, England: Quaternary Science Reviews, v. 12, p. 899–912.

Gray, J.M., 1996, The containment properties of glacial tills: A case study from Hardwick Airfield, Norfolk (UK), *in* Bentley, S.P., ed., Engineering geology of waste disposal: Geological Society [London], Engineering Geology Special Publication 11, p. 299–307.

Gray, J.M., 1997a, Planning and landform: Geomorphological authenticity or incongruity in the countryside?: Area, v. 29, p. 312–324.

Gray, J.M., 1997b, Environment, policy and municipal waste management in the UK: Transactions of the Institute of British Geographers, v. 22, p. 69–90.

Griffith, J., 1987, Crichel Down: The most famous farm in British constitutional history: Contemporary Record, spring, p. 35–40.

Higham, R., 1998, Bases of air strategy: Building airfields for the RAF 1914–1945: Shrewsbury, Airlife Publishing Ltd., 285 p.

Hoskins, W.G., 1955, The making of the English landscape: London, Hodder and Stoughton, 240 p.

House of Commons Defence Committee, 1991, Options for change: Royal Air Force: London, Her Majesty's Stationery Office, 27 p.

Huntingdonshire District Council, 1995, RAF Alconbury planning brief: Huntingdon, Huntingdonshire District Council, 22 p.

Innes, E.B., 1995, British airfield buildings of the Second World War: Leicester, Midlands Publishing, Aviation Pocket Guide No. 1, 128 p.

Institute of Geological Sciences, 1977, Quaternary map of the United Kingdom: Southampton, Ordnance Survey, scale 1:625 000, 2 sheets (north and south).

Jauhiainen, J.S., 1997, Militarisation, demilitarisation and re-use of military areas: The case of Estonia: Geography, v. 82, p. 118–126.

Lowry, B., ed., 1995, 20th century defences in Britain: An introductory guide: York, Council for British Archaeology, Practical Handbooks in Archaeology No. 12, 145 p.

McHardy, L.J., and Holmes, J.Y., 1950, Farming and an airfield: A problem of restoration: Agriculture, v. 57, p. 201–204.

Miller, T., 1973, Military airfields and rural planning: Town Planning Review, v. 44, p. 31–48.

Ministry of Agriculture, Fisheries and Food, 1966, Agricultural land classification: Pinner, Agricultural Land Service, Technical Report No.11, 27 p.

Ministry of Defence, 1994, Front line first: The defence costs study: London, Her Majesty's Stationery Office, 45 p.

Ministry of Defence, Defence Works Services, 1994, Geotechnical investigations for design and construction of airfield pavements: London, Her Majesty's Stationery Office, Defence Works Functional Standards 09, 36 p.

Nairn, L., 1955, Outrage: London, Architectural Press. Reprinted from a special issue of Architectural Review, June, p. 365–456.

National Rivers Authority, 1993, Policy and practice for the protection of groundwater: Bristol, National Rivers Authority, 52 p.

Neal, J.L., 1998, Playas in military operations, *in* Underwood, J.R., and Guth, P.L., eds., Military geology in peace and war: Geological Society of America, Reviews in Engineering Geology, v. 13, p. 165–172.

Network Demilitarised, 1994, The conversion of military sites: A handbook outlining the commercial audit procedure to assist the re-use of former defence establishments: Trowbridge, Wiltshire County Council, in conjunction with EDAW/CR Planning, 37 p.

Newbury District Council, 1994, Greenham Common airbase planning brief: Newbury, Newbury District Council, 21 p.

Newton, D.E., 1960, Clearance of concrete from disused airfields: Journal of the Town Planning Institute, v. 6, p. 169–170.

Pooley, R., and Patel, R., 1998, Pooley's flight guide, United Kingdom, 1998: London, Elstree Aerodrome, Pooley's Flight Guides, 595 p.

Richmond, T.D., and James, D.J., 1995, Disposal of military sites: The need for a land quality statement, *in* Coulson, M., and Baldwin, H., eds., Proceedings, International Symposium on the Environment and Defence: Swansea, University of Wales, NATO Committee on the Challenges of Modern Society Report No. 211, p. 314–320.

Royal Commission on the Historic Monuments of England, 1998, Historic buildings report: RAF Woolfox Lodge, Rutland: Swindon, Royal Commission on the Historic Monuments of England, 18 p.

Segal Quince Wickstead, 1994, Norfolk redundant airbase regeneration study: Swindon, Segal Quince Wickstead, Final report to the Norfolk Airbase Working Party, 79 p. plus appendices.

Sir Alexander Gibb and Partners–Central Electricity Generating Board–Nuclear Industry Radioactive Waste Division, 1988, Site investigation for waste disposal facility: Fulbeck site: London, Sir Alexander Gibb and Partners, Final factual report, 272 p.

Smith, D.J., 1989, Britain's military airfields 1939–45: Cambridge, Patrick Stephens, 249 p.

Stamp, L.D., 1960, Britain's structure and scenery: London, Fontana, 317 p.

Stamp, L.D., 1962, The land of Britain: Its use and misuse (third edition): London, Longmans, 546 p.

Treadgold, R.C., 1945, Post-war adaptation of aerodromes: Journal of the Town Planning Institute, v. 31, p. 125–129.

United States General Accounting Office, National Security and International Affairs Division, 1995, Military bases: Case studies on selected bases closed 1998 and 1991: Washington, D.C., USGAO B-261073, 119 p.

Williams, G., 1995, Flying through fire: FIDO, the fogbuster of World War Two: London, Grange Books, 228 p.

Willis, D., and Holliss, B.S., 1987, Military airfields of the British Isles 1939–1945: Kettering, Enthusiasts Publications, 274 p.

Wills, S., 1994, The redevelopment of redundant RAF airbases: Oxford, Oxford Brookes University, School of Planning, Working Paper No. 157, 61 p.

Wynn, H., 1994, The RAF strategic nuclear defence forces: Their origin, roles and deployment 1946–1969: London, Her Majesty's Stationery Office, 653 p.

MANUSCRIPT ACCEPTED BY THE SOCIETY OCTOBER 27, 2000

Index

[Italic page numbers indicate major references]